A CENTURY OF WISCONSIN DEER

by

OTIS S. BERSING

Second Edition

First Published in 1956

Game Management Division
WISCONSIN CONSERVATION DEPARTMENT
Madison, Wisconsin 53701
1966

Pub. 353-66

Library of Congress Catalog Card Number: 66-63515

ACKNOWLEDGMENTS

The mass of statistical data entered in the first edition of this book was gathered with the assistance of the office associates of the author. Grateful acknowledgment is extended to Walter Wiggins, Robert Waldo, Keith Bohen and Richard Keslin for the assistance given in the initial preparation of deer season and kill data. Special thanks are due Walter Scott for his aid in providing rare source material.

The author is particularly indebted to Lyle Jensen who helped considerably in checking the many statistical compilations, and in verifying factual statements entered in the record. Special acknowledgment is made to James Hale for his work in the much needed editing of the manuscript for publication. The cover picture is reproduced from a drawing by Charles W. Schwartz.

Changes and revisions in this, the second edition, include information relating to deer hunting and related historical happenings during the ten years - 1955 through 1964. In a few instances, recently discovered material has permitted the correction of some data included in the original edition.

In this new material the author is indebted to Mary Grubb for her interest and work in checking references and compiling tables; to George Hartman and Stanley DeBoer for correcting errors that creep into a work of this kind and for furnishing additional source material; to Conservation Department personnel for their encouragement and suggestions as to what the contents should be; and to Ruth Hine for guidance in editing the manuscript.

FOREWORD

The following deer season records and notes are based on available legislative acts, Commission orders, censuses, biennial reports, newspaper items, and special articles covering past deer seasons. In view of the fact that a number of early records are unavailable or incomplete, and short in accuracy, a more correct estimate of the annual kill and season information is lacking.

The author lists a large variety of happenings which were components of the varying deer picture during the last 100 years. This chronology of statistical records and season changes, along with associated historical items, reflects the transitions which have taken place in the field of deer management in Wisconsin. The book covers the period up to, and including, the 1964 deer seasons.

Since weather conditions, deer populations, and amount of range as well as numbers of hunters, are factors determining the annual deer harvest, the kill figures for any county shown in this report are to be construed as showing trends; consequently, the high rank of counties listed during any given year should not necessarily mean that these counties are to be accepted as the best deer areas.

Because of the number of requests each year for deer kill records, this report is prepared as a reference in readily accessible form for use by the many people interested in this field of wildlife management.

L. P. VOIGT
CONSERVATION DIRECTOR

CONTENTS

PREFACE

The fascinating history of the white-tailed deer and deer hunting in Wisconsin is ever with us. For hundreds of years, man's interest in the whitetail was economic. At times venison was the only food source. The skin provided available clothing. The livelihood of the Indian and white man was affected to a large extent by the trade in hides. The sorry story of human behavior, commercial exploitation, and wanton killing, often played a part in the history of deer. Also, a part of the record was general indifference to the welfare of deer for a large number of years after the first white man set foot on Wisconsin soil.

Within the last twenty-five years has come a public awakening to the esthetic value of the graceful buck, doe, and fawn. Also, a scientific interest has developed whereby management, through the continuous study of the ecology of this most important big game animal, has planned and recommended control to maintain the herd at an optimum number for all those concerned, whether their interests are hunting, forestry, or recreational enjoyment.

The history of Wisconsin from prehistoric times through the periods when Wisconsin was a French and then a British colonial possession, the Wisconsin territorial days, and the decades of logging and fire during the first fifty years of Wisconsin statehood, is woven briefly into the story at various points. In restating a portion of the record, the known facts and written statements about deer are arranged in sequence. The citation of references is omitted purposely for the sake of readability. All data given has been interpreted and compiled from source material listed in the bibliography at the end of this book.

The first evidence of deer in prehistoric times is in the animal-shaped mounds scattered throughout the state. It is supposed that these curiously-shaped earthworks where the dead were buried, were built by the Winnebago Indians. Centuries ago the mound-builders flourished, then vanished. The remains of emblematic mounds have been found outlining the figures of man and animal. Effigy mounds built in the shape of deer have been found in Dane, Trempealeau, and other counties. Archeological investigations throughout the state point to the importance of deer to prehistoric Indian tribes. Prehistoric Indian campsites have produced polished bone awls made from the shin bones of deer, and antler-tip arrow points made by hollowing out the base of the tip, for fastening to shafts of wood. Bone skin scrapers and fish hooks made of deer bone have been found. "Bull roars" made from a pierced deer scapula (shoulder blade) attached to a piece of raw deer hide have been uncovered. They were whirled around the head to summon the chiefs to council. This is proof that deer definitely had a place in a primitive culture.

Indian legends handed down by various tribes show the importance of deer long, long ago in naming land and water. The Ojibwa word for lake was "Mitchigan". It meant, "a wooden fence to catch deer near its banks", hence the name Michigan, a translation adopted by the white man. In the Winnebago language, Waupaca meant "stalking place" where one went to shoot deer. The origin of the word, "fence", in naming Fence Lake in the Flambeau area of Vilas County, can be traced to the Winnebago word describing a deer fence near the water. Nebagamon Lake in Douglas County was named by the Chippewas, Nee-bay-gomoh-win, meaning a "place to hunt deer by a fire from the waters".

A chippewa legend associated deer with the origin of the Apostle Islands. The legend tells of Winneboujou, the giant deity who lived on the Brule River during the summer months. While hunting in the Brule Valley and looking over the tree tops, he spotted a deer. Hunting the deer all day, he shot away all of his arrows and threw away his quiver. He then followed the whitetail to the shores of Lake Superior. Disgusted with his failure, he threw rocks at the deer far out in the water. The rocks falling into the water became the Apostle Islands as we see them today.

Before the coming of the white man, the Indian tribesmen relied largely upon hunting for their livelihood. Deer, elk, and buffalo could be found in many places in the land now known as Wisconsin.

The Indians always found uses for all parts of the deer. The Ojibwas used thick buckskin to make mittens and moccasins for hunting and traveling. Shawl-like wraps, robes, and fringed leggings were used by the squaws. Fawn skins were used for fancy work. Thin dressed fawn skins were used by Sauk Indian squaws for summer shirts. The Sauks also wore deerskin war kilts and quilled thongs. The Winnebagos made implements out of antlers. Sometimes chiefs used antlers in front of the headdress as an emblem of power. War shields not used were left in deerskin covers. Drumheads were made from buckskins, and drumsticks were covered with deerskin. Rattles were made from deer hoofs. Buckskin bags were made for pipes and tobacco, and were also found necessary for ceremonial affairs. The Sauks used the marrow of the shin bone as hair oil by breaking the bones and then heating the marrow until it would run. Narrow strips of rawhide were used for the netting within snowshoe frames. Deer meat had medicinal value. The dried meat was boiled with juicy fat bear tissue to make a broth. The bones were saved and used to season corn, hominy, and beans. In tanning hides, the Potowatomi Indians boiled dry deer brains, and soaked the hide in the solution. During the rutting season, the Potowatomi Indians were accustomed to taking two antlers and striking them together loudly to attract a buck, which would think the sound was caused by two other bucks fighting over a doe. Bow-strings were made of the sinews of deer.

There is no authoritative information on the abundance or density of deer in the various parts of Wisconsin during primitive times, or during the years of settlement and changing land-use brought about by logging, railroads, and immigration. No one knows the number killed; however, there are numerous personal chronicles and other historical source materials that furnish us with many references to deer in early Wisconsin history.

The actual beginning of Wisconsin concerns itself with the political regime of New France. In the seventeenth century, the French founded Canada and penetrated the Great Lakes and Upper Mississippi Valley. It was during this period, more than 250 years ago, that we have the first written record of deer by a white man.

In 1634, Jean Nicolet was dispatched by Champlain, the first Governor of New France, to visit and report upon the untraveled Northwest. He landed in Wisconsin, somewhere on the shores of Green Bay. Radison and Grosielliers, roving fur traders, landed in northwestern Wisconsin the winter of 1661-62 and built the first dwelling for whitemen on Chequamegon Bay. "Staggs" were mentioned in their report. They also mentioned "fallow does and bucks". This was the first definite mention of deer in Wisconsin. About this time, Father Claude Allouez, a Jesuit

missionary who founded a mission on Chequamegon Bay, also mentioned the
abundance of large and small "stags" in the Lake Winnebago region, including
the Fox and Wolf River areas.

In 1673, Joliet and Marquette, on their way to exploring and discovering
the Mississippi River, saw many deer on the Wisconsin River, in the area now
known as Crawford, Dane, Grant, Iowa, Richland, and Sauk Counties. In a
letter to Frontenac, the Governor of New France, Joliet told this about the
Indians, "They do not care for deer as a food, but they kill buffaloes which
roam in herds of 30 to 50".

In 1698, LeSuers, an unlicensed trader, tells of hearing "stags" whistle
near the Black River; also how he made a wood whistle to answer, thereby
calling deer to make a kill. He also made the questionable statement that
the rutting season was from the beginning of September to the last of October-
a period at variance with our present-day theory that the breeding season
occurs later in the fall.

Potherie, a French historian, speaks of the Indians hunting deer at all
times in the Green Bay area in the 1650's. In 1721, early history tells of
the Indians at Green Bay receiving the new French Commandant by wading out
to a canoe, placing him on a deerskin robe, and returning to shore. Again
in 1728, the Frenchmen speak of "fallow" deer around Green Bay, and state,
"They are no longer in great numbers, hard to kill any". Could this be an
instance of starvation long before settlement, or the results of deer
slaughter by the Indians?

At the time of the Fox Indian War, which ended about the middle of the
nineteenth century, some traders on the Wisconsin River spoke of deer as
"roebucks". Our white-tailed deer were called "stags", "fallow deer",
"roebucks", and "hinds", during the fur-trade period. These terms apparently were brought from Europe. Not native to this country, the stag had long
been known as the object of the chase in European countries. In England,
ever since the time of the Saxons, stag hunting (with hounds) was the ex-
clusive privilege of royalty. In England a female deer was called a "hind".
In Europe, a small deer less than two feet high which was not native to this
country, was a specie called a "roebuck". The European "fallow" deer with
palmated or flat antlers, also found in the British Isles, was unknown here.
Decades later voyageurs were to speak of "red" deer at Prairie du Chien-a
species native to Europe but not to this country.

In 1763, the territory of New France, including Wisconsin, was formally
ceded by the French to the British who held it for only 20 years. Wisconsin
continued without permanent occupancy-a land with few settlements, French in
language and customs. The wilderness of the country, and fur trading as
the sole industry, prevailed. Logging and farming were to come. When the
British took possession of New France, including Wisconsin, Jonathan Carver,
one of the first English travelers to explore Wisconsin, saw deer on the
Chippewa, Mississippi, and Wisconsin Rivers, and an abundance of deer at the
Wisconsin River portage (1767).

Soon after the Revolutionary War when Wisconsin became a part of the
United States, it was incorporated in an area known as the Northwest Territory, a region including a part of Indiana, Illinois, and Michigan. Deer
continued to be important in the economy of the land. Wisconsin was still
a land of wilderness. At this time the original forest totalled 30 million
acres-6/7 of the area of the state.

An instance of the wasteful deer mortality in the eighteenth century may be illustrated by the hunting of Tomah, an Indian who lived on the Black River. He claimed to excel his brother in deer hunting. Both agreeing to put their skill to the test, they hunted all day; Tomah brought in 10 deer tongues to his brother's 9.

In dealing with the Indians, the white trader handled thousands of deerskins each year. Skins were classified in the market as buck, doe and fawn. The early French traders sold skins by the pound as red skins or summer coat, blue skins or fall coat, and gray skins or winter coat. Light and heavy shaved skins were also sold. In the 1830's at Green Bay, skins sold for from 12 to 28 cents a pound. Thousands were sold. Thousands of pounds of deer tallow were shipped from Green Bay to Mackinac in 1806. In 1804-05, Malhiot, a French clerk with the Northwest Fur Company stationed at Lac du Flambeau, inventoried almost 10,000 deerskins taken by traders in an area now known as Iron, Oneida, and Vilas Counties. As long ago as 1806 and 1810, a trader speaks of Indians wantonly tomahawking deer on the ice, and of deer slaughter on the upper Mississippi River. About 1803 or '04, Michel Curot, a trader, traded rum for 20 skins on the Brule River, and tells of purchases of skins and venison at his post on Yellow Lake in Burnett County. In 1812, one of the very few settlers in the area tells of Indians bringing in 30 deer at the falls of the Chippewa River. After 1820, Schoolcraft, a traveler, writes of many deer at Rice Lake, and south on the Red Cedar River. Deer were still abundant in the Green Bay region, as they were from the earliest times. Apparently deer were found in many regions before the logging period and settlement.

In the early 1800's, the entire state was a wilderness inhabited chiefly by Indians whose numbers probably never exceeded 10,000. The principal source of wealth continued to be the fur trade, and the main streets of Wisconsin were along river banks and at lead-mining posts. Before settlement, southern Wisconsin was an area of hardwood and prairie openings. The white population in the lead-mining area south of the Wisconsin River was estimated at only 200 in 1825. Census figures show no occupancy of northern Wisconsin by settlement. In the 1820's, Green Bay probably had 100 civilians. Prairie du Chien with less than 40 houses, saw Indians trading dressed deerskins with the white man for flour, as there was no circulation of money there at this time (1816).

During this period the deer picture of southern Wisconsin was considered one of abundance. We do not know the variation in deer abundance throughout the oak openings and prairie land. Some regions may have had a density of more than 25 deer per square mile. Students of the history of deer have spoken of "deer retreating northward", and of "being pushed north" following the plow, as man appropriated the southern ranges for farming. These statements are misleading. Deer did not migrate to the north. A more plausible explanation is that the deer population in southern Wisconsin shrank as the result of settlement, unrestricted shooting, and the changing habitat. The north had always had deer, but not in such numbers as after the conversion of pine into brushland as the result of logging, which widened the deer range and accounted in part for the astounding increase in the herd.

Before and after the Black Hawk War in 1832, early settlers tell us of large herds of deer in Walworth County. An abundance was reported near Madison. In 1837, a Captain Frederick Marryat on a trip on the Fox River, speaks of deer tracks being frequent, and of seeing a herd of 15. In 1804, plenty of deer were reported at Milwaukee where purchases were made of what they called summer furs, apparently red skins. Deer were abundant in

- 4 -

Lafayette County in 1834 at the time of the Black Hawk War, on land owned
by a Theodore Rodolf where a settler counted more than 50 in a herd. He
tells of garden damage within a fenced area. Can this be the first deer
damage to crops? In 1834, the editor of the Prairie du Chien Courier wrote
of the red deer on the Mississippi River bluffs. A large number of deer
were found in Grant County near Platteville in the 1830's. In telling of
the early days of Jefferson County, probably in the 1830's, Elisha Keyes
speaks of deer in great abundance. He also states that the early settlers
were not good hunters, and that in those days there were no breechloading
arms. The poor shooting he attributed to "buck fever" -- a pioneer slang
term used today.

The Black Hawk War in 1832 marked a turning point in land-use which
concerned deer in several ways. One of the important results of the war
was the removal of a large number of Indians to reservations west of the
Mississippi River and in northern Wisconsin. Their absence gave the deer
an opportunity to increase for a while in southern Wisconsin. At this time
the civilian population of the state was less than 5,000. Previously, an
estimated 6,000 Winnebago and 4,000 Menominee Indians controlled almost all
of the land in Wisconsin. They had been accustomed to hunting deer during
all seasons of the year, and lived principally on game. Only the lead mines
in southwestern Wisconsin had received a substantial number of people before
the War. The treaty with the Indians gave to the government the land south
and east of the Wisconsin and Fox Rivers. Land offices were opened at
Mineral Point and Green Bay. Agricultural development came fast, and began
to supersede the fur trade and lead mining. A military road was built
between Fort Howard and Green Bay and Fort Crawford at Praire du Chien.

As regular settlement in the southern part of the state began after
the Black Hawk War, prairies were fenced and plowed. Through burning,
pioneers cleared pastures of brush. Towns such as Fond du Lac, Janesville,
Kenosha, and Madison, came into existence. As people moved onto the land,
some animals disappeared. The last buffalo east of the Mississippi River
was shot in Trempealeau County in 1832; the last caribou was seen in
Ashland County in 1840; the last native elk was reported killed in Buffalo
County in 1868.

Wanton deer killing by means of fires, hounding, hunting for the market,
and other unsportsmanlike methods, along with the influx of settlers, accounted for the decline of deer, or the wiping out of the herd, in many
southern counties before the Civil War. The undesirable hunting methods
which were prevalent during the previous years of the British, French, and
Indian trade activities, continued and were adopted by the settler in his
search for a livelihood in the new land.

Many and varied hunting methods accepted commonly during more than
100 years of deer killing, accounted for the change in deer range and the
animals' reaching their lowest point in population in the early 1900's.
Deer were captured along runways by the use of hemp rope snares. Sharp-
pointed stakes were set on creek bank runways where deer were expected to
jump in crossing. Bow and arrow deer hunters were surprised and shocked
to find this rare, illegal method used several years ago, at a drainage
ditch during the Necedah Refuge bow season. Hunting deer with dogs was a
common practice, and it brought strong public opposition, particularly in
the 1880's and '90's. After finding the tracks of a deer, a hunter would
turn the hounds loose to drive the deer to a spot on the runway where the
hunter was posted. Another method of hounding was to drive the deer to
water, then by rowing his boat closely enough, the hunter was able to blow
out the deer's brains, or in the case of the Indian, to kill by tomahawking.

Deer were also hunted by following the hounds on horseback. Although hunting by this method was used considerably in the southern states, it was probably not too common here. Often a bell was tied to the horse, since deer were used to the sound on cattle. It permitted a closer approach to the deer. Within our day in Vilas County, hunters have been known to use Indian ponies for traveling to hunting sites, and for dragging deer to camp, but not while actually hunting. Jacking or floating was a common practice in which the hunter sat behind a powerful light or lantern in a boat, and searched for deer. Generally the hunters began floating for deer in July.

A Sportsman Gazetteer and General Guide published in 1877 describes scaffold shooting. A ladder of slats was nailed to a tree, with a seat 10 to 30 feet high, and the scaffold was placed near a runway. For shooting in July, salt licks were set out during the spring months; however, this Guide recommended stalking as the finest method, and suggested the use of hounds only to retrieve wounded deer.

Shining was common, and both the Indian and white man used torches made from birch bark to approach more closely at night. Candles were used at a later date. In the spring, the torches were thrown to start fires, the purpose of which was to drive deer to the posted hunters. At the time of settlement, the oak openings and prairies of southern Wisconsin were fired to drive deer to selected points for the kill. Sometimes a long line of fires would be started to direct the running of deer to the posted hunters. Bows made from hickory, ash, ironwood, and red cedar, and arrows, were used by the Indians at salt licks, as they had used tomahawks on the ice. Bands of Indians would run down exhausted deer on crusted snow.

Indians used fences to drive deer to a certain point. North of the Menominee River bordering Marinette County, a fence of small trees lapped in one direction was built 50 to 100 yards parallel to the Chicago and Northwestern Railroad line. When deer traveled south, they followed the lane and turned east to find an opening. At the aperture, a scaffold was made from which the killing took place. In the 1880's it was reported that the Indians near Phillips used 12 miles of fence for driving deer, and that a fence 15 miles long was in use at Trout Lake in Vilas County.

The origin of the names Fence, Michigan, and Waupaca, mentioned previously, substantiate the fact that deer fences were used by the Indians before the coming of the white man. Another method of hunting was used in Walworth County. An Elizabeth Baird in 1842 tells of hunting with the men from a sleigh-all were dressed in white. Even the black horse drawing the sleigh was provided with a white sheet as a camouflage. Although the use of set or spring guns, snares, and traps, was prohibited in the 1870's, these illegal methods continued into the 1900's.

Did deer move long distances because of fires, or man's relentless pursuit? Long ago the Indians believed in the general migration of deer. In 1877, a Sportsmen's Guide tells of deer being partially migrant, that they changed their range from north to south in the fall, but they did not desert their range forever. An article in the Forest and Stream Magazine in 1895 tells of migratory deer passing through a certain section in the fall and spring , and that local and migratory deer could be distinguished. In the same magazine in 1900, George Shiras writes of a spring and fall movement which "possessed the characteristics of a true migration". He believed the season should be established to take advantage of the southern migration. In his Preliminary List of Wisconsin Mammals in 1908, Hartley Jackson tells of deer wandering from the regions west and north of

the Wisconsin River to the southern tier of counties during severe winters.
The opinion was also held in the 1870's and '80's, that the construction of
barbed wire fences, particularly along railroads, ended deer migration.

Although the range of deer at the present time is considered to be
quite limited, there is no authentic information regarding the distance a
whitetail will move or migrate to a preferable habitat. All the information we have shows no general migration of deer in Wisconsin. In 1954, a
deer from the Barksdale Powder Plant released at Drummond was killed by a
car west of Spooner, a distance of 56 air miles from the release point.
What the movement of deer is in the woodlots and open fields of the agricultural counties is unknown. They may move great distances. A tagged
deer in Missouri covered a distance of 83 miles. In Illinois (1949), a
tagged deer was shot 98 miles away from the release site.

The first awareness of the public to the unnecessary deer slaughter,
and the need for some sort of deer protection, was brought to the attention
of the legislature more than one hundred years ago. Hardly had Wisconsin
been granted statehood in 1848, and the first legislature and governor
elected, than the first deer control law was passed. It provided for the
protection of deer by closing the season for five months only, from
February 1 to July 1, in 1851.

As early as this time, hunting for sport developed. We read of a
hunter shooting a spike buck on the headwaters of the Wolf River, who met
two unknown hunters that shot at the same animal. The deer was divided
according to the sportsmen's code at the time-the first hunter took the
venison, the strangers the skin.

It appears that deer were a common sight in many counties of the state
in the 1850's; however, most of the northern country was inaccessible.
Roads were little more than winding trails, and they were made for horses,
oxen, and wagon traffic only. In 1850, a primitive road was built from
Green Bay to Wausau, and ten years later a tote road was built through
wilderness from Wausau to Lac Vieux Desert on the Vilas County and Michigan
line.

A hundred years ago, less than 1,700 people lived in what is now the
northern major deer country. Only the woodsmen penetrated the wilderness
areas reported to have had deer; consequently, some wooded habitable areas
in the north not subject to the disastrous fires became natural refuges
awaiting the hunter who moved into the region with logging, railroads, and
settlement. Newspapers and settler chronicles tell of deer being plentiful
in Brown, Douglas, Juneau, St. Croix, and Waupaca Counties. Local papers
told of a band of St. Croix Indians taking 100 deer in the St. Croix-Polk
County region, and of a company of hunters bagging 30 to 40 deer in Richland
County. In 1856, the Whitewater Gazette tells of a Mr. Johnson killing
40 deer during the season in Walworth County.

In the 1860's, at the time of the Civil War, the deer picture began
to show hunting activity in the central and northern counties and disap-
pearance of deer from the oak forests and prairies in the southern part of
the state. In 1866, the Janesville Gazette tells of 3,000 deer being
brought to Eau Claire in three months' time. Deer were said to be plentiful in Lincoln, Marinette, and Polk Counties. Commercialized or market
hunting in the central and northern portions of the state began in earnest.
The lumbering industry, although in its infancy in 1860, began to employ
hunters to shoot for camps. Fires at the time also took a toll of deer.
The Black River, Chippewa, St. Croix, Wisconsin, and Wolf pineries, were
said to be a "raging sea of flame".

- 7 -

The northern half of the state continued to be a forest disturbed only by the hunter, trapper, and lumberman. Only 3% of the state's population lived in the northern areas now comprised of about 24 counties. There was no hunting pressure. During the 1860's, the annual deer seasons lasted 5 or 5½ months each year. During the previous decade, the seasons were 1½ to 2 months each year. Actually the deer seasons at this time did not expire-they were continuous. The only other deer hunting regulation was a legislative act prohibiting the use of set guns. The only law enforcement was by local officers who did not curtail year-round hunting. In the nineteenth century, it was a common belief that one could take whatever wildlife he wanted.

In the 1870's, we read of the enormous amount of saddles, hams, and carcasses shipped, much of it to the Milwaukee and Chicago markets. The winter venison supply was coming into Green Bay, a great deal of it taken within 50 miles of the city. One hunter brought in 30 at one time. The Delavan Republican speaks of 2,500 deer being taken on the Green Bay peninsula in 1878. In the 1870's, deer were being sold for 5 to 6 cents a pound at Eau Claire. Venison was plentiful in the Prairie du Chien market. "In Barron County deer are so plenty that they seriously trouble farmers by foraging upon the growing grain." An indication of the popularity of Wisconsin deer hunting at that time is shown by a guide advertising excellent hunting in Adams, Marinette, Oconto, Portage, and St. Croix Counties. Deer hunting regulations were not uniform throughout the state in the early days. For the most part they were political in nature, and not based on a deer conservation concept. A method of hunting in one portion of the state may have been illegal in another. In the general laws of the 1870's, we find incorporated a number of local or specific laws showing exceptions to the statewide deer season regulations. At times in the 1870's deer hunting laws were confusing to the hunter, since local laws took precedence over general laws. An indication of this lack of uniformity is found in the laws relating to the use of dogs in deer hunting-a method of hunting which was to be a problem for more than 25 years.

In 1871, the legislature passed the first local law for Door County only, prohibiting the use of dogs while deer hunting. A similar law later prevented the use of dogs in Kewaunee County. From 1876 to 1886, a general law prohibited the use of dogs, statewide, but a law, local in naturé, enacted in 1877 and in force until 1888, permitted the use of dogs for hunting deer only in Ashland, Bayfield, and Douglas Counties.

After 1901, hunting of deer with dogs was prohibited, except that in 1901 and 1902 a section of the law permitted their use in 16 southern counties; and in 1903 and 1904, in 28 southern counties. It was in 1905 that the hounding of deer was prohibited statewide-a law that has been in effect up to the present.

Shipment of deer or venison out of state was prohibited statewide in 1878 and 1879, but was permitted again from 1880 to 1882. During this time, however, in 1879, a local law prohibited the shipment of deer out of Door County unless the deer were taken within six miles of the southern county line. From 1883 to 1894, out-of-state shipment was prohibited anywhere. In 1895, shipment was permitted with a limit of two per trip when accompanied by the owner. After 1897, licensed nonresidents could take their legal deer out of the state.

Probably man's activities at the time of large-scale logging, railroad-building, and settlement in the 1880's affected deer (often disastrous) more,

- 8 -

or as much as, during any other decade. With the rapid growth of logging
came the replacement of slash and new growth, which for a time provided an
"edge" that increased the deer population. The opening of the wilderness
of virgin pine, never a habitat for deer, provided both summer and winter
food, and cover as well.

The population of the north jumped from about 35,000 inhabitants in
1870 to over 100,000 in 1880. Man began burning the slash to open the
country for agriculture. The development of railroads in the north at this
time made additional deer areas available to the sport and market hunter.
The Wisconsin Central Railroad completed a line from Milwaukee to Oshkosh,
with branches to Green Bay and Portage (1877). Tracks had been built to
Cable, Eagle River, Minocqua, and Turtle Lake, from Green Bay to Wausau,
across the state to Trempealeau and La Crosse, and northward from the mouth
of the Chippewa River connecting the St. Croix River with Lake Superior.
The railroads advertised the north as a sportsmen's paradise. They told of
hunting conditions and accommodations at Eagle River, Pelican Lake, and
Rhinelander. Maps of the deer counties were made. Only after the coming
of the railroads was a supply of venison available to the city markets.
Newspapers at the time, commented upon the wholesale slaughter of deer.
There were complaints of deer slaughter on the Peshtigo and Pike Rivers in
Marinette County, and of killings by Indians and the white man who left
carcasses in the woods to spoil. Market hunters filled the woods. Slaughter
by night hunting, and the use of dogs, was common.

In 1885, or 70 years ago, it was estimated that 10,000 deer were
shipped out of the state. A large number were shipped to Chicago despite
the law, and labeled "mutton" (1885). A newspaper tells of the oldest and
most experienced hunter in the vicinity of Eau Claire killing 3 tons of venison (1886). In Ashland County in 1887, after the railroad company refused
to receive a deer carcass, it was shipped in a coffin as a corpse. At
Wausau, wagonloads were taken to the city almost every day. Reports of
deer scarcity were made, but there was more evidence of abundance.

In view of the situation, sportsmen advocated shortening the season,
and some suggested closing it for several years (1889). Legislative action
to give the deer some protection was undertaken. In some instances the
laws were strange; for example, in 1885 it was unlawful to take deer except
for food. In 1880 a local law, which continued in force for nine years,
opened Ashland, Bayfield and Douglas Counties in August before the regular
opening in other counties. It is interesting to note that in 1879 a warden
was authorized for Ashland, Bayfield, and Douglas Counties, but the counties
had to pay his expenses and salary. Shining deer and hunting at night were
prohibited, but these practices continued.

During this time any number of deer could be taken. All counties were
open. Most of the seasons averaged from $1\frac{1}{2}$ to $3\frac{1}{2}$ months, and no license of
any kind was required. Hunters still fired the woods, although a forest
fire law ever since 1817, when Wisconsin was part of the Territory of Michigan,
was enacted to prevent the negligent setting of fire to the lands of another,
or allowing a fire to escape.

In 1887, the first actual game wardens were appointed by the governor.
He could have appointed four, but only two were designated at a salary of
$50.00 a month. The wardens could appoint helpers on a fee basis. They were
accused of being political appointments, and of having greater concern for
the conservation of votes than of wildlife. Enforcement of the law continued to be ineffective.

In the 1890's, many areas of the north were described as having plenty of deer; however, the deer were decreasing rapidly because of wasteful killing. Northern Wisconsin was still a land of forests, slash, and forest wastes, and large portions of the region were unoccupied. Prospective settlers were plied with attractive letters advertising its wonderful resources. The area was in a primitive condition agriculturally, and a clearing was to be found only here and there. In the 29 counties of the new north, Boards of Immigration were established to promote settlement.

The hunting of deer with dogs, and wasteful killing continued, as did the unrestricted trade in deer, because of public indifference and indifferent law enforcement. Market hunters were moving through Michigan, Minnesota, and Wisconsin, hunting from one state to another. Woodsmen were employed by logging camps to furnish venison. Entanglement with wire fences along the railroad lines afforded hunters ever easier killing. It was said that illegal game was flooding the Chicago and Milwaukee markets, and that game fences in Milwaukee were receiving carloads of venison, and were acting as clearing houses for illegal shipments to Chicago and St. Louis. A way of evading the law was to ship venison in barrels covered with partridges, and to conceal deer in shipments of Christmas trees. Comments were made often as to the ineffectiveness of the law in preventing the shipment of deer out of the state. Blame was often directed at the express companies. A warden reported wolves and lynx killing many deer in northern Wisconsin, and suggested an increase in bounty payments (wolf bounties had been paid since 1865).

The 1890's marked the peak of lumber production, and provided the hunter with more areas which had been inaccessible in the past. Thousands of miles of logging highways and railroad grades became access routes to the cutover. The lumbering business rapidly provided openings and the eventual clearing of the wilderness. The clearing of railroad right-of-ways resulted in new deer-hunting fields.

Disastrous fires at the time must have accounted for tremendous loss of wildlife and range destruction. The Phillips fire in 1894 burned over 100,000 acres in Price County. Fires continued to rage throughout the state. The Peshtigo fire in 1871 is said to have burned over 1,280,000 acres in an area covering a number of our northeast counties. Settlers and loggers spoke of fires driving deer into new areas, and of many deer of central Wisconsin being driven north to the counties south of Lake Superior. Light fires set on stump farms in the northern and central counties, and slight burning on railroad grades, often actually improved the deer range, as these areas grew up to seedlings, sprouts, and shrubs.

The railroads continued to increase their revenue by publicizing good hunting spots. The Milwaukee, Northwestern, and Wisconsin Central roads hauled many hundreds of nonresidents from Indiana and Ohio. The Northwestern Railroad listed Wisconsin game counties suggested by its station agents. They spoke of good deer-hunting prospects at Ashland, Manitowish, Rhinelander, and Tomahawk Lake. They told of other regions where deer were plentiful. The areas near railroad stations saw a large hunting population and intensive hunting.

In the 1890's, public opinion began to take a turn in favor of deer protection. The shooting of large numbers of does and fawns was deplored. A movement was under way to have a law prohibiting the killing of deer for five years. Abolishment of spring and summer shooting, and prevention of the sale of game at any time, were advocated. In Ashland County, a "Rod, Gun, and Game Protection Club" was organized.

The decline of deer and public demand for changes in the game laws brought considerable legislative action in the 1900's in the form of restrictions upon the hunter. In 1897, a bag limit was established for the first time. The number of deer that could be taken during the season was lowered to two of either sex or any size. Oddly, the law permitted a settler to kill more than two deer for family or neighbor consumption, but not for sale. The owner was required to accompany any deer carcass that was transported. Possession of fawn skins, or skins in the red, was illegal. Hotels and restaurants could serve venison only during the open season. It was lawful to shoot dogs running deer. Closed seasons in various counties were beginning. Fond du Lac and Sheboygan Counties were the first to have closed seasons. Annual seasons began to open in November rather than in October, and the length of the season was reduced. For the first time, deer-hunting licenses were required by both resident and out-of-state hunters. Only in counties frequented by deer, as designated by the legislature, were licenses issued at a fee of $1.00, and nonresident licenses at $30.00.

In spite of these regulations, disregard for the game laws and over-shooting continued in the early 1900's. Although the Lacey Act, a federal law, was passed (which prevented interstate commerce in game killed in violation of local laws), illegal shipments, labeled as butter, eggs, and veal, continued. One of the many ingenious ways to evade game laws or the Lacey Act was shown again by another hunter who shipped two deer to Chicago in a coffin. Resorts were serving venison as mutton. The railroads continued to make their customary campaigns in Illinois, Indiana, and Ohio, to attract deer hunters to Wisconsin.

Probably the deer population reached the lowest point before World War I. In the early 1900's, the awareness of the public to the decline, and grave concern with the problem of increasing the herd, resulted in more legislative restrictions relating to deer hunting. Dogs running deer were declared a public nuisance. The use of salt licks and elevated scaffolds was outlawed. In the southern part of the state, 36 counties were closed in 1907, which marked the first extensive closing of a large area in the state. In 1909, for the first time hunters could bag only one deer instead of two. A forest protection plan was developed, and the first fire lanes were created.

Of far-reaching value in the conservation of deer was the taking of wardens out of politics, and placing them under the merit system. In 1909, civil service examinations were given on a competitive basis. The first school for wardens held three years later received praise from other states. Enforcement of the laws began in earnest in spite of difficulties. In 1916, few of the wardens had automobiles; twenty-five motorcycles were in use. Most of the 63 wardens covered their territory on foot, by train, or by hired livery.

In 1915, the most controversial of all game regulations began, which revolved around the type of deer season best suited for increasing the herd in view of the appalling toll effected in the past by disastrous fires, commercialized hunting, and lack of sufficient enforcement. For several years the storm grew over the need for protecting does and fawns. In 1915, the Conservation Department took a definite stand in favor of a buck season only. Mr. W. E. Barber of the Wisconsin Conservation Commission spoke of deer making their last stand in about twenty counties of the state. He said, "Something must be done to save our deer, as settlements are fast encroaching over the wilderness." The problem of increasing the deer herd was affected by new factors in hunting. High-powered guns became popular, whereas a large number of hunters had used shotguns in the past. Highway development in the state helped make deer hunting one of the major outdoor winter activities, although roads in the early stages were not always in passable condition. The hunter began to use the automobile in moving to the deer country. As late as 1924, a newspaperman spent more than 31 hours to get through a broken road from Rice Lake to Madison. By 1916, 115,000 automobiles were licensed, compared to less than 6,000 in 1910. The influence of the growing popularity of the automobile is shown by the statement in 1917-18 Biennial Report, "Deer, as well as other wild game, have a new weapon pointed at them, more deadly than powder and bullets and much harder to escape, as the range is long and it reaches out into the remote districts where deer once found refuge safe from the pursuit of the hunter. The automobile has annihilated this space, and distance will no longer protect them".

The first one-buck law was passed by the legislature in 1915, and was in effect for two years. At the same time, deer hunting was limited to thirty northern counties. In 1917, for the first time the Conservation Commission was delegated powers relating to deer seasons. The legislature could continue to establish the seasons at each biennial session, but the Commission was empowered to reduce the season, and limit the number of species taken, upon petitions filed and the holding of public hearings.

In 1917, the legislature again established a hunting season which permitted the taking of one deer regardless of age or sex. An estimated 18,000 deer, a kill considerably larger than had been recorded previously, was taken during the reduced season of only ten days. Because of this comparatively large kill, sportsmen from all over the state requested the Commission to use its power to protect does and fawns. The Commission supported the theory that a one-buck law was the only one that would protect the deer and provide an annual open season, but was hesitant in limiting the seasons in contradiction to the wishes of the legislature. It did not make use of its power until 1918 when an any-one-deer season established by the legislature was changed by the Commission to an any-one-deer, except fawns, season. At this time Wisconsin had approximately 53,000 deer hunters who purchased deer tags at a cost of 10 cents each-approximately 1/5 of the number of hunters who bought deer tags during the 1954 season.

In 1919, the any-deer season was termed disastrous, and it was believed that only a one-buck law would safeguard the herd. That same year the Wisconsin Conservationist stated, "A one-buck law is essential to the deer supply, and at the close of the 1921 season, deer probably will be wiped out."

Since by this time the deer population was considered to be at a low level, and public demand for a change in the season increased, the one-buck law management policy was approved by the legislature in 1920. From then on until the 1943 "split" season, 17 buck seasons were established.

Additional protection was given to deer by legislative action in closing some seasons entirely. In 1925, acting under petitions from the deer counties, the legislature passed a law opening and closing the deer season in alternate years. As a consequence, the first closed season in the history of deer hunting occurred in 1925. The alternate years 1927, 1929, 1931, 1933, and 1935, also had closed seasons.

The six-man Commission, a policy-forming body created by the legislature in 1927, was empowered in 1933 to provide open and closed seasons, bag limits, and conditions governing the taking of fish and game. This system of making game regulations has been in effect for about 30 years.

The 1930's witnessed definite and far-reaching changes in the deer picture. The game division of the Conservation Department, organized in 1928, had begun to inform the public of the needs and purposes of deer regulations. Previous to 1933, the legislature had established all fish and game seasons. Hundreds of bills relating to wildlife conservation had been submitted during each biennial session. Many bills were passed which were local in character and not based upon a policy of statewide needs in the interest of deer conservation.

At the same time (1933), the Conservation Congress, an advisory group representing public opinion as registered at annual county hearings, began to assist the Conservation Commission in establishing a deer management policy.

By the middle 1930's, a number of conditions had brought about a substantial increase in the herd, and with it a number of problems unknown to anyone who had hunted deer in the 1920's. The building up of the herd to a new and dangerous high in some areas may be attributed to several factors. Efficient forest protection, which provided a young second growth of food and cover, began to be effective in the 1930's throughout the entire North; the conservation wardens formed an efficient organization in game law enforcement; hounding of deer, market-hunting, and some other illegal deer-hunting methods, disappeared in the 1920's; and restrictive hunting regulations were in force, particularly the one-buck law which was designed to save the deer but actually insured an increase in the herd. Natural predators were eliminated in the deer range areas. Deer refuges were set up.

The growth of the herd since the creation of the Conservation Commission may be shown by the annual field censuses and estimated kills. From 1935 until after the 1937 season, the C.C.C's with their large man power made many drives, and counted approximately 30 deer per section in various areas of northern Wisconsin. This was the first absolute proof of a large deer herd. The C.C.C. census drives showed the Chequamegon National Forest areas as having too large a deer population and the possibility of starvation. Because of the bad browse conditions in 1935, the U. S. Forest Service appealed to the Conservation Commission to permit the killing of 14,000 deer, or 15 deer to the square mile, in a portion of the forest area.

During the 1930's, more than two times as many bucks were taken as were bagged during the buck and any-deer seasons of the 1920's. The annual seasons in the 1940's yielded an estimated harvest of more than one-half million whitetails, a sum twice as large as the combined kill of the 1920's and 1930's. The ever-increasing hunting pressure is shown by the fact that about 400,000 deer licenses were sold in the 1920's, whereas approximately 1 3/4 million big game licenses were sold in the 1940's.

With the astounding increase in the deer population came serious problems of management. In 1930, winter starvation in isolated areas of northwestern Wisconsin was reported. Four years later, deer yard feeding began in the Flag River yard, a project which has been in operation every winter. To date, more than one-half million dollars has been spent for feed costs and distribution. More than 7,000 tons of artificial feed has been fed, an activity not accepted by game managers as the solution to the overpopulation problem. Along with this expensive problem of feeding, we have had deer

- 13 -

damage to crops which, during the 23-year period 1931-1954, has cost more than $400,000.00 in all but 13 of the 71 counties. Paid deer damage claims in the ten-year period 1955-1964 amounted to more than $200,000.00 and included all but 6 counties.

The fact that browse conditions became progressively more critical over an extended period and herd control was necessary, received little consideration from the public. Any relief through more liberal seasons was fought by many, including the "Save the Deer Club" organized to prevent any change.

In 1940 a deer research project began, wherein a study of starvation losses and damage to forest reproduction was made. Since the advent of deer research studies, a public acceptance of the necessity of deer herd control has grown.

After the so-called slaughter of the "split" season of 1943 got under way, providing for a 4-day buck season, a 3-day rest period, and a 4-day antlerless season, it was believed by many that the deer would never come back, although more than eight million acres were closed primarily as a protection to deer. Contrary to the alarmist views of herd extermination at the time, hunters were to see a tremendously high kill of over a half-million during the following eight years.

The year after the "split" season, an any-deer season began for the first time in a number of western and southern agricultural counties. One out of five hunters in this region was successful, a further indication of an increasing deer population. In 1952, Buffalo County, never a major deer county, ranked among the leading deer kill counties. During the 1952 season, the agricultural open counties accounted for one-fifth of the total state deer kill.

In 1946 and 1947, controlled hunts by permit were held in the Necedah National Wildlife Refuge where 32 and 17 deer were taken per square mile. The 1949 antlerless season, and the 1950 and 1951 any-deer seasons, yielded an estimated kill of more than 400,000. For these three years Wisconsin led the nation in the white-tailed deer kill. The growth and spread of the herd is also shown by the number of open counties during the last 25 years. Not until the 1943 "split" season were there more than 35 counties open to deer hunting. Where we had 20 to 30 counties open in the 1930's, we find 40 or more open during most of the 1940's. During the early 1950's, 53 to 55 counties were opened.

The deer herd, while greatly reduced by the statewide liberal seasons of 1949, 1950 and 1951, was not decimated and by the mid-fifties it was apparent again that population controls were needed in many parts of the state.

The Commission, reluctant to open the entire state to an any-deer season, and without the legal authority to directly restrict hunter numbers and the number of deer to be harvested, proposed the party permit system which was enacted into law by the 1957 Legislature under Sec. 29.107 Wisconsin Statutes. Under this law, any four or more licensed hunters could band together and purchase a permit which entitled them to take an extra or "party" deer which could be of any age and either sex.

The party permit system, favored by sportsmen during the first two of its four years of use, lost its appeal in the 1959 and 1960 seasons.

During these years, the distribution of hunters and harvests was poor and as a result, excessively high cropping of deer occurred in a number of areas. In spite of the shortcommings of the party permit law, Wisconsin harvested 330,000 deer during the four annual seasons, 1957 through 1960, when the system was in use.

In order to distribute pressure to more effectively reduce illegal killing, and to better control the harvest, the law was modified to permit the Conservation Commission to directly manage the number of antlerless deer that could be removed. This was the variable quota law, approved by the Legislature in 1961, put into effect in 1963 and used again in 1964. Because of the rapid expansion of the deer population in the central and southern counties, and the liberal seasons in effect in these parts of the state, the variable quota party permit, with its minimum of four hunters, proved inadequate to meet the harvest needs, particularly in the northwestern counties. Therefore, modifications of the basically good variable quota party deer law are being sought.

Today's deer are found in an available range of 18,900,000 acres. They browse within sight of many towns, villages and cities. Changing land use is encouraging deer to creep back and increase in farm areas and in what were formerly farm regions. Deer are found in all counties of Wisconsin, including Milwaukee County.

The problem of deer management is a continuous one. It is one in which the herd must be managed to insure a maximum number of animals without damage to the range or to themselves. This situation will be further complicated by the continuing human population increase. Demands are being made for a large herd as a tourist attraction in resort areas, regardless of browse need. The existing policy on deer management gives official recognition to this value.

Along with the increasingly large number of hunters, has come a degeneration in the sport. The hunter who seeks an unusual rack of antlers or a trophy is scarce. The values found in the old-time deer drives, or moving away from the traveled roads into the back country are appreciated by fewer hunters.

The major deer areas are changing. The central and southwestern counties with their decreasing agriculture, continue to produce more and more deer. The north country is growing up. Many hunting areas once available are now solid and extensive monotype stands of pole-sized hardwoods which offer no browse and poor cover; consequently, the situation provides difficulties in habitat management. Deer like openings and mixed young or uneven stands. They do not get along well in middle-aged or mature forests. If a maximum herd, in keeping with its winter range, is to be maintained, further modification of present legislation covering deer seasons, variable party quotas, and the control of hunter numbers must be made.

Public acceptance of the state's deer management policy continues to improve slowly. If the whitetails had adopted the characteristics of the caribou, among which the females normally have antlers, deer management and season regulations would invite considerably less controversy.

March 1, 1966

Otis S. Bersing

- 15 -

PART ONE

GUN DEER HUNTING

DEER HUNTING SEASONS
1850-1964

Year	Seasons Length	Seasons Type	Number of Open Counties	Estimated Gun Kill	License Sales	Chronology
Before 1851	All year	Any kind or number	Entire state	-	None	Last buffalo killed in Trempealeau County (1832). Last caribou seen in Ashland County in (1840).
1851-1858	July 1- Jan.31 7 mos.	Any kind or number	Entire state	-	None	First game laws. First closed season. Indians permitted to hunt at any time. Wholesale price of venison in Rock County: 3-5¢ per lb. (1857). Venison sold for 5¢ per lb. at Wautoma, Waushara Co. (1856). "Deer have become so lean by starvation that their flesh is not marketable".--Grant County Herald (1857). Deer pelt value 25¢ - Portage.
1859	July 1- Dec.31 6 mos.	Any kind or number	Entire state	-	None	Indians permitted to hunt at any time.

Deer Hunting Seasons (continued)
1850-1964

Year	Seasons		Number of Open Counties	Estimated Gun Kill	License Sales	Chronology
	Length	Type				
1860-1866	Aug. 1 - Jan. 1 5 months	Any kind or number	Entire state	-	None	Sale of Venison prohibited during closed season (1860-1876) Possession of "fresh venison" or skin nor permitted from Feb. 1 to Aug. 1, "uncivilized Indians" excepted (1860). Venison sold for 10-12¢ per lb. at Janesville (1866). More than 3,000 deer brought into Eau Claire for shipment (1866). Last native elk killed in Dunn County (1866). First state-financed bounties on wolves (1865).

Year	Season		Number of Open Counties	Estimated Gun Kill	License Sales	Chronology
	Length	Type				
1867-1874	Aug. 1 - Jan. 15 5½ months	Any kind or number	Entire state	-	None	Possession, sale, and transportation of venison prohibited during closed season (1867-1876). Deer laws did not affect Indians on their own reservations (1868-1896). Set guns prohibited (1869-). Door County the first to prohibit use of dogs (1871). Venison sold for 8-10¢ per lb. in Richland County (1870). Deer plentiful in Sauk and Marquette Counties (1874). Deer shipped from Green Bay to Milwaukee and Chicago market (1870). Wildcat and lynx bountied (1867). Peshtigo forest fire burned 1,280,000 acres in northeastern Wisconsin (1871).

Year	Seasons		Number of Open Counties	Estimated Gun Kill	License Sales	Chronology
	Length	Type				
1875-1876	Aug.15-Dec.15 4 mos.	Any kind or number	Entire state	-	None	Hunting with dogs prohibited in the state in (187 in Kewaunee County in (1875).
						Traps and snares prohibited (1875-).
						Landowner's consent requi to hunt any wild animal in Milwaukee County (1876)
						Complaint of deer damage to wheat and corn crops ir Shawano County (1876)

Deer Hunting Seasons (continued)
1850-1964

Year	Seasons		Number of Open Counties	Estimated Gun Kill	License Sales	Chronology
	Length	Type				
1877-1879	Sept.15-Jan.1 3½ mos.	Any Kind or number	70	-	None	Possession, sale, and transportation prohibited between Jan. 15 and Sept. 15.
	Oct.16-Oct.31 16 days	Any kind or number	Burnett County only	-	None	Sale of venison permitted during open season, and for 15 days thereafter (1877-1888).

Possession, sale, and transportation prohibited between Jan. 15 and Sept. 15.

Sale of venison permitted during open season, and for 15 days thereafter (1877-1888).

Although hunting with **dogs was** prohibited generally, local law permitted their use in Ashland, Bayfield, and Douglas Counties (1877-1888)-repealed in 1889.

Exportation of deer out of state prohibited (1878-1879).

Sale or shipment of deer from Door County illegal, unless deer killed within 6 miles of southern county line (1879).

(continued on the following page)

Year	Seasons		Number of Open Counties	Estimated Gun Kill	License Sales	Chronology
	Length	Type				
1877-1879 period continued						Killing deer for skins only not permitted in Door County (1879). Nets and spring guns prohibited (1878-). Large number of deer killed in swamps and on river islands of Iowa County (1877). Deer reported plentiful in Chippewa, Clark, and Richland Counties (1879). Venison sold in Eau Claire at 5-6¢ per lb. (1879). Plentiful at Prairie du Chien market (1879). 150 deer killed in vicinity of Shiocton, Outagamie County (1878).

Year	Seasons		Number of Open Counties	Estimated Gun Kill	License Sales	Chronology
	Length	Type				
	Sept.1- Nov.30 3 mos.	Any kind or number	All 47ˣ counties north of Columbia, Dodge, Ozaukee, Sauk, Vernon, and Washington.	-	None	Possession of venison illegal after Jan. 15. Shipping out of state permitted (1880-1882).
1880	Aug.16- Nov. 30 3½ mos.	Any kind or number	Ashland, Bayfield, Douglas	-	None	Night hunting and shining of deer prohibited in Door County.
	Oct.16- Oct.31 16 days	Any kind or number	Burnett	-	None	Shipping deer out of Door County prohibited.
	Sept.15- Jan. 1 3½ mos.	Any kind or number	20 remaining counties	-	None	Deer reported plentiful in Barron County-raiding gardens. Venison sold for 8¢ per lb. in Janesville.
	Sept.15- Jan. 1 3½ mos.	Any kind or number	67	-	None	Deer reported numerous in Door County (1882).
1881- 1882	Aug.16- Nov.30 3½ mos.	Any kind or number	Ashland, Bayfield, Douglas	-	None	First resort (northeastern Wisconsin) on Lac Vieux Desert (1882).
	Oct.16- Oct.31 16 days	Any kind or number	Burnett	-	None	Report of two deer shot in Florence County -"weight aggregate-575 lbs."

* Indicates the area comprising the 47 counties at the present time.

Year	Seasons		Number of Open Counties	Estimated Gun Kill	License Sales	Chronology
	Length	Type				
1883-1884	Nov.1-Dec.15 1½ mos.	Any kind or number	68	-	None	Out-of-state shipment of deer prohibited (1883-1894).
	Aug.16-Nov.30 3½ mos.	Any kind or number	Ashland, Bayfield, Douglas			Shining deer prohibited (1883-1916). Last cougar killed in Ashland County (1884).
1885-1886	Oct.1-Nov.30 2 mos.	Any kind or number	68	-	None	Killing deer permitted "only for food" (1885). Possession permitted only during the season.
	Aug.16-Nov.30 3½ mos.	Any kind or number	Ashland, Bayfield, Douglas	-	None	Deer reported destroying gardens in Pestigo (1885). Game slaughter reported in Peshtigo and Pike River areas of Marinette County. Marinette News recommended "Game Constables".

Year	Seasons		Number of Open Counties	Estimated Gun Kill	License Sales	Chronology
	Length	Type				
1887-1888	Oct.1-Nov.10 41 days	Any kind or number	68	-	None	The use of dogs again permitted during the season (1887-1888).

Nighttime hunting prohibited statewide (1887-).

Use of guns not discharged from shoulder prohibited (1887-1930).

First actual game wardens (2) appointed by governor.

Game laws to be published in pamphlet form.

Reports of deer scarcity in northern counties (1888). |
| | Aug.16-Nov.30 3½ mos. | Any kind or number | Ashland, Bayfield, Douglas | - | None | |

Deer Hunting Seasons (continued)
1850-1964

Year	Seasons Length	Seasons Type	Number of Open Counties	Estimated Gun Kill	License Sales	Chronology
1889-1890	Oct.15-Dec. 1 $1\frac{1}{2}$ mos.	Any kind or number	Entire state	-	None	In 1889 hunting with dogs again prohibited (1889-1900). Sale of venison, or possession for sale, prohibited more than 8 days after close of season (1889-1894). Movement by sportsmen to close season for five years First chief warden appointed.
1891-1892	Nov. 1-Dec. 1 31 days	Any kind or number	Entire state	-	None	Hunter killed by a set gun near Chelsea.

Deer Hunting Seasons (continued)
1850-1964

Year	Seasons Length	Type	Number of Open Counties	Estimated Gun Kill	License Sales	Chronology
1893-1894	Oct.1-Nov.1 31 days	Any kind or number	Entire state	-	None	Lawful for any person to kill any dog running or hunting deer. Hunting with dogs common (1893). Unlawful to possess deer after 8 days after close of season (1893-1899). Express or railroad companies could not accept deer for shipment after 8 days after close of season. Hotels and restaurants could not serve venison during closed season. Warden reported wolves and lynx killing many deer in northern Wisconsin. Phillips forest fire burned 100,000 acres in (1894).

Year	Seasons		Number of Open Counties	Estimated Gun Kill	License Sales	Chronology
	Length	Type				
1895	Nov.1-Nov.20 20 days	Any kind or number	70	-	None	Sheboygan first county closed to deer hunting (1895). Although night-time hunting prohibited, "nighttime" defined further by statute as time between 1 hour after sunset to 1 hour before sunrise (1895-1935). Deer carcasses could not be transported unless accompanied by owner (1895-). Carcasses limited to two per trip (1895-1896). Transportation of deer out of state permitted (1895-). Sale of venison not permitted after 3 days following close of season (1895-1896). Restaurants or hotels could not serve venison during closed season.

Year	Seasons		Number of Open Counties	Estimated Gun Kill	License Sales	Chronology
	Length	Type				
1896	Oct.1-Nov.1 31 days	Any kind or number	Entire state	-	None	Last October deer season. Wisconsin Supreme Court, in a decision handed down October 13, 1896, held that what was supposed to be our fish and game laws for 1895-96, never had passed the legislature (legally), and therefore was null; consequently, laws of 1893 deemed in force, and deer season dates were Oct. 1 to Nov. 1, and not Nov. 1 to Nov. 20. Sudden court decision during middle of season confused no small number of deer hunters. Number of hunters, particularly nonresidents, reduced. Ruling actually provided short season.

Year	Seasons		Number of Open Counties	Estimated Gun Kill	Estimated* License Sales	Chronology
	Length	Type				
1897	Nov. 1-Nov. 20 20 days	Number reduced to two, any size, either sex.	69	-	12,000	First bag limit. First deer hunting license required; resident $1.00; nonresident $30.00. Two numbered coupons issued with each license. Licenses sold only in "counties frequented by deer" (Northern counties). Killing deer in water areas prohibited (1897-). Killing deer on ice prohibited (1897-1947). Venison could be sold or transported during first 5 days after close of season (1897-1902). Possession of skins in the red, or spotted coat, unlawful.

(continued on the following page)

* Estimated license sales include nonresident deer licenses from 1897 through 1916.

Deer Hunting Seasons (continued)
1850-1964

| Year | Seasons | | Number of Open Counties | Estimated Gun Kill | Estimated License Sales | Chronology |
	Length	Type				
1897 continued						Settler or resident could kill more than 2 deer during the season, for family or neighbor consumption but not for sale (1897-1898). Wolves reported as being numerous. Moose killed in either Bayfield or Douglas County.
1898	Nov. 1-Nov. 20 20 days	Two deer, any size or sex.	69	-	11,913	Disastrous forest fires occurred in northwestern Wisconsin.
1899	Nov. 1-Nov. 20 20 days	Two deer, any size or sex.	69	1,953*	35,340	Deer Hunting license including license for hunting other game. Deer purchases, sale, and transportation, permitted only between Nov. 6 and Nov. 25, inclusive.

(continued on the following page)
* Deer transported by rail only.

Year	Seasons		Number of Open Counties	Estimated Gun Kill	Estimated License Sales	Chronology
	Length	Type				
1899 continued						Home consumption after the season permitted by written notice to warden (1899-1914). Nonresident deer license fee reduced to $25.00 (1899-1916). 114 deer reported shipped out of state. Height of lumbering production.
1900	Nov. 1-Nov. 20 20 days	Two deer, any size or sex.	69	2,568*	31,856	Twelve hunters killed by firearms. High-power guns popular. 104 deer reported shipped out of state. The Federal Lacey Act prohibited interstate commerce in game killed in violation of local laws.

* Deer transported by rail only.

COUNTIES FREQUENTED BY DEER IN 1897

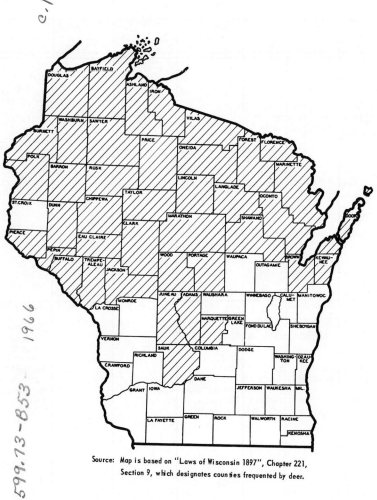

Source: Map is based on "Laws of Wisconsin 1897", Chapter 221, Section 9, which designates counties frequented by deer.

Year	Seasons		Number of Open Counties	Estimated Gun Kill	Estimated License Sales	Chronology
	Length	Type				
1901	Nov. 11- Nov. 30 20 days	Two deer, any size or sex.	67	-	41,000	Dogs found running deer declared public nuisance. Unlawful to sell or transport deer between Dec. 5 and Nov. 15. Hunting with dogs during open season prohibited, except in 16 southern open counties. (1901-1902). Few native moose existed.
	Nov. 21- Nov. 30 10 days	Two deer, any size or sex.	Adams, Columbia, Marquette, Richland, and Sauk.			
1902	Nov. 11- Nov. 30 20 days	Two deer, any size or sex.	62	3,352*	72,635	Number of nonresident deer hunting licenses issued: 293. Nonresident hunters shipped 318 deer.
	Nov. 21- Nov. 30 10 days	Two deer, any size or sex.	Adams, Columbia, Marquette, Richland, and Sauk.			

* Deer transported by rail only.

Year	Seasons		Number of Open Counties	Estimated Gun Kill	Estimated License Sales	Chronology
	Length	Type				
1903	Nov. 11- Nov. 30 20 days	Two deer, any size or sex.	62	-	78,164	Sale of venison prohibited (1903-1954). Hunting with dogs during open season prohibited except in 28 southern counties (1903-1904). Resident hunting licenses issued only to persons 12 years of age or older 1903-1908).
	Nov. 21- Nov. 30 10 days	Two deer, any size or sex.	Adams, Columbia, Marquette, Richland, and Sauk.			Resident licenses issued to settlers by state game warden (1903-1916). Number of nonresident deer hunting licenses issued: 361 Beginning of state forest protection organization.

Year	Seasons		Number of Open Counties	Estimated Gun Kill	Estimated License Sales	Chronology
	Length	Type				
1904	Nov. 11-Nov. 30 20 days	Two deer, any size or sex.	62	-	76,000	Beginning of forestry in Wisconsin. Export limit still 2 deer.
	Nov. 21-Nov. 30 10 days	Two deer, any size or sex.	Adams, Columbia, Marquette, Richland, and Sauk.			
1905	Nov. 11-Nov. 30 20 days	Two deer, any size or sex.	61	-	73,474	Hunting with dogs prohibited (1905-). Use of salt licks prohibited (1905-). Number of nonresident deer hunting licenses issued: 249.
	Nov. 21-Nov. 30 10 days	Two deer, any size or sex.	Adams, Richland, Marquette,			3.3% of population were licensed hunters
1906	Nov. 11-Nov. 30 20 days	Two deer, any size or sex.	61	-	82,000	20 caribou released on Brule River, Douglas County.
	Nov. 21-Nov. 30 10 days	Two deer, any size or sex.	Adams, Richland, Marquette.			Number of nonresident deer hunting licenses issued: 473.

Year	Seasons		Number of Open Counties	Estimated Gun Kill	Estimated License Sales	Chronology
	Length	Type				
1907	Nov. 11- Nov. 30 20 days	Two deer, any size or sex.	35	-	90,000	First extensive closing of counties; 36 southern counties closed. First closed season in Milwaukee County. First closed season on moose. Bag limit of one deer _for nonresident_ hunters. Shipment of carcass prohibited between Dec. 3 and Nov. 12. Dogs not allowed in hunting or logging camps in open counties during season (1907-1908). Use of elevated scaffold prohibited (1907-). A lynx reported killed in Dane County.
1908	Nov. 11- Nov. 30 20 days	Two deer, any size or sex.	35	11,000	100,000	1,209,432 acres burned over. Cougar reported killed in Douglas County.

Deer Hunting Seasons (continued)
1850-1964

Year	Seasons		Number of Open Counties	Estimated Gun Kill	Estimated License Sales	Chronology
	Length	Type				
1909	Nov. 11-Nov. 30 20 days	Any one deer.	31	3,985*	103,000	For first time, residents limited to taking one deer. Age limit of licensee--15 years, citizenship required (1909-1938). Hunting with dogs, or having dogs in possession, prohibited during November in open season deer counties (1909-1917). Unlawful to ship by carrier or private conveyance, any carcass between Dec. 3 and Nov. 12. "The Fish and Game Warden may issue permits to breed or domesticate deer, moose, elk, and caribou....". Increase of deer in Sauk County. Cougar reported seen in Marinette County.

(continued on the following page)

* Deer transported by rail only.

Deer Hunting Seasons (continued)
1850-1964

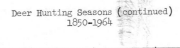

Year	Seasons Length	Seasons Type	Number of Open Counties	Estimated Gun Kill	Estimated License Sales	Chronology
1909 continued						Wisconsin Fish and Game Protective Association organized (incorporated in 1916).
1910	Nov. 11-Nov. 30 20 days	Any one deer.	31	-	113,000	Record deer head reported taken in Vilas County. Maximum outside spread: $30\frac{1}{2}$"; weight 256 lbs. dressed.
1911	Nov. 11-Nov. 30 20 days	Any one deer.	33	6,555*	125,000	First fire lanes. Forest Protection plan developed.
1912	Nov. 11-Nov. 30 20 days	Any one deer.	33	5,853*	123,000	Deer common in 24 counties. Timber wolves common in northern Wisconsin.
1913	Nov. 11-Nov. 30 20 days	Any one deer.	31	6,969*	147,000	First closed season on elk. Carload of elk shipped from Yellowstone National Park to 300-acre enclosure at Trout Lake, Vilas County; only two survived. Shipment of deer carcass between Dec. 3 and Nov. 12 prohibited.

* Deer transported by rail only.

APPROXIMATE RANGE OF WHITE-TAILED DEER-1912

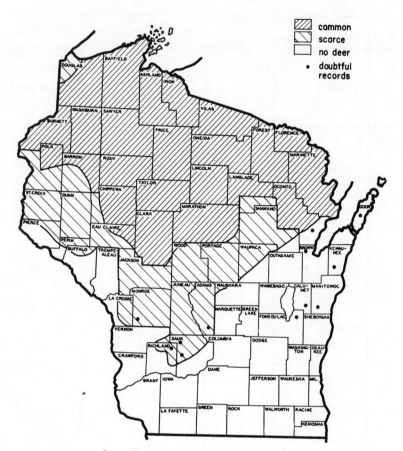

Source: "Mammals of Illinois and Wisconsin" by C. B. Cory.

Deer Hunting Seasons (continued)
1850-1964

Year	Seasons		Number of Open Counties	Estimated Gun Kill	Estimated License Sales	Chronology
	Length	Type				
1914	Nov. 11-Nov. 30 20 days	Any one deer.	31	7,347*	155,000	Newspaper report showed 24 hunters killed, and 26 injured during season. "Richland County now boasts of about one hundred deer, while Sauk has about four hundred."

* Deer transported by rail only.

Deer Hunting Seasons (continued)
1850-1964

Year	Seasons		Number of Open Counties	Estimated Gun Kill	Estimated License Sales	Chronology
	Length	Type				
1915	Nov. 11-Nov. 30 20 days	Any one buck. ("Bucks in the velvet, or in red, blue, or spotted coat, or does-- none.")	30	3,257*	134,000	First one-buck law. Transportation of deer permitted between Nov. 12 and Dec. 3. Resident possession of legal deer permitted at any time; written notice to Commission required (1915-1916). Game (deer, elk, moose...) farmers' license issued. "One-half of all deer killed are killed by market hunters". First game refuge established; two townships closed in Forest County. Five hunters reported killed.
1916	Nov. 11-Nov. 30 20 days	Any one buck. ("Bucks in the velvet, or in red, blue, or spotted coat, or does-- none.")	30	7,000 (3,647)*	125,000	Automobile popular. 115,645 autos licensed. Number of non-resident deer hunting licenses issued: 173

* Deer transported by rail only.

Deer Hunting Seasons (continued)
1850-1964

Year	Seasons		Number of Open Counties	Estimated Gun Kill	Deer Tag Sales*	Chronology
	Length	Type				
1917	Nov. 21-Nov. 30 10 days	Any one deer. ("Any deer in the velvet, or in the red or blue coat - none".)	30	18,000	53,593	Commission empowered to reduce game laws as to manner, numbers, places, and times of taking game, upon petition filed and the holding of public hearings. Department stated: "A one-buck law is the only law that will protect the deer and provide an annual open season". Legislature rejected one-buck law. Deer tags (paper) required for first time; cost 10¢. Nonresident big game license fee increased to $50.00 (1917-1954). First settler license issued. First guide license issued. Indians hunting, fishing, or trapping off Indian reservation lands subject to all game laws.

(continued on the following page)

Deer tag sales represent only resident license sales from 1917 through 1936.

Deer Hunting Seasons (continued)
1850-1964

Year	Seasons		Number of Open Counties	Estimated Gun Kill	Deer Tag Sales	Chronology
	Length	Type				
1917 continued						No person while hunting or in possession of firearms, could have in possession any light for purpose of hunting deer (1917-).
						Home consumption of deer permitted at any time (1917-1938).
						Hunting with dogs, or having dogs in possession during period from Nov. 1 to Dec. 10, prohibited in open seasons (1917-1922).
						Moose seen in Ashland County.
						Second carload of elk, 32 cows and 8 bulls, secured from Jackson Hole, Wyoming, and shipped to Vilas County.
1918	Nov. 21-Nov. 30 10 days	Any one deer, except fawns.	30	17,000	50,260	Fawn protected by Commission Order pursuant to power authorized in 1917-first use of this power.

Deer Hunting Seasons (continued)
1850-1964

Year	Seasons		Number of Open Counties	Estimated Gun Kill	Deer Tag Sales	Chronology
	Length	Type				
1919	Nov. 21-Nov. 30 10 days	Any one deer	27	25,152	70,504	Deer could be moved to railroad station for shipment two days after season close. Owner required to accompany carcass. Number of deer shipped by express: 6,253. "The close of the hunting season in 1921 will see Wisconsin deer practically wiped out".
1920	Nov. 21-Nov. 30 10 days	One buck with horns not less than three inches.	27	20,025	69,479	First use of metal deer tags, to be fastened "at the hock joint back of the tendon and around the leg"; cost 10¢. Serving venison in resorts fairly common as late as 1920.

Year	Seasons		Number of Open Counties	Estimated Gun Kill	Deer Tag Sales	Chronology
	Length	Type				
1921	Nov. 13-Nov. 22 10 days	One buck not less than one year old.	27	14,845	63,848	Price of deer tag increased to 25¢. Carrying guns in open season counties five days previous to opening of seasons prohibited, unless gun was knocked down or in carrying case. "Our instructions to the conservation wardens are that all deer found in possession of a hunter, with horns less than three inches in length, is a fawn and should be confiscated". Deer damage to fruit trees and winter grain in Sauk County. Moose found swimming in Allouez Bay, Douglas County. Four fatalities and 1 injury reported during deer season.
1922	Nov. 13-Nov. 22 10 days	One buck not less than one year old	23	9,255	59,436	"Deer territory is narrowed to twenty counties." Last known wolverine trapped in Sawyer County.

Year	Seasons		Number of Open Counties	Estimated Gun Kill	Deer Tag Sales	Chronology
	Length	Type				
1923	Nov. 13-Nov. 22 10 days	One buck not less than one year old.	27	9,000	51,140	Price of deer tag increased to 50¢. Hunting with dogs, or having dogs in possession 5 days before open season to 5 days after close of season prohibited in open counties.
1924	Nov. 13-Nov. 22 10 days	One buck not less than one year old.	27	7,000	50,212	
1925	First closed season.					Beginning of alternate annual closed and open seasons established by Legislature.
1926	Dec. 1-Dec. 10 10 days	One buck not less than one year old.	24	12,000	47,330	Season may have been open past rutting stage - possibly into yarding period.
1927	No open season.					Six-man Commission created.

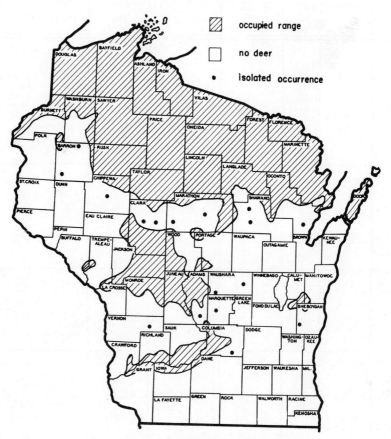

Source: Big game survey made by Aldo Leopold for the Sporting
Arms and Ammunition Manufacturers' Institute.

Year	Seasons		Number of Open Counties	Estimated Gun Kill	Deer Tag Sales	Chronology
	Length	Type				
1928	Dec. 1-Dec. 10 10 days	One buck not less than one year old.	22	17,000	69,049	Transportation permitted between second day of season, and 11:00 p.m. of third day after close of season (1928-1946). Deer hunters required to wear official conservation button while hunting (1928-1932). Game division of Conservation Department created.
1929	No open season					Survey undertaken by wardens and sportsmen revealed following counties as having no deer: Brown, Buffalo, Dane, Dodge, Fond du Lac, Green, Jefferson, Kenosha, Kewaunee, La Crosse, Lafayette, Milwaukee, Outagamie, Pierce, Rock, Vernon, Walworth, Washington, Waukesha, and Waushara. First licensing of deer farms. Bobcats kill deer in Oneida County.

DEER POPULATION - 1929

Source: Game survey undertaken by conservation wardens and
selected sportsmen in 65 counties.

Deer Hunting Seasons (continued)
1850-1964

Year	Seasons		Number of Open Counties	Estimated Gun Kill	Deer Tag Sales	Chronology
	Length	Type				
1930	Dec. 1-Dec. 10 10 days	One buck not less than one year old.	22	23,000	77,284	Starvation in isolated areas reported. Price of confiscated deer: entire carcass 30¢ per lb. Forest fire devastation brought under control.
1931	No open season					First annual Legislative appropriation for deer and bear damage - $12,000.00 in each year in which open season occurs (1931-1941). First game census card return required of hunters. Use of bow and arrow authorized (1931-).
1932	Nov. 21-Nov. 30 10 days	One buck not less than one year old.	21	36,009	70,245	Price of deer tag increased to $1.00 (1932-1950). Moose seen in Douglas County.
1933	No open season					Commission given power to set open season dates on all game. Beginning of Conservation Congress.

Deer Hunting Seasons (continued)
1850-1964

Year	Seasons		Number of Open Counties	Estimated Gun Kill	Deer Tag Sales	Chronology
	Length	Type				
1934	Nov. 24-Nov. 30 7 days	One buck not less than one year old.	22	21,251	83,938	First bow and arrow deer season. Artificial feeding began in Flag River deer yard. Price of confiscated deer 20¢ per lb.
1935	No open season.					CCC deer census drives began (1935-1937). Count: Average of 30 deer per section. Legislation passed allowing state to fence areas having continuous deer damage. "Somewhat alarming starvation losses noted." Overbrowsing in Flag yard. U.S. Forest Service requested removal of 14,000 deer by controlled hunting in the Chequamegon area of Ashland, Price, and Sawyer Counties.

Deer Hunting Seasons (continued)
1850-1964

| Year | Seasons | | Number of Open Counties | Estimated Gun Kill | Deer Tag Sales | Chronology |
	Length	Type				
1936	Nov. 21-Nov. 27 7 days	Forked-horn buck or larger.	28	29,676	97,735	Although night-time hunting continued to be illegal, day-time was defined as one-half hour before sunrise to sunset (1936-). First removal of deer (150) from Barksdale enclosure, Bayfield County. Estimate of 100 deer between Arcadia and Marshland in Trempealeau County. Price of confiscated deer 25¢ per lb.

Deer Hunting Seasons (continued)
1850-1964

Year	Seasons		Number of Open Counties	Estimated Gun Kill	Deer Tag Sales*	Chronology
	Length	Type				
1937	Nov. 26-Nov. 28 3 days	Forked-horn buck or larger	30	14,835	90,906	Shortest deer season on record. Voluntary sportsman license law passed; fee-$5.00 (1937-1948). Portions of fund to be used for acquiring refuges and public hunting grounds. Minimum age for licensee - 15 years. 192 deer killed by cars and salvaged by wardens. Moose seen in Florence County. Large timber wolf (103 lb.) trapped in Bayfield County.

* Includes Resident and Voluntary Sportsmen's License Sales (1937-1939).

Year	Seasons		Number of Open Counties	Estimated Gun Kill	Deer Tag Sales	Chronology
	Length	Type				
1938	Nov. 19-Nov. 25 7 days	Forked-horn buck or larger.	30	32,855	103,721	Use of .22 rifle and .410 gauge shotgun, incendiary or tracer shells, prohibited (1938-1954). "Polk County has 1,478 deer" based upon a 150 man deer drive. "60 counties inhabited by deer." 3,352,000 acres of public lands in northern Wisconsin open to deer hunting. First deer damage claim in Dane County. Seized deer sold for 25¢ per lb.
1939	Nov. 25-Dec. 1 7 days	Forked-horn buck or larger. Antler to have fork one inch long or over.	30	25,730	109,630	Use of buckshot prohibited for first time (1939-1942). Licensees between ages of 12 and 16 required to be accompanied by parent or guardian (1939-). Unlawful to possess venison after April 1 (1939-1941). 255,000 acres closed for protection of deer.

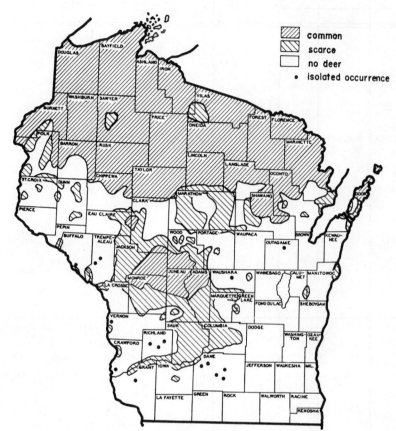

WHITE-TAILED DEER IN WISCONSIN
SUMMER RANGE
AS OF 1938

Source: "The Problem of Managing Wisconsin Deer" by Ernest Swift.

Deer Hunting Seasons (continued)
1850-1964

Year	Seasons		Number of Open Counties	Estimated Gun Kill	Deer Tag Sales*	Chronology
	Length	Type				
1940	Nov. 23-Nov. 30 8 days	Forked-horn buck or larger. Antler to have fork one inch long or over.	32	33,138	105,198	Specialized survey of deer yards began under Pittman-Robertson research project. First protection of albino or white deer at all times (1940-1957). Price of confiscated deer: 20¢ per lb.
1941	Nov. 22-Nov. 30 9 days	Forked-horn buck or larger. Antler to have fork one inch long or over.	32	40,403	124,305	Deer predators uncommon. Timber wolves nearing extinction.

* Deer Tag Sales Include Resident, Voluntary Sportsmen and Nonresident Big Game Licenses, 1940-1964.

Year	Seasons		Number of Open Counties	Estimated Gun Kill	Deer Tag Sales	Chronology
	Length	Type				
1942	Nov. 21-Nov. 29 9 days	Forked-horn buck or larger. Antler to have fork one inch long or over.	31	45,188	120,605	Back tags first required by Commission Order. Unlawful to possess venison after June 1; storage other than at home required permit (1942). Heavy loss of fawns by starvation. Probable date when deer herd reached peak. Citizens' Deer Committee for survey of deer yards appointed. Additional funds were needed annually to provide for increased deer and bear damage (1942-1948).

Year	Seasons		Number of Open Counties	Estimated Gun Kill	Deer Tag Sales	Chronology
	Length	Type				
1943	Nov. 18-Nov. 21 4 days	Forked-horn buck or larger. Antler to have fork one inch long or over.	44	66,252	157,824	First doe and fawn season in 24 years. Unlawful to possess venison After August 1; storage other than at home required permit (1943-1944). Resident hunting license fee increased to $1.50 (1943-1950).
	Nov. 25-Nov. 28 4 days	Antler-less deer - does and fawns.	33	62,044 ─────── 128,296		Use of buck-shot legal. Deer tag revenue earmarked by the Legislature for deer yard purchase and deer feeding (50¢ from sale of each $1.00 tag). Price of seized deer, entire carcass - 30¢ per lb. (1943-).

Deer Hunting Seasons (continued)
1850-1964

Year	Seasons		Number of Open Counties	Estimated Gun Kill	Deer Tag Sales	Chronology
	Length	Type				
1944	Nov. 25-Nov. 30 6 days	Forked-horn buck, antler to have fork one inch long or over. Either sex	34 7	28,537	127,643	First annual opening of any-deer season in agricultural counties. Buckshot again prohibited (1944-). Annual deer kill based on special deer hunter poll (1944-1954). "Save Wisconsin Deer" committee organized; newspaper published.
1945	Nov. 24-Nov. 28 5 days	Forked-horn buck, antler to have fork one inch long or over.	41	37,527	133,548	No license required for servicemen living in Wisconsin for duration of World War II. Law enacted requiring wearing of red clothing while hunting. First use of shotgun only, loaded with ball or slug in certain counties as control measure. Home consumption permitted at any time (1945-). Total known deer yards in state - 537.

Year	Seasons		Number of Open Counties	Estimated Gun Kill	Deer Tag Sales	Chronology
	Length	Type				
1946	Nov. 23-Dec. 1 9 days	Forked-horn buck, antler to have fork one inch long or over. Either sex.	39 3	55,276	201,061	First controlled antlerless deer hunt in Necedah National Wildlife Refuge, Juneau County (32 deer taken per square mile). First aerial survey of deer concentration. 390 deer killed by cars. Deer seen in Kenosha County.
1947	Nov. 22-Nov. 30 9 days	Forked-horn buck, antler to have fork one inch long or over. Either sex	34 7	53,520	222,935	Transportation permitted for 3 days after close of season. Owner required to accompany deer (1947-). Second controlled antlerless deer hunt in Necedah National Wildlife Refuge and Meadow Valley Unit of CWCA, Dec. 6 to Dec. 14, resulting in 18-day season in portions of Juneau County. Survey of deer damage to forest reproduction began. More than 6,000 illegal kills found in 502,000 acres in central Wisconsin

Deer Hunting Seasons (continued)
1850-1964

Year	Seasons		Number of Open Counties	Estimated Gun Kill	Deer Tag Sales	Chronology
	Length	Type				
1948	Nov. 20-Nov. 28 9 days	Forked-horn buck, antler to have fork one inch long or over	38	41,954	248,609	Hunting conditions unfavorable. 10-point doe bagged in Taylor County, Largest number of paid deer damage claims - 554, at the largest cost - $57,091.30, during any calendar year.
		Either sex	7			
1949	Nov. 19-Nov. 23 5 days	Antler-less deer, and forked-antler with fork not in excess of two inches.	47	159,112	286,299	Hunters not permitted to purchase deer tags during season (1949-1958). The voluntary sportsmens' license fee increased to $6.50 (1949-1956). Madeline Island deer kill: 310 850,000 acres, not including wildlife refuges, closed primarily for protection of deer. $40,000 appropriated annually for deer and bear damage (1949-). Commission authorized deer killing permits for Bayfield County deer damage farmers.

Deer Hunting Seasons (continued)
1850-1964

| Year | Seasons | | Number of Open Counties | Estimated Gun Kill | Deer Tag Sales | Chronology |
	Length	Type				
1950	Nov. 18-Nov. 24 7 days	Any one deer	47	167,911	312,570	First "any-deer" season since 1919. 1,057,280 acres closed primarily for protection of deer. Chambers Island, Door County open; had been closed since 1913. Shooting hours began at 8:00 a.m. on opening day only. Unprecedented purchase of 1,131 tons of deer feed at cost of $50,049.34. Permits to shoot deer doing damage offered to Oconto County muck farmers.

Deer Hunting Seasons (continued)
1850-1964

Year	Seasons		Number of Open Counties	Estimated Gun Kill	Deer Tag Sales	Chronology
	Length	Type				
1951	Nov. 17-Nov. 23 7 days	Any one deer	55	129,475	296,795	Separate licenses required for resident small game and deer hunting. Deer hunting license, including tag, $2.50 (1951-1956). For first time, Department personnel permitted to issue big game licenses. Orange-colored clothing now included in red clothing law (1951-1958). 760,000 acres closed primarily for protection of deer. Deer killed by automobiles: 448 1951-52 fiscal year deer damage paid claims: $21,378.55 lowest amount since 1943. Deer hunting licenses issued to servicemen at resident fees, providing they are stationed in Wisconsin, or are Wisconsin residents on furlough or leave.

(continued on the following page)

Deer Hunting Seasons (continued)
1850-1964

Year	Seasons		Number of Open Counties	Estimated Gun Kill	Deer Tag Sales	Chronology
	Length	Type				
1951 continued						For third consecutive season, Wisconsin led nation in white-tailed deer kill.
1952	Nov. 22-Nov. 28 7 days	Forked-horn buck or larger, antler to have fork one inch long or over. Either sex.	44 9	27,504	238,287	License sales showed decrease of 19.7% from previous years. 1,767,282 acres closed primarily for protection of deer. Necedah National Wildlife Refuge closed to deer gun hunting (1952-57 Deer killed by automobiles: 465. Pre-season fire hazards causes uncertainty of opening date.

Deer Hunting Seasons (continued)
1850-1964

| Year | Seasons | | Number of Open Counties | Estimated Gun Kill | Deer Tag Sales | Chronology |
	Length	Type				
1953	Nov. 28-Dec. 4 7 days	Forked-horn buck or larger, antler to have fork one inch long or over	53	19,823 (15,880)*	234,032	License sales showed decrease of 1.8% from previous year. Minimum age of sportsmen and settler licensee reduced by Legislature to 12 years. Members of armed forces stationed in Wisconsin, or Wisconsin residents on furlough or leave, permitted to purchase license at resident fee after season opened. First season gun deer hunters required to register deer at checking stations. Hunters per deer taken: 14.7

* 15,880 deer were recorded at checking stations in 1953 in accordance with the new regulation which required all successful hunters to register their deer.

Deer Hunting Seasons (continued)
1850-1964

| Year | Seasons | | Number of Open Counties | Estimated Gun Kill | Deer Tag Sales | Chronology |
	Length	Type				
1954	Nov. 20-Nov. 26 7 days	Forked-horn buck or larger, to have fork one inch long or over.	55	24,698 (19,877)*	247,310	License sales showed an increase of 5% over previous years. Washington County open for the first time since 1906. Two-thirds of bucks harvested were less than three years old. Hunters per deer taken: 12.4.

* 19,877 deer were recorded at checking stations in 1954, in accordance with the regulation which required all successful hunters to register their deer.

Deer Hunting Seasons (continued)
1850-1964

Year	Seasons		Open Counties	Registered Gun Kill	License Sales	Chronology
	Length	Type				
1955	Nov. 19-Nov. 27 9 days Nov. 19-Nov. 22 4 days	Forked-horn buck Any deer	58 7	35,060	267,612	License sales showed an 8.2% increase over previous year. The harvest showed an increase of 76% over the previous 1954 forked-antler season. Portions of Walworth and Waukesha Counties and all of Jefferson County open for first time since 1906. Buffalo County with a kill of 1,564 deer placed second in rank among the heavy harvest counties. Six closed counties - Green, Kenosha, Lafayette, Milwaukee, Racine and Rock. Hunters per deer taken: 7.6. Law Enforcement Personnel increased to 134 Officers.

Deer Hunting Seasons (continued)
1850-1964

Year	Seasons		Number of Open Counties	Registered Gun Kill	Deer Tag Sales	Chronology
	Length	Type				
1956	Nov. 17- Nov. 25 9 days	Buck with three-inch spike or larger.	65	35,562	284,645	One hundredth established gun deer season. Lafayette County open for the first time since 1906. Deer hunting permitted in the McCoy military reservation by permit issued by the commanding officer. The Conservation Commission called for deer management by designated areas, rather than on a uniform statewide basis. The state was divided into 77 deer management units to serve as a basis for zoned harvests. Hunters per deer taken: 8.0.

Deer Hunting Seasons (continued)
1850-1964

Year	Seasons		Number of Open Counties	Registered Gun Kill	Deer Tag Sales	Chronology
	Length	Type				
1957	Nov. 16-Nov. 24 9 days	One buck, antler not less than three inches.	56	Reg. Lic. 42,779 Party Permit 25,359 Total 68,138	288,903 Party Permits 32,027	Resident big game license fee increased to $4.00 (tag included). Voluntary sportsmen license fee increased to $10.00. Legislature enacted first party permit (deer hunter law-29.107). License fee $5.00. Nonresident hunters from 21 states took 808 deer in 43 counties (276 by party permit). Department agents authorized landowner or lessee by permit to capture or destroy wild animals doing damage. Legislature designated the white-tailed deer as the state animal. Hunters 12 to 16 years of age may obtain license, but must be accompanied by parent or guardian while hunting. From 1952 through 1957, 60% of the deer were shot during the opening two days. A total of 109,720 acres were closed to deer hunting. Kill registered by township. Timber wolves and Canadian Lynx protected at all times. Chapter 157, Laws of 1957. Law Enforcement established cooperative agreement with State Crime Laboratory relating to technical work. Hunters per deer taken: Regular License: 6.8; Party Permit: 1.3.
	Nov. 16-Nov. 18 3 days &	Either sex	9 Mississippi River Zone counties			
	Nov. 19-Nov. 24 6 days	Spike buck				
	Nov. 16-Nov. 24 9 days	Either sex	Northeast Bayfield County and the Apostle Islands, except Madeline Island.			
	Nov. 16-Nov. 24 9 days	Party permit	29			

Deer Hunting Seasons (continued)
1850-1964

Year	Seasons		Number of Open Counties	Registered Gun Kill	Deer Tag Sales	Chronology
	Length	Type				
1958	Nov. 15- Nov. 30 16 days	Spike buck and party permit	Counties north of U.S. Highway 8	Reg. Lic. 50,247 Party Permit 44,987	335,866 Party Permits 58,438	Longest deer gun season since 1916. Rock County open for first time since 1906. Necedah Refuge open to gun hunting for first time since 1951. (nine days). Harvest - regular license - 56, party permit - 97.
	Nov. 15- Nov. 23 9 days	Spike buck and party permit	Counties south of U.S. Highway 8	Total 95,234		
	Nov. 15- Nov. 17 3 days	Either sex				Total state harvest 40% over the previous season.
	Nov. 18- Nov. 23 6 days	Spike buck	Mississippi River Zone- 8 counties			First harvest by management unit (in northwest and northeast areas only). 62% of the harvest was taken in the opening two days. Nonresidents from 21 states took 1,101 deer. About one-half hunted in the northwest area. A fee of $2.00 was offered to hunters for reporting eartagged deer. White deer protected at all times (1958-19-). Hunters per deer taken: Regular License: 6.6; Party Permit: 1.3.

Year	Seasons		Number of Open Counties	Registered Gun Kill	Deer Tag Sales	Chronology
	Length	Type				
1959	Nov. 14- Nov. 29 16 days	Spike buck and party permit	North of highways 70, 53 and 8, in 15 counties or parts of counties.	Reg. Lic. 57,900 Party Permit 47,696 Total 105,596	349,443 Party Permits 61,018	First registration of deer by management unit statewide. Horicon National Wildlife Refuge closed to deer hunting.
	Nov. 14- Nov. 29 16 days	Spike buck	Restricted area: Management Units 34B, 36 and 37 in Vilas and Oneida Counties.			Bright yellow clothing included in the bright orange or red deer hunter clothing law (1959-19-).
	Nov. 21- Nov. 29 9 days	Spike buck and party permit	South of Highways 70, 53 and 8, in 42 counties or parts of counties.			Game Management Division took over responsibility for coordination of deer program.
	Nov. 21- Nov. 29 9 days	Spike buck	West Central restricted area, in 8 counties or parts of counties.			First open season in Kenosha County since 1906. Deer may be killed by persons authorized to do so by the licensee on licensed deer farms of not less than 10 acres in area. Chapter 382, Laws of 1951.
	Nov. 21- Nov. 23 3 days &	Either sex	Mississippi River Zone, 8 counties			
	Nov. 24- Nov. 29 6 days	Spike buck				Hunters permitted to purchase deer license after opening of season.
	Nov. 21- Nov. 29 9 days	Either sex	7 Southeastern counties.			Hunters per deer taken: Regular License: 6.0; Party Permit: 1.3.

Deer Hunting Seasons (continued)
1850-1964

Year	Seasons		Number of Open Counties	Registered Gun Kill	Deer Tag Sales	Chronology
	Length	Type				
1960	Nov. 19-Nov. 27 9 days	Spike buck and party permit	North of Highway 29, 27 counties or parts of counties.	Reg. Lic. 35,490 Party Permit 25,515 Total 61,005	338,208 Party Permit 47,522	77% of the deer were taken on the opening two days.
		Spike buck	South of Highway 29, 36 counties or parts of counties.			Registration method required; two members of party permit to be present when deer was
	Nov. 19-Nov. 20 2 days &	Either sex	Mississippi River Zone, 8 counties.			registered. Green and Racine Counties open for first time since 1906.
	Nov. 21-Nov. 27 7 days	Spike buck				It was unlawful to transport deer from the time it was
	Nov. 19-Nov. 21 3 days	Either sex	Southeastern block, 5 counties			killed to time of registration, unless it was openly exposed in such a manner that the locked tag could not be manipulated by the occupant of the vehicle. All counties open except Milwaukee. First verified report of moose Burnett County.

(continued on following page)

Deer Hunting Seasons (continued)
1850-1964

| Year | Seasons | | Number of Open Counties | Registered Gun Kill | Deer Tag Sales | Chronology |
	Length	Type				
1960 continued						Hunters not permitted to purchase deer license after opening of season. 1960 - Law Enforcement Division develops air patrol system. Hunters per deer taken: Reg. License 9.5 Party Permit 1.9

Year	Seasons		Number of Open Counties	Registered Gun Kill	Deer Tag Sales	Chronology
	Length	Type				
1961	Nov. 18- Nov. 26 9 days	Spike buck with antler not less than three inches.	63	38,772	307,863	Issuance of party permit licenses prohibited by legislative action, Chapter 91, 103, effective 1961 and 1962.
	Nov. 18- Nov. 19 2 days	Either sex	Southeast block - 8 counties.			Variable quota deer management plan passed by Legislature authorizing the Conservation Commission to issue party permits in areas where the population of the deer herd was such that additional cropping was necessary to properly manage the herd. 29.107 Effective July 1, '63.
						The County of Menominee was established, making a total of 72 counties in the state.
						Resident big game license fee increased from $4.00 to $5.00.
						Hunters required to carry deer openly while transporting until registration.
						62% of harvest taken first dwo days. Ten-year $50-million Outdoor Recreation Act Program effective in 1961. Hunters per deer taken: 7.9.

DISTRIBUTION OF DEER, FALL RANGE AS OF 1961.

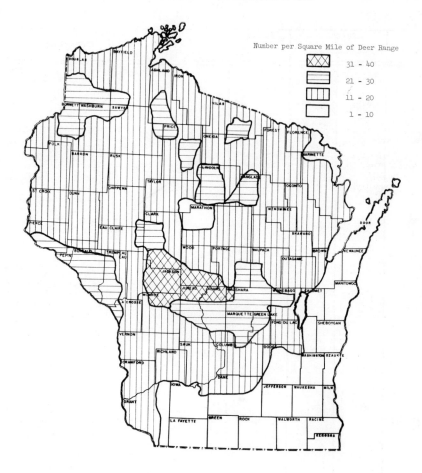

Deer Hunting Seasons (continued)
1850-1964

Year	Seasons		Number of Open Counties	Registered Gun Kill	Deer Tag Sales	Chronology
	Length	Type				
1962	Nov. 17-Nov. 25 9 days	Spike buck	53	45,835	331,035	Deer population in excess of 400,000. Largest county deer kill- Buffalo County - 2,465
	Nov. 17-Nov. 18 2 days &	Either sex	Mississippi River Zone (6)			66.2% of the harvest was taken during the first two days of the season.
	Nov. 19-Nov. 23 5 days	Spike buck	Mississippi River Zone (6)			Hunters per deer taken: 7.2.
	Nov. 17-Nov. 18 2 days	Either sex	Southern Zone (12)			

Deer Hunting Seasons (continued)
1850-1964

Year	Seasons		Number of Open Counties	Registered Gun Kill	Deer Tag Sales	Chronology
	Length	Type				
1963	Nov. 23-Dec. 1	Spike buck	71	Reg. Lic. 60,507	360,552	First issuance of quota party permits for eight management unit problem areas involving 3,519 square miles of deer range.
	9 days			Party Permit 4,513	Party Permits 5,578	
	Nov. 23-Nov. 24	Either sex		Total 65,020		
	2 days &		Mississippi River Zone 10 counties			Largest black bear on record in Wisconsin shot in Ashland County (665 pounds).
	Nov. 25-Dec. 1	Spike buck				
	7 days					
	Nov. 23-Nov. 24	Either sex				First managed bear gun hunt permitting the use of dogs. Two-day season in limited areas.
	2 days &		Eastern Zone 7 counties			
	Nov. 25-Dec. 1	Spike buck				
	7 days					Assassination of the President reduced hunting pressure.
	Nov. 23-Nov. 24	Either sex	Southern Zone 12 counties			
	2 days					Hunters per deer taken: Regular License: 6.0; Party Permit: 1.2.

Deer Hunting Seasons (continued)
1850-1964

Year	Seasons		Number of Open Counties	Registered Gun Kill	Deer Tag Sales	Chronology
	Length	Type				
1964	Nov. 21- Nov. 29 9 days	Spike buck	71	Reg. Lic. 73,888 Party Permit 19,557 Total 93,445		Party permit quota areas extended to 32 management units.
	Nov. 21- Nov. 22 2 days &	Either sex	Mississippi River Zone 11 counties			Shooting hours annually have continued to be one-half hour before sunrise to sunset since the 1950 season.
	Nov. 23- Nov. 29 7 days	Spike buck				
	Nov. 21- Nov. 23 3 days	Either sex	Southern Zone 12 counties			Largest antlered buck kill on record - 65,052, 70% of the total harvest.
	Nov. 21- Nov. 29 9 days	Either sex	Quota Areas 36 counties			Highest annual deer mortality on highways - 8,107.
						Hunters per deer taken: Regular License - 5.2; Party Permit - 1.3

OPENING WEEK DAYS OF ANNUAL DEER SEASONS

1851-1964 Inclusive

	Monday	Tuesday	Wednesday	Thursday	Friday	Saturday	Sunday
Y E A R S	1897 1901 1907 1912 1922 1930 1932	1851-58 1889-90 1898 1902 1913 1923	1860-66 1880 1899 1903 1908 1914 1917 1926	1867-74 1881-82 1883-84 1885-86 1896 1900 1909 1915 1918 1924 1943	1859 1895 1904 1910 1919 1937	1877-79 1887-88 1905 1911 1916 1928 1934 1936 1938-42 1944-64	1875-76 1891-92 1893-94 1906 1920-21
Total	7	14	14	21	6	37	9

Season	Hunting Conditions	Kill	
1944	Satisfactory	28,537;	forked horn buck season
1945	Satisfactory	37,527	"
1946	Satisfactory	55,276	"
1947	Satisfactory	53,520	"
1948	Unfavorable; snowstorm, 2-9 inches	41,954	"
1949	Frequent wet snow reduced visibility; poor tracking in the north; no tracking snow in West Central and Southern Areas	159,112;	any deer except forked horn buck
1950	Very favorable	167,911;	any deer
1951	Wet woods; poor visibility; flooded marshlands; closed roads	129,475	"
1952	Extremely dry noisy conditions; no snow in Northeast and central counties on opening day.	27,504;	forked horn buck season
1953	Postponement of season because of drought conditions; weather satisfactory	15,880	"
1954	Unfavorable; no tracking snow; dry noisy conditions	19,877	"
1955	Satisfactory	35,060	"
1956	Hampered by heavy snows; varied undesirable conditions	35,562;	spike buck season
1957	Rain; lack of snow in Northwest Area	42,779 25,359;	" party permit
1958	Mild weather; no snow	50,247; 44,987;	spike buck season party permit
1959	Good tracking snow	57,900; 47,696;	spike buck season party permit
1960	Poor; no snow in state; warm; woods noisy	35,490; 25,515;	spike buck season party permit
1961	Fair; unusual weather conditions; wet snow and water-filled marshes; unfavorable in Southern Area	38,772;	spike buck season
1962	Fair; mild temperatures, dry noisy woods in north and central forest areas; snow cover on seventh day of season; road conditions good.	45,835;	spike buck and any deer season
1963	Fair; heavy rains on preceding two days followed by cold temperatures (10-20 degrees on opening day) produced noisy conditions in some areas; some tracking snow; roads generally good; marshes fairly dry	60,507; 4,513;	spike buck season party permit
1964	Good; two to five inches snow in south and two central areas; traces of snow in northern area; near zero temperatures on opening day - moderating; trails good except in northern part of Northwest Area on last weekend when snow closed the woods trail	73,888; 19,557;	spike buck season party permit

LENGTH OF DEER SEASONS
1851-1964

Days	Month or More	20 Days	10 Days	9-16 Days	9 Days	8 Days	7 Days	6 Days	5 Days	3 Days	Closed
No. of Years	45	21	12	2	13	2	9	1	2	1	6
Time	1851-94 1896	1895 1897-1916	1917-24 1926 1928 1930 1932	1958 1959	1941-42 1946-48 1955-57 1960-64	1940 1943	1934 1936 1938-39 1950-54	1944	1945 1949	1937	1925 1927 1929 1931 1933 1935

TYPE OF DEER SEASONS
1851-1964

TYPE	YEARS	NO. OF YEARS
Any kind or number	1851 through 1896	46
Any two deer	1897 through 1908	12
Any one deer	1909 through 1914, 1917, 1919, 1950, 1951	10
One buck deer	1915 and 1916	2
Any one deer except fawns	1918	1
One buck - horns over three inches	1920	1
One buck - over one year old	1921 through 1924, 1926, 1928, 1930, 1932, 1934	9
Fork horn buck	1936 through 1942, 1944 through 1948, 1952 through 1955	16
Fork horn buck and antlerless	1943	1
Any deer except fork horn buck	1949	1
Spike buck and party permit	1957, 1958, 1959, 1960, 1963, 1964	6
Spike buck	1956, 1961, 1962	3
		108

COUNTIES CLOSED TO DEER GUN HUNTING
1850-1964

County	Total No. of Years	Years Closed*
Adams	30	1907 through 1936
Ashland	6	1925, 1927, 1929, 1931, 1933 and 1935
Barron	6	1925, 1927, 1929, 1931, 1933 and 1935
Bayfield	6	1925, 1927, 1929, 1931, 1933 and 1935
Brown	48	1907 through 1954
Buffalo	34	1909 through 1942
Burnett	6	1925, 1927, 1929, 1931, 1933 and 1935
Calumet	54	1901 through 1954
Chippewa	6	1925, 1927, 1929, 1931, 1933 and 1935
Clark	12	1922, 1925 through 1935
Columbia	35	1905 through 1939
Crawford	39	1907 through 1942; 1944, 1946 and 1950
Dane	42	1907 through 1942; 1945 through 1950
Dodge	44	1907 through 1950
Door	41	1907 through 1910; 1913 through 1949
Douglas	6	1925, 1927, 1929, 1931, 1933 and 1935
Dunn	31	1917 through 1947
Eau Claire	9	1925; 1927 through 1933; 1935
Florence	6	1925, 1927, 1929, 1931, 1933 and 1935
Fond du Lac	56	1897 through 1950; 1952 and 1953
Forest	6	1925, 1927, 1929, 1931, 1933 and 1935
Grant	37	1907 through 1942; 1947
Green	53	1907 through 1959
Green Lake	42	1907 through 1942; 1944 through 1947; 1949, 1950
Iowa	36	1907 through 1942
Iron	6	1925, 1927, 1929, 1931, 1933, and 1935
Jackson	19	1903, 1904; 1919 through 1935
Jefferson	48	1907 through 1954
Juneau	21	1907, 1908; 1917 through 1935
Kenosha	52	1907 through 1958
Kewaunee	48	1907 through 1954
La Crosse	40	1903 through 1942
Lafayette	50	1907 through 1955; 1959
Langlade	6	1925, 1927, 1929, 1931, 1933 and 1935
Lincoln	6	1925, 1927, 1929, 1931, 1933 and 1935
Manitowoc	54	1901 through 1954
Marathon	17	1919 through 1935
Marinette	6	1925, 1927, 1929, 1931, 1933 and 1935
Marquette	38	1907 through 1942; 1944; 1947
Menominee**	--	
Milwaukee	58	1907 through 1964
Monroe	33	1903 through 1935
Oconto	7	1922, 1925, 1927, 1929, 1931, 1933 and 1935
Oneida	6	1925, 1927, 1929, 1931, 1933 and 1935
Outagamie	44	1907 through 1950
Ozaukee	48	1907 through 1954
Pepin	38	1909 through 1946
Pierce	21	1925, 1927, 1929, 1931; 1932 through 1948
Polk	8	1915, 1916, 1925, 1927, 1929, 1931, 1933 and 1935
Portage	34	1909 through 1942
Price	6	1925, 1927, 1929, 1931, 1933 and 1935
Racine	53	1907 through 1959
Richland	37	1907 through 1942; 1948
Rock	51	1907 through 1957

Counties Closed to Deer Gun Hunting (continued)

County	Total No. of Years	Years Closed*
Rusk	6	1925, 1927, 1929, 1931, 1933 and 1935
St. Croix	18	1925, 1927, 1929, 1931, 1932 through 1943; 1945, 1947
Sauk	37	1905 through 1939; 1942, 1945
Sawyer	6	1925, 1927, 1929, 1931, 1933 and 1935
Shawano	14	1909, 1910, 1922, 1925, 1927 through 1936
Sheboygan	59	1895; 1897 through 1954
Taylor	9	1925 through 1931; 1933, 1935
Trempealeau	28	1903 through 1906; 1919 through 1942
Vernon	48	1903 through 1950
Vilas	6	1925, 1927, 1929, 1931, 1933 and 1935
Walworth	51	1907 through 1954; 1956 through 1958
Washburn	6	1925, 1927, 1929, 1931, 1933 and 1935
Washington	47	1907 through 1953
Waukesha	48	1907 through 1954
Waupaca	40	1909 through 1948
Waushara	37	1907 through 1942; 1944
Winnebago	47	1907 through 1950; 1952 through 1954
Wood	16	1913 through 1916; 1922; 1925 through 1935

* All counties were closed during the years 1925, 1927, 1929, 1931, 1933 and 1935

** New county created from parts of Shawano and Oconto Counties in 1961.

FIRST CLOSED COUNTIES

Year	Counties
1895	Sheboygan
1897	Fond du Lac
1901	Calumet and Manitowoc
1903	Jackson, La Crosse, Monroe, Trempealeau and Vernon
1905	Columbia and Sauk
1907	First general closing - 36 counties
1932	Greatest number of closed counties - 50
1960-64	Smallest number of closed counties since 1895 - 1 (Milwaukee)

THE FOLLOWING COUNTIES WERE CLOSED ONLY DURING THE PERIOD OF ALTERNATE YEAR, STATEWIDE CLOSING IN 1925, 1927, 1929, 1931, 1933 and 1935

Ashland	Florence	Oneida
Barron	Forest	Price
Bayfield	Iron	Rusk
Burnett	Langlade	Sawyer
Chippewa	Lincoln	Vilas
Douglas	Marinette	Washburn

			TOTAL NUMBER OF COUNTIES CLOSED YEARLY				
Year	Number of Closed Cos.	Year	Number of Closed Cos.	Year	Number of Closed Cos.	Year	Number of Closed Cos.
Prior to		1911	38	1929	All	1947	30
1895	None	1912	38	1930	49	1948	26
1895	1	1913	40	1931	All	1949	24
1896	None	1914	40	1932	50	1950	24
1897	2	1915	41	1933	All	1951	16
1898	2	1916	41	1934	49	1952	18
1899	2	1917	41	1935	All	1953	18
1900	2	1918	41	1936	43	1954	16
1901	4	1919	44	1937	41	1955	6
1902	4	1920	44	1938	41	1956	6
1903	9	1921	44	1939	41	1957	6
1904	9	1922	48	1940	39	1958	5
1905	10	1923	44	1941	39	1959	4
1906	10	1924	44	1942	40	1960	1
1907	36	1925	All	1943	27	1961	1
1908	36	1926	47	1944	30	1962	1
1909	40	1927	All	1945	30	1963	1
1910	40	1928	49	1946	29	1964	1

ANNUAL ESTIMATED DEER GUN KILL IN OPEN COUNTIES
1912-1954

Year Season County	1912* Nov. 11-Nov. 30 Any one deer	1913* Nov. 11-Nov. 30 Any one deer	1914* Nov. 11-Nov. 30 Any one deer
Ashland.	247	310	583
Barron	41	34	35
Bayfield	557	797	785
Brown.	(c)	1(c)	2(c)
Burnett.	10	32	1
Chippewa	348	167	201
Clark.	109	85	86
Door	73	(c)	(c)
Douglas.	345	516	470
Dunn	30	24	17
Eau Claire	16	16	25
Florence	124	71	308
Forest	73	111	93
Iron	224	190	255
Jackson.	54	26	16
Juneau	9	5	7
Langlade	87	75	104
Linclon.	80	101	147
Marathon	30	14	26
Marinette.	137	195	205
Monroe	6(c)	2(c)	5(c)
Oconto	37	20	58
Oneida	414	629	577
Polk	12	22	18
Price.	360	487	529
Portage.	(c)	1(c)	2(c)
Rusk	411	508	368
Sawyer	782	968	811
Shawano.	8	7	4
Taylor	405	599	667
Trempealeau. . . .	-	-	1
Vilas.	543	657	284
Washburn	166	232	447
Wood	-	(c)	(c)
Michigan	50	-	29
Unidentified . . .	65	67	59
Picked up by expressmen . . .	-	-	-
TOTALS	5,853	6,969	7,375
ESTIMATED KILL	8,500	9,750	9,850
HUNTING LICENSE SALES (Estimated)	123,000	147,000	155,000

* Previous to 1912, no records disclose a kill by county. The annual kill records show only the number shipped. It was estimated at this time that approximately twice this number were killed, as very few native hunters brought home deer by train. There was no large number of migrant hunters from the more heavily populated southern counties. Less than 55,000 automobiles were in use in the state during this period.
(c) County closed.

Annual Estimated Deer Gun Kill Open Counties (continued)
1912-1954

Year Season County	1915* Nov. 11-Nov. 30 Any one buck	1916** Nov. 11-Nov. 30 Any one buck	1917** Nov. 11-Nov. 30 Any one deer
Ashland.	182	-	-
Barron	18	-	-
Bayfield	386	-	-
Burnett.	2	-	-
Chippewa	118	-	-
Clark.	34	-	-
Douglas.	195	-	-
Dunn.	-	-	(c)
Eau Claire	4	-	-
Florence	132	-	-
Forest	42	-	-
Iron	140	-	-
Jackson.	7	-	-
Juneau	4	-	(c)
Langlade	39	-	-
Linclon.	39	-	-
Marathon	5	-	-
Marinette.	76	-	-
Monroe	3(c)	(c)	(c)
Oconto	31	-	-
Oneida	258	-	-
Pierce	-	-	-
Polk	9(c)	(c)	-
Price.	145	-	-
Rusk	185	-	-
St. Croix.	-	-	-
Sawyer	502	-	-
Shawano.	4	-	-
Taylor	255	-	-
Trempealeau. . . .	-	-	-
Vilas.	178	-	-
Washburn	178	-	-
Wood	(c)	(c)	-
Michigan Pts. . .	32	-	-
Unidentified . . .	-	-	-
Picked up by expressmen.	54	-	-
TOTALS	3,257		
ESTIMATED KILL	5,000	7,000	18,000
HUNTING LICENSE SALES (Estimated)	134,000	125,000	53,593***

* The county kill shown for the 1915 season shows only the number shipped by train and not the number taken by private conveyances or shot by local hunters.

** County kill is not available.
In 1917, three-fourths of the harvest was estimated to be does and fawns.

*** Deer tags were required for the first time.

(C) County closed.

- 89 -

Annual Estimated Deer Gun Kill in Open Counties (continued)
1912-1954

Year	1918*	1919*	1920*
Season	Nov. 21-Nov. 30	Nov. 21-Nov. 30	Nov. 21-Nov. 30
	Any one deer	Any one deer	One buck with
	except fawns		horns not less
County			than 3 inches
Ashland.	-	-	-
Barron	-	-	-
Bayfield	-	-	-
Burnett.	-	-	-
Chippewa	-	-	-
Clark.	-	-	-
Douglas.	-	-	-
Eau Claire	-	-	-
Florence	-	-	-
Forest	-	-	-
Iron	-	-	-
Jackson.	-	(c)	(c)
Langlade	-	-	-
Lincoln.	-	-	-
Marathon	-	(c)	(c)
Marinette.	-	-	-
Oconto	-	-	-
Oneida	-	-	-
Pierce	-	-	-
Polk	-	-	-
Price.	-	-	-
Rusk	-	-	-
St. Croix.	-	-	-
Sawyer	-	-	-
Shawano.	-	-	-
Taylor	-	-	-
Trempealeau. . . .	-	(c)	(c)
Vilas.	-	-	-
Washburn	-	-	-
Wood	-	-	-
TOTALS		6,253	
ESTIMATED KILL	17,000	25,152	20,025
DEER TAG SALES	50,260	70,504	69,479

* County kill is not available.
  The county kill shown for the 1919 season shows only the number shipped
  by train and not the number taken by private conveyances or shot by
  local hunters.

(c) County closed.

Annual Estimated Deer Gun Kill in Open Counties (continued)
1912-1954

Year	1921*	1922*	1923*
Season	Nov. 13-Nov. 22	Nov. 13-Nov. 22	Nov. 13-Nov. 22
	One buck one	One buck one	One buck one
	year of age	year of age	year of age
County	or older	or older	or older
Ashland.	327	187	129
Barron	30	5	2
Bayfield	606	343	263
Burnett.	37	26	15
Chippewa	54	16	18
Clark.	95	(c)	23
Douglas.	493	280	180
Eau Claire	38	5	14
Florence	148	95	46
Forest	218	116	67
Iron	162	136	90
Langlade	150	50	32
Lincoln.	158	65	32
Marinette.	120	65	33
Oconto	42	15(c)	11
Oneida	152	133	86
Pierce	-	-	3
Polk	22	12	5
Price.	318	329	205
Rusk	249	150	116
St. Croix.	-	-	1
Sawyer	417	328	231
Shawano.	-	(c)	-
Taylor	144	170	103
Vilas.	284	276	97
Washburn	-	57	29
Wood	25	(c)	12
Miscellaneous. . .	-	10	8
TOTALS	4,289	2,869	1,851
ESTIMATED KILL	14,845	9,255	9,000
AVERAGE WEIGHT	160	163	174
DEER TAG SALES	63,848	59,436	51,140

* County kill and average weight record was based on a post card deer kill
  census return required of the tag purchaser for the first time. Total
  kill is incomplete.

(c) County closed.

Annual Estimated Deer Gun Kill in Open Counties (continued)
1912-1954

Year Season County	1924* Nov. 13-Nov. 22 One buck one year of age or older	1925**	1926* Dec. 1-Dec. 10 One buck one year of age or older	1927
Ashland.	-	FIRST	-	C
Barron	-		-	
Bayfield	-		-	L
Burnett.	-		-	
Chippewa	-		-	O
Clark.	-		(c)	
Douglas.	-	STATEWIDE	-	S
Eau Claire	-		-	
Florence	-		-	E
Forest	-		-	
Iron	-		-	D
Langlade	-		-	
Lincoln.	-	CLOSED	-	
Marinette.	-		-	
Oconto	-		-	S
Oneida	-		-	
Pierce	-		-	E
Polk	-		-	
Price.	-	SEASON	-	A
Rusk	-		-	
St. Croix.	-		-	S
Sawyer	-		-	
Shawano.	-		-	O
Taylor	-		(c)	
Vilas.	-		-	N
Washburn	-		-	
Wood	-		(c)	
TOTALS	7,000		12,000	
DEER TAG SALES	50,212		47,330	

*   County kill is not available.

** Beginning of alternate closed and open seasons (1925-1935).

Annual Estimated Deer Gun Kill in Open Counties (continued)
1912-1954

Year	1928*	1929	1930*	1931
Season	Dec. 1-Dec. 10 One buck one year of age		Dec. 1-Dec. 10 One buck one year of age	
County	or older		or older	
Ashland.	-	C	-	C
Barron	-		-	
Bayfield	-	L	-	L
Burnett.	-		-	
Chippewa	-	O	-	O
Douglas.	-		-	
Florence	-	S	-	S
Forest	-		-	
Iron	-	E	-	E
Langlade	-		-	
Lincoln.	-	D	-	D
Marinette.	-		-	
Oconto	-		-	
Oneida	-		-	
Pierce	-	S	-	S
Polk	-		-	
Price.	-	E	-	E
Rusk	-		-	
St. Croix.	-	A	-	A
Sawyer	-		-	
Vilas.	-	S	-	S
Washburn	-		-	
		O		O
		N		N
TOTALS	17,000		23,000	
DEER TAG SALES	69,049		77,284	

* County kill is not available.

Year	1932	1933	1934	1935
Season	Nov. 21-Nov. 30		Nov. 24-Nov. 30	
	One buck one		One buck not less	
	year of age		than one year old	
County	or older		(spike horn)	
Ashland	2,981	C	1,631	C
Barron	184		141	
Bayfield	3,398	L	2,336	L
Burnett	672		540	
Chippewa	548	O	395	O
Douglas	1,530		754	
Eau Claire	(c)	S	422	S
Florence	1,216		536	
Forest	2,044	E	1,352	E
Iron	1,129		598	
Langlade	931	D	576	D
Lincoln	683		621	
Marinette	1,346		679	
Oconto	661		347	
Oneida	2,422	S	1,796	S
Polk	292		266	
Price	3,599	E	1,515	E
Rusk	2,128		1,184	
Sawyer	4,411	A	2,553	A
Taylor	2,028		613	
Vilas	3,104	S	1,914	S
Washburn	702		482	
		O		O
		N		N
TOTALS	36,009		21,251	
DEER TAG SALES	70,245		83,938	

Annual Estimated Deer Gun Kill in Open Counties (continued)
1912-1954

Year	1936	1937	1938
Season	Nov. 21-Nov. 27	Nov. 26-Nov. 28	Nov. 19-Nov. 25
	One buck with	One buck with	One buck with
	forked horn	one or more	one or more
	per season	forked horns	forked horns
County		per season	per season
Adams.	(c)	187	285
Ashland.	1,877	786	1,658
Barron	105	46	118
Bayfield	2,555	1,139	2,709
Burnett.	846	628	1,165
Chippewa	259	147	253
Clark.	692	331	688
Douglas.	1,581	757	1,551
Eau Claire	213	153	276
Florence	1,071	500	1,250
Forest	1,765	714	1,722
Iron	1,288	563	1,486
Jackson.	951*	605	890
Juneau	420	256	535
Langlade	614	261	638
Lincoln.	494	341	603
Marathon	127	63	159
Marinette.	1,269	660	1,496
Monroe	282	174	438
Oconto	344	203	542
Oneida	2,244	989	2,305
Polk	294	137	489
Price.	1,955	906	2,074
Rusk	807	351	770
Sawyer	2,505	946	2,390
Shawano.	(c)	29	76
Taylor	807	382	818
Vilas.	3,050	1,302	3,250
Washburn	777	302	785
Wood	468	294	495
Miscellaneous. . .	16	683	941
TOTALS	29,676	14,835	32,055
DEER TAG SALES	97,735	90,476	103,061
VOLUNTARY SPORTSMEN		430	660
TOTAL TAG SALES	97,735	90,906	103,721

* The Town of Knapp was closed in 1936.
  The central counties of Adams, Jackson, Juneau, Monroe, and Wood were
  opened (1936) to deer hunting after having been closed for a number of
  years.

(c) County closed.

Annual Estimated Deer Gun Kill in Open Counties (continued)
1912-1954

Year	1939	1940
Season	Nov. 25-Dec. 1	Nov. 23-Nov. 30
	Forked-antlered buck	Forked-antlered buck
	season-Antler to	season-Antler to
	have fork one inch	have fork one inch
County	long or over	long or over
Adams.	365	502
Ashland.	1,198	1,466
Barron	86	160
Bayfield	2,317	3,010
Burnett.	987	1,510
Chippewa	138	174
Clark.	382	626
Columbia	(c)	- *
Douglas.	1,436	1,898
Eau Claire	219	336
Florence	1,023	1,116
Forest.	1,210	1,444
Iron	977	1,150
Jackson.	1,198	1,082
Juneau	309	254**
Langlade	363	630
Linclon.	476	620
Marathon	50	140
Marinette.	1,348	1,564
Monroe	213***	392
Oconto	424	610
Oneida	1,907	2,302
Polk	349	694
Price.	1,513	2,168

(continued on following page)

* In Columbia County, parts of the Towns of Lewiston and Newport lying
north and east of the Wisconsin River were open in 1940.

** The area in Juneau County north of State Highway 21 was open in 1940.

*** The area in Monroe County south of State Highway 16 was closed in 1939.
Approximately one-half the county was closed.

(c) County closed.

Annual Estimated Deer Gun Kill in Open Counties (continued)
1912-1954

Year	1939 (continued)	1940 (continued)
Season	Nov. 25-Dec. 1	Nov. 23-Nov. 30
	Forked-antlered buck	Forked-antlered buck
	season-Antler to	season-Antler to
	have fork one inch	have fork one inch
County	long or over	long or over
Rusk	568	904
Sauk	(c)	- *
Sawyer	1,799	2,450
Shawano.	44	78
Taylor	484	682
Vilas.	2,820	3,166
Washburn	697	1,034
Wood	315**	508***
Miscellaneous . .	515	468
TOTALS	25,730	33,138
DEER TAG SALES	107,477	102,288
VOLUNTARY SPORTSMEN	2,153	2,840
NONRESIDENT BIG GAME****		70
TOTAL TAG SALES	109,630	105,198

*   In Sauk County, parts of the Towns of Delton, Fairfield, and Greenfield were open in 1940.

**   The area in Wood County south of State Highway 73 and west of the Wisconsin River was open in 1939. Approximately three-fourths of the county was closed.

***   The area in Wood County south of State Highway 73 and west of the Wisconsin River, plus the Towns of Saratoga and Grand Rapids, was open in 1940.

****   Nonresident big game licenses sold previous to 1940 are included in the annual deer tag sales.

(c)   County closed.

Annual Estimated Deer Gun Kill in Open Counties (continued)
1912-1954

Year Season County	1941 Nov. 22-Nov. 30 Forked-antlered buck season-Antler to have fork one inch long or over	1942 Nov. 21-Nov. 29 Forked-antlered buck season-Antler to have fork one inch long or over
Adams	465	757
Ashland	2,123	2,214
Barron.	153	209
Bayfield.	3,485	4,291
Burnett	1,324	1,656
Chippewa.	178	166
Clark	882	1,284
Columbia.	236*	226*
Douglas	2,090	2,595
Eau Claire. . . .	482	528
Florence.	1,568	1,706
Forest.	1,699	1,696
Iron.	1,377	1,145
Jackson	1,357	1,975
Juneau.	415	800
Langlade.	636	627
Lincoln	902	979
Marathon.	101	143
Marinette	2,178	2,393
Monroe.	410	471
Oconto.	884	1,125
Oneida.	3,075	2,887
Polk.	452	833
Price	2,769	2,625

(continued on following page)

* In Columbia County, all of the Towns of Newport and Caledonia, and parts
of the Towns of Lewiston, Pacific, and Dekorra, were open in 1941 and
1942.

Annual Estimated Deer Gun Kill in Open Counties (continued)
1912-1954

Year Season County	1941 (continued) Nov. 22-Nov. 30 Forked-antlered buck season-Antler to have fork one inch long or over	1942 (continued) Nov. 21-Nov. 29 Forked-antlered buck season-Antler to have fork one inch long or over
Rusk.	915	873
Sauk.	186*	(c)
Sawyer.	3,219	3,206
Shawano	75	129
Taylor.	751	767
Vilas	3,879	4,527
Washburn.	892	1,158
Wood.	726**	1,029**
Miscellaneous . .	519	168
TOTALS	40,403	45,188
DEER TAG SALES	120,734	116,674
VOLUNTARY SPORTSMEN	3,419	3,788
NONRESIDENT BIG GAME	152	143
TOTAL TAG SALES	124,305	120,605

*   The area in Sauk County east and north of a line formed by the junction
    of the following highways: County Trunk K, State Highway 23-33, State
    136, U.S. Highway 12-13, County ZZ, State Highway 78, and State 113,
    was open in 1941.

** The area in Wood County south of State Highway 73, west of the Wisconsin
    River, plus the Towns of Saratoga and Grand Rapids, were open in 1941
    and 1942.

(c) County closed.

Annual Estimated Deer Gun Kill in Open Counties (continued)
1912-1954

Year Season County	THE 1943 "SPLIT" SEASON			
	4 days Nov. 18-Nov. 21 Forked-antlered deer, antler to have fork one inch or over	Inter- vening Closed Season 3 days	4 days Nov. 25-Nov. 28 Antlerless deer, or deer with antler not to exceed one inch	Total Kill
Adams.	619		(c)	619
Ashland.	2,458		2,431	4,889
Barron	241		137	378
Bayfield	4,866		5,075	9,941
Buffalo*	100		100	200
Burnett.	2,731		3,045	5,776
Chippewa	218		(c)	218
Clark.	1,106		(c)	1,106
Columbia*.	514		555	1,069
Crawford*.	18		9	27
Dane*.	77		59	136
Douglas.	3,578		3,127	6,705
Eau Claire	1,097		(c)	1,097
Florence	2,331		2,130	4,461
Forest	3,045		2,494	5,539
Grant*	23		23	46
Green Lake*. . . .	196		269	465
Iowa*.	105		82	187
Iron	1,520		1,502	3,022
Jackson.	2,440		(c)	2,440
Juneau	787		(c)	787
La Crosse*	50		82	132
Langlade	706		592	1,298
Lincoln.	979		473	1,452
Marathon	146		(c)	146
Marinette.	3,661		3,218	6,879
Marquette*	733		646	1,379
Monroe . . . , . .	387		(c)	387
Oconto	1,848		1,652	3,500
Oneida	5,007		5,244	10,251
Polk	1,525		1,370	2,895
Portage.	73		(c)	73
Price.	3,751		3,837	7,588
Richland*.	9		9	18
Rusk	1,976		2,699	4,675
Sauk*.	337		291	628
Sawyer	4,971		6,300	11,271
Shawano.	123		(c)	123
Taylor	1,316		1,366	2,682
Trempealeau* . . .	173		159	332
Vilas.	6,892		9,864	16,756
Washburn	1,384		1,552	2,936

(continued on following page)

* Open to shotgun loaded with buckshot or ball, and bow and arrow only.

(c) County closed.

Annual Estimated Deer Gun Kill in Open Counties (continued)
1912-1954

Year Season County	THE 1943 "SPLIT" SEASON (continued)			
	4 days Nov. 18-Nov. 21 Forked-antlered deer, antler to have fork one inch or over	Inter- vening Closed Season 3 days	4 days Nov. 25-Nov. 28 Antlerless deer, or deer with antler not to exceed one inch	Total Kill
Waushara*.	105		64	169
Wood	742		(C)	742
Miscellaneous. . .	1,288		1,588	2,876
TOTALS	66,252		62,044	128,296
DEER TAG SALES				150,805
VOLUNTARY SPORTSMEN				6,662
NONRESIDENT BIG GAME				357
TOTAL TAG SALES				157,824

* Open to shotgun loaded with buckshot or ball, and bow and arrow only.
(C) County closed.

NOTE: The Conservation Department had recommended a nine-day antlerless
       season which was rejected by the Commission. The Department then
recommended a "split" season, a four-day forked antler, and a five-day
antlerless season. The Conservation Congress requested the protection of
spike bucks during the antlerless season.

The controversial "split" season resulted in the ominous prediction
by many that the deer herd was damaged beyond recovery. No one foresaw a
season kill larger by 30,000 six years later (1949), after five intervening
bucks seasons.

A special inquiry addressed to deer hunters furnished more than 38,000
returns which disclosed the following items relating to hunting:
   1. Four out of ten hunted both seasons.
   2. One out of five hunted for the first time.
   3. The number of days spent hunting averaged 3.9.
   4. Approximately 43% of the total kill was recorded on the opening
       days of each season.

In retrospect, the very large amount of closed areas (more than eight
million acres) in twenty-nine of the forty-four open counties, was
particularly significant in maintaining a large deer population. Also
noteworthy was the closing of the central Wisconsin counties during the
antlerless season: namely, Adams, Jackson, Juneau, Monroe, and Wood
Counties.

The following table shows an estimate of the areas closed primarily
for the protection of deer.

- 101 -

County	Total Land Acreage	Closed (acres)	% Closed	Open (acres)
Forked-antlered buck season - Nov. 18 to Nov. 21 - Rifle or Shotgun				
Adams	433,280		none	433,280
Chippewa	656,000		none	656,000
Clark	782,080		none	782,080
Eau Claire	415,360		none	415,360
Jackson	640,000		none	640,000
Juneau	508,800		none	508,800
Marathon	1,013,760		none	1,013,760
Monroe	585,600		none	585,600
Portage	518,400	492,480	95%	25,920
Shawano	752,640		none	752,640
Wood	519,680	311,808	60%	207,872
TOTALS	6,825,600	804,288	11.8%	6,021,312
Forked-antlered buck - Nov. 18-21, and Antlerless - Nov. 25-28 - Shotguns only				
Buffalo	455,680	364,550	80%	91,130
Columbia	497,920	397,336	80%	100,584
Crawford	375,040	318,784	85%	56,256
Dane	766,080	651,168	85%	114,912
Green Lake	227,200		none	227,200
Grant	747,520	598,016	80%	149,504
Iowa	487,040	243,520	50%	243,520
La Crosse	300,160	180,095	60%	120,065
Marquette	292,480		none	292,480
Richland	373,760	317,696	85%	56,064
Sauk	537,600	483,840	90%	53,760
Trempealeau	472,960	402,016	85%	70,944
Waushara	401,920		none	401,920
TOTALS	5,935,360	3,957,021	66.7%	1,978,339
Antlerless season - Nov. 25-28 - Rifle or Shotgun				
Ashland	663,680	221,227	33%	442,453
Barron	554,240	332,544	60%	221,696
Bayfield	943,360	47,168	5%	896,192
Burnett	537,600	107,520	20%	430,080
Douglas*	838,400		none	838,400
Florence*	312,960		none	312,960
Forest	646,400	40,000	6%	606,400
Iron	477,440	119,360	25%	358,080
Langlade	549,120	274,560	50%	274,560
Lincoln	576,000	345,600	60%	230,400
Marinette	888,320	355,328	40%	532,992
Oconto	707,840	530,880	75%	176,960
Oneida*	712,960		none	712,960
Polk	597,760	298,880	50%	298,880
Price	811,520	162,304	20%	649,216
Rusk	582,400	232,960	40%	349,440
Sawyer	814,720	162,944	20%	651,776
Taylor	626,560	313,280	50%	313,280
Vilas	554,880	45,575	8%	509,305
Washburn	522,240	208,896	40%	313,344
TOTALS	12,918,400	3,799,026	29.4%	9,119,374

TOTAL AREA OF OPEN COUNTIES   25,679,360 acres
TOTAL CLOSED AREA   8,560,335 acres (33.3%)

* Commission Order G-602 opened entire county.

Annual Estimated Deer Gun Kill in Open Counties (continued)
1912-1954

Open Counties	THE 1944 SEASON Kill	Notes
Adams	234	
Ashland	1,220	
Barron.	175	
Bayfield.	2,329	Six-day, forked-antlered buck season from November 25 to November 30.
Buffalo	108	
Burnett	904	
Chippewa.	173	Definition of a forked-antlered buck: One whose antler has a branch or fork one inch long or over.
Clark	943	
Columbia.	442	
Dane.	261	
Douglas	1,600	First opening of an any-deer season in the western and southern agricultural counties: Buffalo, Dane, Grant, Iowa, La Crosse, Richland, and Trempealeau Counties, were open for one deer of any age or either sex, with either rifle or shotgun loaded with a single slug or ball.
Eau Claire.	981	
Florence.	1,104	
Forest.	1,448	
Grant	81	
Iowa.	68	
Iron.	770	
Jackson	1,477	
Juneau.	593	Vilas and Bayfield Counties each attracted more than 10,000 hunters.
La Crosse	354	
Langlade.	293	
Lincoln	535	Columbia County was open north of Highway 60 and west of Highway 44 only.
Marathon.	68	
Marinette	1,662	
Monroe.	316	Local hunters were more successful than migrant hunters.
Oconto.	623	
Oneida.	1,713	
Polk.	459	The use of buckshot was again prohibited.
Portage	150	
Price	892	
Richland.	32	One hunter out of 4.4 was successful in bagging a deer.
Rusk.	487	
St. Croix	28	
Sauk.	134	The average number of days spent hunting was 3.94.
Sawyer.	1,542	
Shawano	180	
Taylor.	351	The number of hunters who purchased tags but did not hunt was about 5,500.
Trempealeau	348	
Vilas	2,170	
Washburn.	495	Nine out of ten deer were killed with a rifle.
Wood.	794	

TOTAL	28,537

DEER TAG SALES	117,052
VOLUNTARY SPORTSMEN	10,152
NONRESIDENT BIG GAME	439
TOTAL TAG SALES	127,643

Open Counties	Kill	THE 1945 SEASON Notes
Adams	656	
Ashland	1,319	Five-day, forked-antlered buck season from November 24 to November 28.
Barron	95	
Bayfield	2,714	Definition of forked-antlered buck: One whose antler has a branch or fork one inch long or over.
Buffalo	86	
Burnett	1,194	
Chippewa	270	
Clark	1,800	One forked-antlered buck could be taken with a shotgun only (slug or ball only) in the counties of Buffalo, Crawford, Grant, Iowa, La Crosse, Richland, and Trempealeau.
Columbia	555	
Crawford	14	
Douglas	1,959	
Eau Claire	752	
Florence	1,648	
Forest	1,878	Grant County was open north of U.S. Highway 18 only. Iowa County was open north of U.S. Highway 18 only.
Grant	19	
Iowa	68	
Iron	443	
Jackson	2,107	The deer kill showed a 32% increase over previous year.
Juneau	1,374	
La Crosse	21	Jackson and Clark Counties showed a 60% increase in kill over the previous year.
Langlade	892	
Lincoln	683	
Marathon	510	
Marinette	2,581	Complete destruction of the deer range on Chambers Island in Door County resulted in the removal of 250 deer by Department personnel.
Marquette	226	
Monroe	884	
Oconto	1,010	
Oneida	1,739	
Polk	632	Vilas and Marinette Counties attracted the largest number of hunters.
Portage	160	
Price	1,245	One hunter out of 3.4 was successful in bagging a deer.
Richland	11	
Rusk	553	
Sawyer	1,493	The number of hunters who purchased deer tags but did not hunt was about 4,800.
Shawano	248	
Taylor	640	
Trempealeau	21	The average number of days spent hunting was 3.46.
Vilas	2,543	
Washburn	872	
Waushara	275	
Wood	1,337	

TOTAL	37,527

DEER TAG SALES	119,955
VOLUNTARY SPORTSMEN	13,193
NONRESIDENT BIG GAME	400
TOTAL TAG SALES	133,548

Open Counties	Kill	THE 1946 SEASON Notes
Adams	1,145	Nine-day, forked-antlered buck season, from November 23 to December 1.
Ashland	1,596	
Barron.	144	
Bayfield.	3,593	Definition of forked-antlered buck: One whose antler has a branch or fork one inch long or over.
Buffalo	354	
Burnett	1,747	
Chippewa.	252	
Clark	2,646	One forked-antlered buck could be taken with shotgun only (slug or ball only) in Columbia, Grant, Iowa, Richland, and Sauk Counties.
Columbia.	349	
Douglas	2,729	
Eau Claire. . . .	839	
Florence.	1,134	One deer of any age or either sex could be taken with shotgun only (slug or ball only) in Buffalo, La Crosse, and Trempealeau Counties.
Forest.	2,503	
Grant	19	
Iowa.	20	
Iron.	794	
Jackson	3,419	The Town of Union was closed in Eau Claire County.
Juneau.	3,609	
La Crosse	613	One hunter out of 3.2 was successful in bagging a deer.
Langlade.	1,296	
Lincoln	1,580	
Marathon.	156	Approximately 68,000 more licenses were sold than in 1945.
Marinette	3,110	
Marquette	278	
Monroe.	970	The kill was 47% higher than the previous year.
Oconto.	1,507	
Oneida.	2,752	The number of hunters who purchased tags but did not hunt was about 6,000.
Polk.	1,089.	
Portage	321	
Price	2,310	Of the total number of hunters, 14% were trying their skill for the first time.
Richland.	19	
Rusk.	833	
St. Croix	240	
Sauk.	152	Controlled hunting in the 32,000-acre Necedah National Wildlife Refuge in Juneau County was concurrent with the state-wide season. Gun hunting in this area was permitted for the first time since 1939. 1,637 antlerless deer were taken in the refuge, an average of 32 deer per square mile. Three out of 4 hunters were successful. Two out of 3 deer were killed in the morning. There were no hunting accidents. A total of 3,000 permits was issued, and 2,226 hunters participated.
Sawyer.	1,937	
Shawano	244	
Taylor.	550	
Trempealeau . . .	473	
Vilas	4,300	
Washburn.	1,387	
Waushara.	320	
Wood.	1,947	
TOTAL	**55,276**	
DEER TAG SALES	182,304	The deer kill on Madeline Island amounted to 171.
VOLUNTARY SPORTSMEN	17,886	
NONRESIDENT BIG GAME	871	The Conservation Department had recommended a four-day, any-deer season. The Conservation Congress voted for a nine-day, forked-horn buck season.
TOTAL TAG SALES	201,061	

Open Counties	Kill	THE 1947 SEASON Notes
Adams.	1,158	
Ashland.	1,593	
Barron	309	
Bayfield	3,328	
Buffalo.	627	
Burnett.	1,374	
Chippewa	298	
Clark.	2,462	
Columbia	489	
Crawford	205	
Douglas.	2,851	
Eau Claire . . .	552	
Florence	1,422	
Forest	2,894	
Iowa	139	
Iron	843	
Jackson.	2,939	
Juneau	3,678	
La Crosse. . . .	447	
Langlade	1,307	
Lincoln.	1,561	
Marathon	292	
Marinette. . . .	3,137	
Monroe	1,320	
Oconto	1,665	
Oneida	2,670	
Pepin.	186	
Polk	1,032	
Portage.	395	
Price.	1,631	
Richland	20	
Rusk	1,017	
Sauk	293	
Sawyer	1,964	
Shawano.	228	
Taylor	966	
Trempealeau. . .	359	
Vilas.	2,959	
Washburn	1,024	
Waushara	534	
Wood	1,352	
TOTAL	53,520	
DEER TAG SALES	199,234	
VOLUNTARY SPORTSMEN	22,438	
NONRESIDENT BIG GAME	1,263	
TOTAL TAG SALES	222,935	

Nine-day, forked-antlered buck season from November 22 to November 30.

Definition of forked-antlered buck: One whose antler has a branch or fork one inch long or over.

One deer of any age or either sex could be taken with shotgun only (slug or ball only) in the counties of Buffalo, Crawford, Iowa, La Crosse, Pepin, Richland and Trempealeau. These agricultural counties accounted for 3.7% of the total kill.

One hunter out of 3.6 was successful in bagging a deer.

The number of hunters who purchased deer tags but did not hunt was about 6,300.

Cranberry marsh deer damage in central Wisconsin resulted in the use of gas exploders, patrolling of the area, and the shooting of 23 deer by Department personnel.

Controlled Hunting - the Necedah National Wildlife Refuge and portions of the Meadow Valley Unit of the Central Wisconsin Conservation Area (62,713 acres), were open to antlerless deer hunting after the regular buck season, December 6 to 14. 1,518 antlerless deer, or 16 deer per square mile, were taken. More than a third of the hunters were successful. There were 19,664 applications for the 6,000 permits issued. This area was also open to forked-horn bucks during the regular season from November 22 to 30.

The Conservation Department had recommended a five-day, any-deer season. The Conservation Congress had recommended the usual buck season.

THE 1948 SEASON

Open Counties	Kill
Adams	996
Ashland	801
Barron.	240
Bayfield.	2,739
Buffalo	283
Burnett	1,331
Chippewa.	381
Clark	1,587
Columbia.	207
Crawford.	22
Douglas	1,719
Dunn.	275
Eau Claire. . . .	871
Florence.	889
Forest.	1,681
Grant	172
Green Lake. . . .	162
Iowa.	23
Iron.	937
Jackson	2,907
Juneau.	1,193
La Crosse	284
Langlade.	1,153
Lincoln	1,396
Marathon.	647
Marinette	3,065
Marquette	319
Monroe.	561
Oconto.	1,611
Oneida.	2,075
Pepin	41
Polk.	785
Portage	205
Price	1,730
Rusk.	524
St. Croix	149
Sauk.	205
Sawyer.	1,701
Shawano	590
Taylor.	643
Trempealeau . . .	192
Vilas	2,292
Washburn.	960
Waushara.	354
Wood.	1,056
TOTAL	**41,954**
DEER TAG SALES	220,004
VOLUNTARY SPORTSMENT	27,042
NONRESIDENT BIG GAME	1,563
TOTAL TAG SALES	**248,609**

Notes

Nine-day, forked-antlered buck season from November 20 to November 28.

Definition of a forked-antlered buck: One whose antler has a branch or fork one inch long or over.

One deer of any age or either sex could be taken with a shotgun only (ball or slug only) in the counties of Buffalo, Crawford, Grant, LaCrosse, Pepin, Polk (south of U.S. Highway 8), and Trempealeau.

One forked-antlered buck could be taken with shotgun only (slug or ball only) in the counties of Dunn, Iowa, and St. Croix.

Polk County had a rifle season for forked-antlered deer north of U.S. Highway 8, and a shotgun season for any deer south of U.S. Highway 8.

Iowa County had a shotgun season north of U.S. Highway 18, but was closed south of U.S. Highway 18.

One hunter out of five was successful in bagging a deer.

Occupation of hunters:

Farmers	37%
Businessmen	14%
Professional men	6%
Misc. occupations	43%

The number of hunters who purchased a deer tag but did not hunt was about 7,000.

Checking station data recorded the following heavy dressed weights in the Mississippi River deer counties, and the western agricultural counties of Polk and Pepin:

	Number	Average weight
Adult bucks	25	160 lbs.
Adult does	118	116.3 lbs.

The Conservation Congress voted for an any-deer season. The Department and Commission recommended a 9-day, any-deer season. It was turned down by the governor whose approval must be given to all game season orders.

Open Counties	Kill	THE 1949 SEASON Notes
Adams.	2,538	Five-day, antlerless-deer season, from November 19 to November 23.
Ashland.	3,717	
Barron	196	
Bayfield	8,981	The antlerless deer season permitted the shooting of does, fawns, spike bucks, and forked-antlered bucks with a fork or branch less than two inches long.
Buffalo.	261	
Burnett.	4,389	
Chippewa	556	
Clark.	8,359	There was a shotgun season for antlerless deer (ball or slug only) in the counties of Barron, Buffalo, Columbia, Crawford, Dunn, Grant, Iowa, La Crosse, Marathon, Marquette, Pepin, Pierce, Richland, St. Croix, Shawano, Trempealeau, Waupaca, and Waushara.
Columbia	302	
Crawford	116	
Douglas.	7,367	
Dunn	757	
Eau Claire . . .	4,559	
Florence	5,062	
Forest	6,781	
Grant.	132	All other hunting except waterfowl was prohibited during the deer season.
Iowa	61	
Iron	2,208	Polk County had a rifle season north of U.S. Highway 8, and a shotgun season south of U.S. Highway 8.
Jackson.	16,263	
Juneau	7,086	
La Crosse. . . .	153	Three hunters out of five were successful in bagging a deer.
Langlade	2,245	
Lincoln.	2,764	
Marathon	315	The number of hunters who purchased deer tags but did not hunt was about 10,000.
Marinette. . . .	9,597	
Marquette. . . .	695	
Monroe	3,934	
Oconto	4,764	Rifles preferred by hunters (in order of preference by caliber):
Oneida	8,583	
Pepin.	268	1. 30-30 6. 35
Pierce	453	2. 32 special & others 7. 30 unspecified
Polk	2,217	3. 30-06 8. 30-40
Portage.	547	4. 8 mm 9. 39-55
Price.	5,515	5. 300 10. 303
Richland	108	
Rusk	2,319	One-fourth of the hunters used shotguns.
St. Croix. . . .	432	
Sauk	308	Nonresidents from 22 states bagged 1,445 deer.
Sawyer	5,516	
Shawano.	594	Approximately 62% of all licensed hunters in the state purchased deer tags.
Taylor	1,591	
Trempealeau. . .	92	
Vilas.	14,773	The Conservation Congress went on record for a 9-day, forked-buck season with controlled hunting. The Conservation Department had also recommended a buck season with controlled hunting on about a million acres. Since the Legislature failed to pass the controlled hunting bill (restriction of issuance of deer tags and permits, and designation of areas to be hunted) the Department recommended a five-day, antlerless and spike buck season.
Washburn	2,489	
Waupaca.	871	
Waushara	879	
Wood	7,399	
TOTAL	159,112	
DEER TAG SALES	263,489	
VOLUNTARY SPORTSMEN	21,084	
NONRESIDENT BIG GAME	1,726	
TOTAL TAG SALES	286,299	

Open Counties	Kill	THE 1950 SEASON Notes

Open Counties	Kill
Adams	2,892
Ashland	5,230
Barron	556
Bayfield	10,785
Buffalo	442
Burnett	4,644
Chippewa	578
Clark	8,489
Columbia	792
Door	173
Douglas	7,863
Dunn	780
Eau Claire	1,856
Florence	5,971
Forest	8,540
Grant	130
Iowa	24
Iron	3,402
Jackson	8,878
Juneau	3,621
La Crosse	171
Langlade	2,583
Lincoln	3,878
Marathon	573
Marinette	12,262
Marquette	1,106
Monroe	2,245
Oconto	5,721
Oneida	10,520
Pepin	200
Pierce	372
Polk	3,142
Portage	848
Price	7,168
Richland	32
Rusk	2,851
St. Croix	369
Sauk	795
Sawyer	7,559
Shawano	590
Taylor	2,296
Trempealeau	215
Vilas	16,558

Seven-day any-deer (one deer of either sex or any age) season, from November 18 to November 24.

There was a closed season on all species of wild animals, except deer and migratory birds, south of an east-west line along State Highway 29 and U.S. Highway 12.

For the first time the season began at 8:00 a.m. on the opening day. The usual opening time since 1935 had been one-half hour before sunrise.

In Polk County hunting was permitted with rifles north of U.S. Highway 8, and with shotguns south of U.S. Highway 8.

Wisconsin led the nation in the kill of white-tailed deer. This was the first year that more than 300,000 deer-hunting licenses were sold. Deer tag sales increased about 9% over the preceding year.

Two-thirds of all the hunters in the state bought deer tags.

Of the total number of deer tag purchasers, 11,500 did not hunt.

The kill in the six Mississippi River counties: Buffalo, Grant, La Crosse, Pepin, Pierce, and Trempealeau; and the 11 other agricultural counties: Columbia, Dunn, Eau Claire, Iowa, Marathon, Marquette, Richland, St. Croix, Shawano, Waupaca, and Waushara, was about 10,000, or less than 7% of the total harvest. These counties were open to shotgun hunting only.

The central counties of Admas, Jackson, Juneau, Monroe, and Wood, accounted for approximately 13% of the kill. In these same counties during the previous year the hunters had bagged 23% of the total kill.

Chambers Island only, which constitutes about 2,600 acres of Door County, was open after having been closed for 36 years. A total of 173 deer was taken.

(continued on the following page)

Annual Estimated Deer Gun Kill in Open Counties (continued)
1912-1954

Open Counties	Kill	THE 1950 SEASON (continued) Notes
Washburn.	3,137	An estimated 200 deer were taken from Madeline Island, Ashland County.
Waupaca	1,692	
Waushara.	1,212	
Wood.	4,170	Approximately one out of two hunters bagged their deer.
TOTAL	167,911	Hunting pressure was low after the first three days. Less than ten per cent of the hunters hunted more than five days.
DEER TAG SALES	289,420	Hunters spent an average of 3.2 days in the field.
VOLUNTARY SPORTSMEN	20,035	Out-of-state hunters from 23 states bagged 2,439 whitetails.
NONRESIDENT BIG GAME	3,115	Both the Congress and the Department had recommended a 9-day, any-deer season. The Commission agreed on this type of season, but reduced the length to 7 days.
TOTAL TAG SALES	312,570	

Open Counties	Kill	THE 1951 SEASON Notes
Adams.	3,284	
Ashland.	4,463	
Barron	193	
Bayfield	7,695	
Buffalo.	878	
Burnett.	4,741	
Chippewa	830	
Clark.	2,878	
Columbia	1,141	
Crawford	126	
Dane	238	
Dodge.	195	
Door	446	
Douglas.	6,622	
Dunn	667	
Eau Claire . . .	2,235	
Florence	4,768	
Fond du Lac. . .	30	
Forest	6,376	
Grant.	97	
Green Lake . . .	983	
Iowa	136	
Iron	2,614	
Jackson.	4,309	
Juneau	2,414	
La Crosse. . . .	367	
Langlade	3,070	
Lincoln.	3,613	
Marathon	1,539	
Marinette. . . .	8,979	
Marquette. . . .	1,186	
Monroe	880	
Oconto	4,657	
Oneida	6,730	
Outagamie. . . .	869	
Pepin.	169	
Pierce	460	
Polk	2,064	
Portage.	966	
Price.	7,057	
Richland	51	
Rusk	2,176	
St. Croix. . . .	256	

Notes column:

Seven-day, any-deer (one deer of either sex or any age) season, from November 17 to Nov. 23.

There was an open season in 55 counties. Not since 1906 were there more counties open.

Newly Opened Counties	Year of Last Open Season
Dodge	1907
Fond du Lac	1897
Outagamie	1907
Winnebago	1907

The Mississippi River counties (Buffalo, Crawford, La Crosse, Pepin, Pierce, Trempealeau, and Vernon) were open to shotgun loaded with single slug or ball only, and they accounted for about 2% of the total kill. Additional counties open to shotgun hunting were: Dodge, Fond du Lac, Green Lake, Marquette, Waushara, Winnebago, Outagamie, Waupaca, Shawano, St. Croix, Richland, Monroe, Jackson, Dunn, the southern portion of Polk, Barron, Eau Claire, and Clark Counties, and the southern portion of Iowa County.

The central counties - Admas, Juneau, and Wood (rifle), Jackson, and Monroe (shotgun), accounted for approximately 10% of the total kill. About 3,800 less deer were taken than during the previous season.

21% of the state's male population, 12 years of age or older, bought big game hunting licenses.

For the first time Jackson and Monroe were among the 22 counties having a nonrifle season.

Almost every other hunter was successful in bagging a deer.

More than 6,000 hunters who purchased deer tags did not hunt.

(continued on following page)

Open Counties	THE 1951 SEASON (continued) Kill	Notes

THE 1951 SEASON (continued)

Open Counties	Kill	Notes
Sauk	465	Hunters who lived in counties which were open were about 8% more successful than the hunters who came from counties which had no open deer season.
Sawyer	5,514	
Shawano	1,409	
Taylor	2,344	
Trempealeau . . .	388	About 3 out of 4 of the nonresident hunters representing 15 states, were successful in getting their deer.
Vernon	145	
Vilas	6,030	
Washburn	3,528	The Legislature enacted a new law to legalize the wearing of orange as well as red (29.233). A new law also required that any person involved in a hunting accident must submit a report to the State Conservation Commission within 10 days after the accident.
Waupaca	2,083	
Waushara	1,532	
Winnebago	32	
Wood	2,557	
TOTAL	129,475	
DEER TAG SALES	260,136	The Conservation Department and Congress had recommended a 9-day, any-deer season. The Deer Committee of the Congress recommended a 16-day any-deer season.
VOLUNTARY SPORTSMEN	33,909	
NONRESIDENT BIG GAME	2,750	
TOTAL TAG SALES	296,795	

Open Counties	THE 1952 SEASON Kill	Notes
Adams.	396	
Ashland.	720	
Barron	223	
Bayfield	1,192	
Buffalo.	1,128	
Burnett.	443	
Chippewa	281	
Clark.	388	
Columbia	153	
Crawford	296	
Dane	221	
Dodge.	62	
Door	113	
Douglas.	1,257	
Dunn	119	
Eau Claire . . .	292	
Florence	1,032	
Forest	2,095	
Grant.	303	
Green Lake . . .	75	
Iowa	310	
Iron	529	
Jackson.	1,534	
Juneau	356	
La Crosse. . . .	418	
Langlade	747	
Lincoln.	1,280	
Marathon	363	
Marinette. . . .	1,493	
Marquette. . . .	169	
Monroe	417	
Oconto	970	
Oneida	1,206	
Outagamie. . . .	316	
Pepin.	30	
Pierce	117	
Polk	176	
Portage.	321	
Price.	1,087	
Richland	64	
Rusk	416	
St. Croix. . . .	33	
Sauk	70	

Notes:

Seven-day, forked-antlered buck season, from November 22 to November 28.

Definition of a forked-antlered buck: One whose antler has a branch or fork one inch long or over.

One deer of any age or sex could be taken with shotgun only (ball or slug only) in the nine counties of Buffalo, Crawford, Dane, Grant, Iowa, La Crosse, Richland, Trempealeau, and Vernon.

One forked-antlered buck could be taken by shotgun only (ball or slug only) in the 12 counties of Columbia, Dodge, Dunn, Green Lake, Marquette, Outagamie, Pepin, Pierce, St. Croix, Shawano, Waupaca, and Waushara.

Barron and Polk Counties, open to forked-antlered bucks, had a rifle season north of U.S. Highway 8, and a shotgun season south of U.S. Highway 8.

Eau Claire County open to forked-antlered buck had a rifle season north and east of U.S. Highway 12, and a shotgun season south of U.S. Highway 12.

Approximately one out of 6 of the state's male population 12 years of age or older bought big game licenses.

More than 13,000 hunters who purchased deer tags did not hunt.

One out of eight hunters belonged to an age group below 21 years.

Hunters averaged 3.9 days hunting in one or more of the 53 open counties.

(continued on following page)

Open Counties	THE 1952 SEASON (continued) Kill	Notes
Sawyer.	1,064	All of the Necedah National Wildlife Refuge was closed to gun hunting.
Shawano	188	
Taylor.	458	
Trempealeau . .	384	More than 13,000 hunters invaded the Mississippi River counties.
Vernon.	235	
Vilas	612	Buffalo County for the first time ranked among the leading deer kill counties.
Washburn. . . .	480	
Waupaca	488	
Waushara. . . .	213	
Wood.	171	Farming counties permitting shotgun hunting only accounted for almost one-fifth of the total number of deer taken.
TOTAL	27,504	The Conservation Department recommended a spike-antlered season, with legal bucks to have a 2-inch spike or longer. The Commission followed the recommendations of the Congress and their Executive Council in authorizing a forked-horn buck season with a 1-inch fork or longer as legal deer.
DEER TAG SALES	199,944	
VOLUNTARY SPORTSMEN	37,101	
NONRESIDENT BIG GAME	1,242	
TOTAL TAG SALES	238,287	

Open Counties	Kill	THE 1953 SEASON Notes
Adams	258	Seven-day, forked-antlered buck season from November 28 to December 4. The season was originally established to open on November 21 for 7 days, but was postponed due to near-drought conditions resulting in extreme forest fire hazards.
Ashland	656	
Barron	36	
Bayfield	764	
Buffalo	217	
Burnett	347	
Chippewa	83	Definition of a forked-antlered buck: One whose antler has a branch or fork one inch long or over.
Clark	721	
Columbia	168	
Crawford	32	
Dane	20	The 53 counties open were the same as during the 1952 season. The any-deer or antlerless season established previously in a number of western and southern agricultural counties was discontinued.
Dodge	20	
Door	30	
Douglas	733	
Dunn	72	
Eau Claire . . .	616	
Florence	477	One forked-antlered buck could be taken with shotgun only in the 22 counties of Buffalo, Columbia, Crawford, Dane, Dodge, Door, Dunn, Grant, Green Lake, Iowa, La Crosse, Marquette, Outagamie, Pepin, Pierce, Richland, St. Croix, Shawano, Trempealeau, Vernon, Waupaca, and Waushara.
Forest	898	
Grant	84	
Green Lake . . .	20	
Iowa	13	
Iron	210	
Jackson	1,447	
Juneau	592	
La Crosse . . .	74	
Langlade	449	Barron and Polk Counties had a rifle season north of U.S. Highway 8, and a shotgun season south of U.S. Highway 8.
Lincoln	789	
Marathon	112	
Marinette	1,216	177,590 acres were closed primarily for the protection of deer. The closed acreage showed a reduction of 90% from the previous year. The Conservation Congress opposed closed deer hunting areas on all public land, and resolved "that such designated closed areas on private lands not exceed 10 per cent of the land area of any one county during the 1953 season".
Marquette	129	
Monroe	522	
Oconto	496	
Oneida	1,131	
Outagamie	52	
Pepin	40	
Pierce	54	
Polk	345	One out of 11 hunters was successful in bagging a deer.
Portage	261	
Price	1,193	An estimated 14,000 hunters who purchased deer tags did not hunt.
Richland	20	
Rusk	318	One out of 9 hunters belonged to an age group below 21 years.
St. Croix	35	
Sauk	71	Hunters averaged 3.8 days hunting in one or more of the open counties. About 9 out of 10 hunters hunted during the opening two days.

(continued on following page)

Open Counties	THE 1953 SEASON (continued) Kill	Notes

DEER REGISTRATION

For the first time, all successful hunters were required to exhibit their deer at checking stations where a special tag was affixed, and the deer recorded after inspection. The kill figures shown by the registration method were as follows:

Open Counties	Kill			
Sawyer	641			
Shawano	189			
Taylor	398			
Trempealeau	84			
Vernon	20			
Vilas	1,483			
Washburn	307			
Waupaca	365			
Waushara	195			
Wood	320			

County	Kill	County	Kill
Adams	224	Marathon	154
Ashland	519	Marinette	844
Barron	63	Marquette	137
Bayfield	595	Monroe	619
Buffalo	139	Oconto	329
Burnett	432	Oneida	892
Chippewa	91	Outagamie	112
Clark	559	Pepin	36
Columbia	86	Pierce	46
Crawford	14	Polk	241
Dane	5	Portage	145
Dodge	22	Price	858
Door	35	Richland	4
Douglas	621	Rusk	309
Dunn	107	St. Croix	26
Eau Claire	399	Sauk	59
Florence	434	Sawyer	611
Forest	855	Shawano	181
Grant	37	Taylor	319
Green Lake	34	Trempealeau	63
Iowa	12	Vernon	5
Iron	302	Vilas	872
Jackson	1,084	Washburn	311
Juneau	283	Waupaca	268
La Crosse	36	Waushara	162
Langlade	425	Wood	295
Lincoln	569	TOTAL	15,880

TOTAL	19,823
DEER TAG SALES	192,687
VOLUNTARY SPORTSMEN	40,227
NONRESIDENT BIG GAME	1,118
TOTAL TAG SALES	234,032

The Conservation Commission followed the recommendations of the Department in authorizing the forked-horn buck season. The statewide Congress had passed a motion for a 7-day gun deer season. The Congress county meetings favored a deer season by a vote of 59 to 12.

Open Counties	Kill	THE 1954 SEASON Notes
Adams.	280	
Ashland.	731	
Barron	152	
Bayfield	746	
Buffalo.	263	
Burnett.	599	
Chippewa	90	
Clark.	675	
Columbia	344	
Crawford	17	
Dane	28	
Dodge.	29	
Door	74	
Douglas.	1,008	
Dunn	149	
Eau Claire . . .	496	
Florence	953	
Fond du Lac. . .	52	
Forest	1,345	
Grant.	59	
Green Lake . . .	97	
Iowa	14	
Iron	479	
Jackson.	1,213	
Juneau	862	
La Crosse. . . .	89	
Langlade	531	
Lincoln.	778	
Marathon	297	
Marinette. . . .	1,327	
Marquette. . . .	342	
Monroe	459	
Oconto	851	
Oneida	999	
Outagamie. . . .	184	
Pepin.	137	
Pierce	130	
Polk	530	
Portage.	365	
Price.	1,197	
Richland	20	
Rusk	520	
St. Croix. . . .	82	
Sauk	30	
Sawyer	894	
Shawano.	271	
Taylor	291	
Trempealeau. . .	112	

Notes:

A seven-day, forked-antlered buck season from November 20 to November 26. Definition of a forked-antlered buck: One whose antler has a branch or fork one inch long or over.

A total of 55 counties was open. As in 1951, more counties were open than during any other year since 1906 when 61 counties were open. Counties open were the same as during the 1953 season, plus Fond du Lac and Washington. One forked-horn buck in the 24 counties of Adams, Buffalo, Columbia, Crawford, Dane, Dodge, Dunn, Fond du Lac, Grant, Green Lake, Iowa, La Crosse, Marquette, Outagamie, Pepin, Pierce, Richland, St. Croix, Shawano, Trempealeau, Vernon, Washington, Waupaca, and Waushara. Barron and Polk Counties had a rifle season north of U.S. Highway 8, and a shotgun season south of U.S. Highway 8.

Deer of any age or either sex could be taken by rifle and shotgun on the Apostle Islands, except Madeline, and with shotgun only on the islands of Detroit and Rock in Door County.

A total of 162,435 acres (less than 2% of the total state deer range - 16,200,000 acres) were closed primarily as a protection for deer.

One out of ten hunters were successful. An estimated 12,000 deer tag purchasers did not hunt at all. About one out of six of the male population of Wisconsin 12 years of age or older bought a big game license.

The kill showed an increase of 24% over the 1953 kill. A total of 354 deer of any age or either sex was taken on the Apostle Islands, including 41 bucks from Madeline Island. A total of 63 deer was taken on the Door County islands: Detroit 51, and Rock 12.

(continued on following page)

Open Counties	THE 1954 SEASON (continued) Kill	Notes

Vernon.	84
Vilas	1,648
Washburn.	347
Washington. . . .	14
Waupaca	479
Waushara.	385
Wood.	550

TOTAL	24,698
DEER TAG SALES	205,022
VOLUNTARY SPORTSMEN	41,163
NONRESIDENT BIG GAME	1,125
TOTAL TAG SALES	247,310

One out of 8 hunters belonged to an age group below 21 years. One out of 16 hunters was inexperienced.

About 9 out of 10 hunters were in the field during the opening 2 days. There was a considerable drop in the number of hunters on the third day. There was no substantial increase in the number of hunters during the Thanksgiving holiday. These patterns of hunting activity were the same as during the 1952 and 1953 seasons.

Hunters averaged 4.14 days of hunting as compared with 3.8 in 1953, and 3.9 in 1952.

DEER REGISTRATION

For the second time, all successful hunters were required to register their deer at checking stations. The following kill figures show the number of deer registered:

Adams	173	Grant	56	Portage	254
Ashland	810	Green Lake	75	Price	901
Barron	96	Iowa	37	Richland	8
Bayfield	600	Iron	341	Rusk	398
Buffalo	226	Jackson	977	St. Croix	64
Burnett	454	Juneau	443	Sauk	102
Chippewa	165	La Crosse	97	Sawyer	655
Clark	626	Langlade	508	Shawano	299
Columbia	200	Lincoln	619	Taylor	345
Crawford	48	Marathon	284	Trempealeau	129
Dane	8	Marinette	1,201	Vernon	32
Dodge	17	Marquette	226	Vilas	1,109
Door	63	Monroe	466	Washburn	409
Douglas	692	Oconto	647	Washington	11
Dunn	181	Oneida	1,008	Waupaca	442
Eau Claire	373	Outagamie	192	Waushara	324
Florence	532	Pepin	48	Wood	451
Fond du Lac	24	Pierce	88		
Forest	1,022	Polk	321	TOTAL	19,877

The Conservation Commission approved a forked-antlered buck season in all but 16 of the 71 counties.

The Department requested the Conservation Congress to consider either a 3-inch polished horn, or a forked-horn buck season followed by, or concurrent with, the last days of the general season, with a 2-day, any-deer season in the critical areas of a number of northern counties.

The Wisconsin Conservation Congress favored a 7-day, forked-horn buck season by a 43 to 24 vote.

The county congress meetings favored a forked or polished horn season.

Annual Registered Deer Gun Kill in Open Counties
1955-1964

THE 1955 SEASON *

Counties	Kill	Notes
Adams.	705	
Ashland.	970	65 counties were open to gun deer hunting.
Barron	190	
Bayfield	1,064	A nine-day forked horn buck season
Brown.	50	November 19 - November 27.
Buffalo.	1,564	
Burnett.	928	Shotgun only in 23 counties: Brown,
Calumet.	38	Calumet, Columbia, Crawford, Dane, Dodge,
Chippewa	226	Door (including Detroit and Rock Islands),
Clark.	798	Fond du Lac, Grant, Green Lake, Jefferson,
Columbia	287	Kewaunee, Manitowoc, Outagamie, Ozaukee,
Crawford	64	Shawano, Sheboygan, Walworth (only por-
Dane	13	tion open), Washington, Waukesha (only
Dodge.	36	portion open), Waupaca, Waushara and
Door	54	Winnebago.
Douglas.	1,131	
Dunn	1,482	Definition of a forked-horn buck:
Eau Claire . . .	576	One whose antler has a branch one inch
Florence	733	or more.
Fond du Lac. . .	27	Except the following areas:
Forest	1,434	
Grant.	77	Mississippi River Zone
Green.	C	
Green Lake . . .	165	A four-day (November 19-22) either
Iowa	86	sex season in seven counties: Buffalo,
Iron	304	Dunn, La Crosse, Pepin, Pierce, Trem-
Jackson.	1,439	pealeau and St. Croix.
Jefferson. . . .	39	
Juneau	677	A nine-day either sex season on the
Kenosha.	C	Apostle Islands with shotgun or rifle
Kewaunee	56	except Madeline Island which was open for
La Crosse. . . .	838	forked-horn bucks only.
Lafayette. . . .	C	
Langlade	820	The Conservation Department and the
Lincoln.	999	statewide Conservation Congress recom-
Manitowoc. . . .	147	mended a nine-day spike buck season (bucks
Marathon	358	with a three-inch minimum spike).
Marinette. . . .	1,664	
Marquette. . . .	423	The Conservation Commission estab-
Milwaukee. . . .	C	lished the less liberal forked-horn buck
Monroe	565	season.
Oconto	854	
Oneida	1,542	
Outagamie. . . .	267	
Ozaukee.	2	
Pepin.	286	
Pierce	528	
Polk	577	
Portage.	419	
Price.	1,554	
Racine	C	

(continued on following page)

Annual Registered Deer Gun Kill in Open Counties (continued)
1955-1964

	THE 1955 SEASON (continued)*	
Counties	Kill	
Richland.	38	
Rock.	C	
Rusk.	620	
St. Croix	470	
Sauk.	177	
Sawyer.	1,013	
Shawano	419	
Sheboygan	34	
Taylor.	669	
Trempealeau . . .	696	
Vernon.	66	
Vilas	1,287	
Walworth.	13	
Washburn.	727	
Washington. . . .	21	
Waukesha.	30	
Waupaca	623	
Waushara.	478	
Winnebago	68	
Wood.	555	
TOTAL	35,060	
DEER TAG SALES	219,611	
SPORTSMEN LICENSES	46,549	
NONRESIDENT BIG GAME LICENSES	1,452	
TOTAL SALES	267,612	

* Age and sex not available.

Annual Registered Deer Gun Kill in Open Counties (continued)
1955-1964

THE 1956 SEASON

Counties	Kill
Adams.	654
Ashland.	1,046
Barron	151
Bayfield	1,296
Brown.	53
Buffalo.	438
Burnett.	935
Calumet.	39
Chippewa	264
Clark.	1,079
Columbia	404
Crawford	99
Dane	42
Dodge.	39
Door	64
Douglas.	1,210
Dunn	205
Eau Claire . . .	696
Florence	812
Fond du Lac. . .	45
Forest	1,612
Grant.	134
Green.	C
Green Lake . . .	205
Iowa	128
Iron	489
Jackson.	2,121
Jefferson. . . .	26
Juneau	924
Kenosha.	C
Kewaunee	55
La Crosse. . . .	151
Lafayette. . . .	19
Langlade	869
Lincoln.	908
Manitowoc. . . .	115
Marathon	340
Marinette. . . .	1,986
Marquette. . . .	449
Milwaukee. . . .	C
Monroe	755
Oconto	1,034
Oneida	1,960
Outagamie. . . .	308
Ozaukee.	9
Pepin.	106
Pierce	149
Polk	539
Portage.	457
Price.	1,687
Racine	C
Richland	51

Notes

65 Open Counties

A nine-day spike buck season from November 17 - November 25.

Shotgun only in 27 counties: Brown, Buffalo, Calumet, Crawford, Dane, Dodge, Door*, Dunn*, Fond du Lac, Grant, Jefferson, Kewaunee, La Crosse, Lafayette, Manitowoc, Outagamie, Ozaukee, Pepin*, Pierce, St. Croix, Shawano, Sheboygan, Trempealeau, Washington, Waupaca, Winnebago and Waukesha**.

* No open season on Chambers Island, Door County or on Nine Mile Island in Dunn and Pepin Counties.

** Portion of Waukesha County closed.

Definition of a spike buck: One with antlers not less than 3 inches in length.

Except in the following area:

A nine-day either-sex season on the Apostle Islands, except Madeline Island which was open to spike buck only.

Not since 1934 had there been an open season on spike bucks during the buck only season.

Approximately one out of five deer taken were spike buck. About 6 out of 10 deer were taken on the opening weekend.

A total of 116,119 acres, less than 1% of the deer range, was closed. Kill per square mile of deer range: 1.43.

A record 533 deer were taken in 42 counties by nonresident hunters from 17 states. Approximately 3 out of 10 nonresident hunters were successful.

The Conservation Congress at county hearings and the state meeting approved the 9-day spike buck season proposed by the joint Law Enforcement and Game Management Board of the Wisconsin Conservation Department.

(continued on following page)

Annual Registered Deer Gun Kill in Open Counties (continued)
1955-1964

Counties	THE 1956 SEASON (continued) Kill
Rock.	C
Rusk.	628
St. Croix	84
Sauk.	174
Sawyer.	1,229
Shawano	520
Sheboygan	47
Taylor.	539
Trempealeau . . .	187
Vernon.	146
Vilas	1,795
Walworth.	C
Washburn.	783
Washington. . . .	28
Waukesha.	28
Waupaca	690
Waushara.	625
Winnebago	77
Wood.	825
TOTAL	35,562
RESIDENT LICENSE SALES (BIG GAME)	229,297
SPORTSMEN LICENSES	53,482
NONRESIDENT LICENSES	1,866
TOTAL	284,645

Kill by Age and Sex

Total	Spike Buck	Forked-Horn Buck	Misc.*
35,562	7,141	27,790	631

* Includes 129 does and fawns taken on the Apostle Islands.

Annual Registered Deer Gun Kill in Open Counties (continued)
1955-1964

THE 1957 SEASON

Counties	Total	Kill Regular License	Kill Party Permit	Notes
Adams	1,311	741	570	65 Counties Open
Ashland	1,406	914	492	
Barron	292	180	112	A nine-day spike buck season in
Bayfield	3,280	2,778	502	56 counties November 16 - November 24.
Brown	31	31	-	
Buffalo	1,618	1,618	-	Shotgun only in 18 counties:
Burnett	1,692	981	711	Brown, Calumet, Dane, Dodge, Door,
Calumet	47	47	-	Dunn, Fond du Lac, Jefferson, Ke-
Chippewa	416	240	176	waunee, Manitowoc, Lafayette,
Clark	2,079	1,109	970	Outagamie, Ozaukee, Sheboygan, Wash-
Columbia	398	398	-	ington, Waukesha, Waupaca and
Crawford	423	423	-	Winnebago.
Dane	29	29	-	Definition of a spike buck: a
Dodge	47	47	-	buck whose spike is 3 inches or more
Door	67	67	-	in length.
Douglas	1,889	1,272	617	
Dunn	365	207	158	Except the following areas:
Eau Claire	1,514	653	861	The first party permit season
Florence	1,493	766	727	November 16 - November 24 provided a
Fond du Lac	36	36	-	nine-day either sex season in all or
Forest	3,219	1,652	1,567	parts of 29 counties in the North-
Grant	351	351	-	west, Northeast and West Central
Green	C	-	-	areas. The law allowed groups of
Green Lake	201	201	-	four or more hunters to apply for a
Iowa	131	131	-	hunting party permit which entitled
Iron	880	522	358	the party to one deer of either sex
Jackson	4,998	2,347	2,651	or any age. 32,027 permits issued.
Jefferson	37	37	-	
Juneau	2,041	979	1,062	Mississippi River Zone
Kenosha	C	-	-	A split season in nine Missis-
Kewaunee	56	56	-	sippi River counties: a three-day
La Crosse	704	704	-	either sex season November 16 -
Lafayette	22	22	-	November 18 followed by a six-day
Langlade	1,506	861	645	spike buck season November 19 -
Lincoln	1,887	1,044	843	November 24. Shotgun only in
Manitowoc	129	129	-	Buffalo, Grant, La Crosse, Pierce,
Marathon	415	415	-	St. Croix and Trempealeau counties.
Marinette	4,475	2,256	2,219	Rifle permitted in Crawford, Pepin,
Marquette	474	474	-	and Vernon counties.
Milwaukee	C	-	-	A nine-day either sex season
Monroe	1,191	659	532	November 16 - November 24 in north-
Oconto	2,370	1,286	1,084	east Bayfield County and the Apostle
Oneida	3,775	2,024	1,751	Islands, except Madeline Island,
Outagamie	340	340	-	where the spike buck and party permit
Ozaukee	15	15	-	seasons were applicable.
Pepin	359	359	-	
Pierce	365	365	-	
Polk	1,083	588	495	
Portage	486	486	-	

(continued on following page)

Annual Registered Deer Gun Kill in Open Counties (continued)
1955-1964

THE 1957 SEASON (continued)

Counties	Total	Kill Regular License	Party Permit	Notes
Price	2,843	1,809	1,034	Managed Deer Gun Hunt on the
Racine	C	-	-	Horicon National Wildlife Refuge, two
Richland	46	46	-	days, December 21 - December 22.
Rock	C	-	-	Either sex. There were 4,963 appli-
Rusk	1,156	693	463	cations for the 250 available reser-
St. Croix	253	253	-	vations to hunt during the two-day
Sauk	174	174	-	season. Each reservation entitled
Sawyer	2,337	1,375	962	the holder to bring one guest. 627
Shawano	546	546	-	hunters took 162 deer in the 8-9,000
Sheboygan	52	52	-	acres deer area during the two-day
Taylor	1,035	585	450	season.
Trempealeau	806	806	-	Yearling deer comprised more than
Vernon	411	411	-	one-half of the legal buck shot in the
Vilas	3,480	1,760	1,720	regular license areas.
Walworth	C	-	-	Harvest per square mile of deer
Washburn	1,398	844	554	range - 2.7.
Washington	25	25	-	The Conservation Congress ap-
Waukesha	27	27	-	proved the nine-day statewide spike
Waupaca	814	814	-	buck season and the party permit
Waushara	656	656	-	season.
Winnebago	63	63	-	The Conservation Commission
Wood	2,073	1,000	1,073	adopted the Congress recommendation
TOTAL	68,138	42,779	25,359	with only minor changes, i.e., the highway boundary to be changed from Highway 8 to Highway 64.

Summary of Kill by Age and Sex

Type of License	Total Kill	Antlered Forked Buck	Spike Buck	% Spike Buck	Antlerless Adult Doe	Fawn Buck	Fawn Doe	Unknown
Regular License	42,779	30,554	7,547	19.5	2,406	936	896	440
Party Permit	25,359	207	1,164	84.9	15,557	4,806	3,573	52
Total	68,138	30,761	8,711	22.0	17,963	5,742	4,469	492

License Sales

Resident Big Game License Sales	235,125
Voluntary Sportsmen's Licenses	51,669
Nonresident Big Game License Sales	2,109
Total License Sales	288,903
Party Permit Sales	32,027

THE 1958 SEASON

Counties	Total	Kill Regular License	Party Permit	Notes
Adams	1,881	848	1,033	66 Open Counties.
Ashland	2,012	1,218	794	
Barron	411	234	177	Second party permit season extended to 58 counties.
Bayfield	2,936	1,814	1,122	
Brown	135	69	66	A 16-day spike buck and party
Buffalo	2,117	2,117	-	permit season in counties north of
Burnett	2,106	1,082	1,024	U.S. Highway 8, including Madeline
Calumet	132	63	69	Island, November 15 - November 30.
Chippewa	443	259	184	
Clark	2,785	1,255	1,530	Definition of a spike buck:
Columbia	1,250	545	705	One whose spike is not less than
Crawford	345	345	-	three inches long.
Dane	98	56	42	
Dodge	150	71	79	A nine-day spike buck and party
Door	196	118	78	permit season in counties south of
Douglas	2,563	1,622	941	U.S. Highway 8, except Green, Kenosha,
Dunn	504	234	270	Milwaukee, Racine and Walworth
Eau Claire	1,701	697	1,004	Counties which were closed, November 15 - November 23. Shotgun only
Florence	2,169	1,013	1,156	in 20 counties: Brown, Calumet,
Fond du Lac	157	70	87	Dane, Dodge, Dunn, Fond du Lac, Jef-
Forest	3,815	1,933	1,882	ferson, Kewaunee, Lafayette, Mani-
Grant	436	436	-	towoc, Outagamie, Ozaukee, Rock, St.
Green	C	-	-	Croix, Shawano (south of Highway 29),
Green Lake	723	300	423	Sheboygan, Washington, Waukesha,
Iowa	326	155	171	Waupaca and Winnebago.
Iron	1,149	643	506	Except in the following areas:
Jackson	5,824	2,270	3,554	
Jefferson	121	45	76	(1) Mississippi River Zone
Juneau	2,497	1,073	1,424	
Kenosha	C	-	-	A split season which provided
Kewaunee	199	78	121	for a three-day either sex season,
La Crosse	658	658	-	November 15 - November 17 followed by
Lafayette	82	40	42	a six-day spike buck season, Novem-
Langlade	1,737	1,003	734	ber 18 - November 23 in Buffalo*,
Lincoln	2,380	1,361	1,019	Crawford, Grant, La Crosse*, Pepin*,
Manitowoc	431	168	263	Pierce*, Trempealeau* and Vernon
Marathon	855	519	336	Counties.
Marinette	5,351	2,509	2,842	*Nonrifle season, November 15 -
Marquette	1,543	599	944	November 17. Rifle season, November
Milwaukee	C	-	-	18 - November 23.
Monroe	1,485	706	779	
Oconto	3,075	1,362	1,713	A 16-day either sex season,
Oneida	5,585	2,826	2,759	November 15 - November 30 on the
Outagamie	1,170	522	648	Apostle Islands, except Madeline
Ozaukee	33	15	18	Island.
Pepin	371	371	-	
Pierce	317	317	-	A nine-day spike buck and
Polk	1,346	646	700	party permit season in the Necedah
Portage	1,254	591	663	National Wildlife Refuge (northern
Price	4,207	2,622	1,585	portion), November 15 - November 23.
Racine	C	-	-	Regular License harvest - 56. Party Permit - 97. Total - 153.

(continued on following page)

Annual Registered Deer Gun Kill in Open Counties (continued)
1955-1964

THE 1958 SEASON (continued)

Counties	Total	Kill Regular License	Party Permit	Notes
Richland	85	46	39	**Horicon National Wildlife Refuge**
Rock	46	35	11	
Rusk	1,915	1,156	759	Second annual managed shotgun
St. Croix	158	96	62	hunt in the Horicon National Wildlife
Sauk	478	228	250	Refuge, December 27 and December 28.
Sawyer	3,549	2,031	1,518	6,553 applications for the 250 reser-
Shawano	1,693	844	849	vations that were available. 161
Sheboygan	125	59	66	deer taken by 647 hunters.
Taylor	1,204	736	468	
Trempealeau	899	899	-	Public acceptance of the party
Vernon	334	334	-	permit system was evidenced by the
Vilas	4,136	1,857	2,279	fact that the Conservation Congress
Walworth	C	-	-	voted for the same season as 1957.
Washburn	2,066	1,199	867	
Washington	85	34	51	The Conservation Commission
Waukesha	89	51	38	liberalized the regulations by ex-
Waupaca	2,183	1,027	1,156	tending the party permit system to
Waushara	2,290	867	1,423	58 counties and prolonging the sea-
Winnebago	291	151	140	son in the northern counties to
Wood	2,547	1,099	1,448	16 days.
TOTAL	95,234	50,247	44,987	

Type of License	Total Harvest	Antlered Forked Buck	Spike Buck	% Spike	Antlerless Adult Doe	Doe Fawn	Buck Fawn	Unknown
Summary of Kill by Age and Sex								
Regular License	50,247	38,437	7,976	17.1	1,730	787	732	585
Party Permit	44,987	317	2,799	89.8	28,154	7,467	5,718	532
Total	95,234	38,754	10,775	21.8	29,884	8,254	6,450	1,117

License Sales

Big Game Licenses	**276,808**
Voluntary Sportsmen's License Sales	56,428
Nonresident Big Game License Sales	2,630
Total	335,866
Party Permit Sales	58,438

THE 1959 SEASON

Counties	Total	Kill Regular License	Party Permit	Notes
Adams	2,460	937	1,523	
Ashland	3,068	1,765	1,303	67 Open Counties.
Barron	582	405	177	
Bayfield	4,132	2,134	1,998	A 16-day spike buck and party permit season, November 14 - November 29, north of Highways 70, 53 and 8, including Madeline Island.
Brown	187	78	109	
Buffalo	2,818	2,818	-	
Burnett	3,108	1,529	1,579	A nine-day spike buck and party permit season November 21 - November 29, south of Highways 70, 53 and 8.
Calumet	198	85	113	
Chippewa	691	408	283	
Clark	1,174	1,170	4	
Columbia	1,477	573	904	Definition of a spike buck: One whose antler is not less than three inches in length.
Crawford	526	526	-	
Dane	606	606	--	
Dodge	257	113	144	Except the following areas:
Door	216	126	90	
Douglas	3,213	1,730	1,483	(1) Northeast Restricted Area
Dunn	787	339	448	A 16-day spike buck only season, November 14 - November 29 in management units 34B, 36 and 37 in Vilas and Oneida Counties.
Eau Claire	589	589	-	
Florence	3,098	1,137	1,961	
Fond du Lac	276	121	155	
Forest	4,730	1,992	2,738	
Grant	640	640	-	(2) Mississippi River Zone
Green	C	-	-	
Green Lake	929	344	585	A split season which provided for a three-day either sex season, November 21 - November 23, followed by a six-day spike buck only season, November 24 - November 29, in Buffalo*, Crawford, Grant, La Crosse**, Pepin, Pierce*, Trempealeau** and Vernon Counties.
Iowa	540	222	318	
Iron	1,439	679	760	
Jackson	1,747	1,747	-	
Jefferson	413	413	-	
Juneau	1,140	1,065	75	
Kenosha	25	25	-	
Kewaunee	220	97	123	
La Crosse	877	877	-	* Shotgun only.
Lafayette	C	-	-	
Langlade	1,988	1,004	984	** Shotgun only, November 21- November 23. Rifle season, November 24 - November 29.
Lincoln	2,676	1,424	1,252	
Manitowoc	516	201	315	
Marathon	1,237	679	558	(3) West Central Restricted Area
Marinette	5,631	2,478	3,153	A nine-day spike buck season, November 21 - November 29, in Eau Claire, Jackson, Monroe and portions of Chippewa, Juneau, Clark, Adams, Marathon and Wood Counties.
Marquette	1,767	573	1,194	
Milwaukee	C	-	-	
Monroe	652	652	-	
Oconto	2,990	1,318	1,672	
Oneida	5,962	2,983	2,979	(4) Southeast Block
Outagamie	1,473	626	847	
Ozaukee	38	14	24	A nine-day either sex season, November 21 - November 29, in Dane, Jefferson*, Kenosha*, Rock*, Walworth*, Washington* and Waukesha* Counties.
Pepin	542	542	-	
Pierce	463	463	-	
Polk	1,131	547	584	
Portage	1,542	669	873	
Price	5,851	3,063	2,788	* Shotgun only.

(continued on following page)

Counties	Total	THE 1959 SEASON (continued) Kill Regular License	Party Permit	Notes
Racine	C	–	–	A 31-day either sex season,
Richland	202	82	120	October 1 – October 31 on the Apostle
Rock	164	164	–	Islands, except Madeline Island.
Rusk	2,773	1,450	1,323	
St. Croix	177	99	78	A three-day spike buck season
Sauk	806	324	482	during last three days of regular
Sawyer	5,570	2,653	2,917	season, November 27, 28 and 29 on the
Shawano	2,129	1,034	1,095	Necedah National Wildlife Refuge.
Sheboygan	250	101	149	More than 4,000 hunters, 80 hunters
Taylor	1,743	1,002	741	per square mile, were in the open
Trempealeau	1,433	1,433	–	area of approximately 33,000 acres.
Vernon	521	521	–	Some portions had 140 hunters per
Vilas	3,402	1,620	1,782	square mile. Unsportsmanlike hunting
Walworth	157	157	–	prevailed. The illegal kill was
Washburn	2,710	1,407	1,303	estimated at 820 deer. Legal kill –
Washington	343	343	–	313.
Waukesha	332	332	–	
Waupaca	2,711	1,098	1,613	Closed counties – Green, La-
Waushara	2,271	787	1,484	fayetee, Milwaukee and Racine.
Winnebago	315	128	187	
Wood	963	639	324	Estimated sex and age ratios of
County Unknown	2	–	2	the herd: Adult buck – 20%, Adult doe – 40% and fawn – 40%.
TOTAL	105,596	57,900	47,696	State deer kill was 10.9% over the previous season: 4.1 per square mile of deer range.

License Sales

Resident Big Game Licenses	284,693
Voluntary Sportsmen's Licenses	61,863
Nonresident Big Game Licenses	2,887
Total	349,443
Party Permit Sales	61,018

State deer kill was 10.9% over the previous season: 4.1 per square mile of deer range.

The Conservation Congress recommended opening the season a week earlier in the northern counties during the November gun season. The Conservation Commission supported the recommendation.

Summary of Kill by Age and Sex

Type of License	Total Harvest	Antlered Forked Buck	Spike Buck	% Spike Buck	Antlerless Adult Doe	Fawn Buck	Fawn Doe	Unknown
Regular License	57,900	41,905	8,660	28.9	3,528	1,852	1,473	482
Party Permit	47,696	455	1,653	94.7	29,657	7,902	7,438	591
Total	105,596	42,360	10,313	76.2	33,185	9,754	8,911	1,073

1959 DEER HARVEST

By
Unit and County within Management Unit

Unit	County	Total	Unit	County	Total	Unit	County	Total
1.	Douglas	473	13.	Ashland	96	22.	Barron	124
				Bayfield	530		Chippewa	4
2.	Douglas	649		Sawyer	1,821		Dunn	69
	Bayfield	393		Misc.	11		Polk	3
	Misc.	145		Total	2,458		St. Croix	3
	Total	1,187					Misc.	3
			14.	Ashland	1,116		Total	206
3.	Bayfield	994		Price	357			
	Misc.	26		Sawyer	228	23.	Barron	22
	Total	1,020		Misc.	7		Chippewa	293
				Total	1,708		Rusk	251
4.	Douglas	560					Misc.	7
			15.	Barron	30		Total	573
5.	Bayfield	1,140		Burnett	378			
				Polk	325	24.	Chippewa	80
6.	Ashland	590		Washburn	30		Rusk	390
	Bayfield	473		Misc.	5		Taylor	73
	Misc.	29		Total	768		Misc.	2
	Total	1,092					Total	545
			16.	Barron	20			
7.	Ashland	578		Burnett	33	25.	Price	1,128
	Iron	129		Polk	365		Rusk	178
	Misc.	10		Misc.	47		Taylor	145
	Total	717		Total	465		Misc.	5
							Total	1,456
8.	Burnett	432	17.	Barron	202			
	Douglas	674		Rusk	36	26.	Taylor	1,191
	Washburn	336		Washburn	96			
	Misc.	4		Misc.	13	27.	Clark	10
	Total	1,446		Total	347		Taylor	211
							Misc.	10
9.	Bayfield	560	18.	Rusk	794		Total	231
	Douglas	1,047		Sawyer	261			
	Sawyer	152		Misc.	34	28.	Ashland	490
	Washburn	253		Total	1,089		Iron	366
	Misc.	6					Misc.	12
	Total	2,018	19.	Rusk	1,056		Total	868
				Sawyer	2,421			
10.	Burnett	1,300		Misc.	15	29.	Ashland	107
	Polk	107		Total	3,492		Iron	681
	Misc.	3					Oneida	5
	Total	1,410	20.	Price	1,446		Price	463
				Rusk	22		Vilas	337
11.	Burnett	879		Sawyer	431		Misc.	4
	Washburn	429		Misc.	10		Total	1,597
	Misc.	4		Total	1,909			
	Total	1,312				30.	Price	1,959
			21.	Polk	304			
12.	Sawyer	156		St. Croix	26	31.	Lincoln	29
	Washburn	1,451		Misc.	31		Oneida	3,243
	Misc.	14		Total	361		Price	259
	Total	1,621					Vilas	28
							Misc.	4
							Total	3,563

- 129 -

Unit	County	Total	Unit	County	Total	Unit	County	Total
32.	Lincoln	1,511	42.	Langlade	714	51.	Marinette	393
	Price	103		Lincoln	132		Oconto	514
	Taylor	109		Oneida	113		Misc.	4
	Misc.	13		Misc.	7		Total	911
	Total	1,736		Total	966			
						52.	Langlade	4
33.	Lincoln	21	43.	Forest	63		Lincoln	774
	Marathon	27		Langlade	639		Oneida	128
	Taylor	2		Oneida	80		Misc.	3
	Misc.	3		Misc.	3		Total	909
	Total	53		Total	785			
						53.	Adams	1,340
34.	Iron	250	44.	Forest	1,172		Portage	21
	Vilas	601		Langlade	251		Waushara	41
	Misc.	8		Oconto	315		Wood	446
	Total	859		Misc.	2		Juneau	128
				Total	1,740		Misc.	49
35.	Forest	171					Total	2,025
	Vilas	1,866	45.	Forest	745			
	Misc.	13		Marinette	1,487	54.	Adams	818
	Total	2,050		Oconto	174		Juneau	251
				Misc.	8		Marquette	90
36.	Oneida	145		Total	2,414		Monroe	18
	Vilas	415					Waushara	3
	Misc.	3	46.	Langlade	85		Misc.	9
	Total	563		Lincoln	146		Total	1,189
				Marathon	366			
37.	Lincoln	2		Shawano	7	55.	Clark	403
	Oneida	582		Misc.	-		Jackson	1,461
	Misc.	4		Total	604		Monroe	293
	Total	588					Misc.	5
			47.	Shawano	569		Total	2,162
38.	Forest	83		Langlade	21			
	Langlade	18		Misc.	11	56.	Clark	9
	Lincoln	20		Total	601		Jackson	15
	Oneida	1,321					Juneau	551
	Vilas	33	48.	Langlade	232		Monroe	68
	Misc.	-		Oconto	351		Wood	207
	Total	1,475		Shawano	179		Misc.	110
				Misc.	6		Total	960
39.	Florence	78		Total	768			
	Forest	1,997				57.	Adams	19
	Oneida	164	49.	Marinette	2,139		Clark	53
	Vilas	71		Oconto	1,070		Marathon	413
	Misc.	1		Misc.	7		Portage	497
	Total	2,311		Total	3,216		Waushara	8
							Wood	306
40.	Florence	1,773	50.	Florence	1,172		Misc.	15
	Forest	398		Forest	10		Total	1,311
	Misc.	6		Marinette	784			
	Total	2,177		Misc.	2	58.	Chippewa	33
				Total	1,968		Clark	690
41.	Marinette	692					Eau Claire	352
							Misc.	8
							Total	1,083

Unit	County	Total	Unit	County	Total	Unit	County	Total
59.	Buffalo	4	65.	Portage	627	72.	Crawford	6
	Chippewa	256		Waupaca	543		Juneau	8
	Clark	8		Waushara	247		La Crosse	130
	Dunn	537		Misc.	24		Monroe	215
	Eau Claire	235		Total	1,441		Richland	167
	Jackson	261					Vernon	256
	La Crosse	694	66.	Waupaca	457		Misc.	3
	Monroe	39		Waushara	1,191		Total	785
	Pepin	143		Winnebago	143			
	Taylor	9		Misc.	24	73.	Crawford	2
	Trempealeau	422		Total	1,815		Grant	467
	Misc.	4					Misc.	4
	Total	2,612	67.	Columbia	109		Total	473
60.	Dunn	164		Green Lake	615			
	Pepin	34		Marquette	1,529	74.	Crawford	504
	Pierce	206		Waushara	678		La Crosse	3
	St. Croix	148		Misc.	45		Vernon	263
	Misc.	5		Total	2,976		Misc.	2
	Total	557	68.	Columbia	34		Total	772
61.	Buffalo	2,804		Dodge	62	75.	Dane	20
	La Crosse	49		Fond du Lac	150		Grant	7
	Pepin	365		Green Lake	268		Iowa	85
	Pierce	257		Waushara	43		Total	112
	Trempealeau	1,009		Winnebago	51			
	Misc.	21		Misc.	10	76.	Columbia	15
	Total	4,505		Total	618		Dane	114
			69.	Calumet	10		Dodge	184
62.	Marathon	400		Fond du Lac	126		Jefferson	406
	Portage	354		Manitowoc	26		Rock	13
	Shawano	799		Ozaukee	35		Washington	110
	Waupaca	1,005		Sheboygan	240		Waushara	309
	Misc.	24		Washington	232		Misc.	3
	Total	2,582		Dodge	3		Total	1,154
63.	Brown	99		Misc.	5	77.	Jefferson	6
	Calumet	2		Total	677		Kenosha	25
	Oconto	475					Rock	151
	Outagamie	1,417	70.	Adams	230		Walworth	157
	Shawano	552		Columbia	1,281		Waukesha	22
	Waupaca	641		Dane	466		Misc.	1
	Winnebago	111		Iowa	295		Total	362
	Misc.	10		Juneau	138			
	Total	3,307		Marquette	77	Misc.		1,140
64.	Brown	78		Richland	30			
	Calumet	184		Sauk	796	Total		105,596
	Door	212		Misc.	6			
	Kewaunee	127		Total	3,319			
	Manitowoc	481						
	Outagamie	2	71.	Grant	159			
	Misc.	90		Iowa	154			
	Total	1,174		Richland	3			
				Sauk	1			
				Total	317			

DEER MANAGEMENT UNITS

0 10 20 30 40 50
Scale of Miles

THE 1960 SEASON

Counties	Total	Kill Regular License	Party Permit	Notes
Adams	507	507	-	70 Counties Open.
Ashland	1,887	960	927	
Barron	402	194	208	A 9-day spike buck and party
Bayfield	3,045	1,441	1,604	permit season, November 19 - November 27, in area north of Highway 29,
Brown	63	42	21	including Madeline Island.
Buffalo	2,051	2,051	-	
Burnett	2,222	1,049	1,173	A nine-day spike buck season,
Calumet	49	49	-	November 19 - November 27 in area
Chippewa	559	262	297	south of Highway 29.
Clark	774	765	9	
Columbia	253	253	-	Definition of a spike buck: One
Crawford	360	360	-	whose antler is not less than three
Dane	17	17	-	inches in length.
Dodge	61	61	-	
Door	76	76	-	Except in the following areas:
Douglas	2,638	1,412	1,226	
Dunn	696	225	471	Mississippi River Zone
Eau Claire	408	408		
Florence	857	307	550	1. A split season which provided a 2-day either sex season,
Fond du Lac	62	62	-	November 19 and November 20, followed
Forest	1,776	787	989	by a 7-day spike season, November 21-
Grant	435	435	-	November 27, in Buffalo*, Crawford,
Green	51	51	-	Grant, La Crosse**, Pepin*, Pierce*,
Green Lake	134	134	-	Trempealeau** and Vernon counties.
Iowa	151	151	-	
Iron	870	415	455	* Shotgun only
Jackson	1,635	1,635	-	
Jefferson	69	69	-	** Shotgun only November 19 -
Juneau	554	554	-	November 20; rifle season November 21-
Kenosha	8	8	-	November 27.
Kewaunee	52	52	-	
La Crosse	434	434	-	Southeast Block
Lafayette	58	58	-	
Langlade	1,508	705	803	2. A 3-day either sex season
Lincoln	1,357	1,021	1,336	in Jefferson, Kenosha, Racine, Walworth and Waukesha counties. Shotgun
Manitowoc	111	111	-	only.
Marathon	669	368	301	
Marinette	3,651	1,525	2,126	A 44-day either sex season in
Marquette	280	280	-	the Apostle Islands (except Madeline)
Milwaukee	C	-	-	Ocotober 15 - November 27.
Monroe	637	637	-	
Oconto	2,126	821	1,305	A nine-day spike buck season in
Oneida	3,487	1,410	2,077	the Necedah National Wildlife Refuge,
Outagamie	297	297	-	November 19 - November 27. Approximately 85% of the Refuge was open.
Ozaukee	13	13	-	There were 9 hunters per square mile,
Pepin	378	378	-	compared to 80 hunters per square
Pierce	376	376	-	mile the previous year. Harvest -
Polk	1,192	563	629	31 deer.
Portage	360	360	-	
Price	3,816	1,860	1,956	

(continued on following page)

Annual Registered Deer Gun Kill in Open Counties (continued)
1955-1964

THE 1960 SEASON (continued)

Counties	Total	Kill Regular License	Party Permit	Notes
Racine	7	7	-	The third annual managed shotgun either sex season in the Horicon National Wildlife Refuge, November 30 and December 1. 2,877 applications. 629 hunters took 146 deer.
Richland	41	41	-	
Rock	12	12	-	
Rusk	1,643	807	836	
St. Croix	185	82	103	
Sauk	160	160	-	
Sawyer	2,844	1,255	1,589	The Conservation Congress approved the basic regulations proposed by the Joint Board of the Wisconsin Conservation Department. The Conservation Commission concurred, fixing the dividing line for Party Permit at Highway 29.
Shawano	1,344	746	598	
Sheboygan	82	82	-	
Taylor	1,774	839	935	
Trempealeau	992	992	-	
Vernon	237	237	-	
Vilas	3,123	1,184	1,939	
Walworth	38	38	-	
Washburn	1,843	835	1,008	
Washington	19	19	-	
Waukesha	64	64	-	
Waupaca	831	831	-	
Waushara	399	399	-	
Winnebago	58	58	-	
Wood	766	766	-	
County Unknown	71	27	44	
TOTAL	61,005	35,490	25,515	

License Sales

Resident Big Game License Sales   269,867
Voluntary Sportsmen's License Sales   65,371
Nonresident Big Game License Sales   2,970
                Total   338,208

Summary of Kill by Age and Sex

Type of License	Total Kill	Antlered Forked Buck	Spike Buck	% Spike Buck	Antlerless Adult Doe	Fawn Buck	Fawn Doe	Unknown
Regular License	35,490	25,484	6,173	19.5	1,751	1,030	799	253
Party Permit	25,515	170	1,011	85.6	16,114	4,452	3,693	75
Total	61,005	25,654	7,184	21.9	17,865	5,482	4,492	328

By
Unit and County within Management Unit

Unit	County	Total	Reg. Lic.	Party Permit	Unit	County	Total	Reg. Lic.	Party Permit
1.	Douglas	236	166	70	12.	Sawyer	85	36	49
						Washburn	952	437	515
2.	Bayfield	308	150	158		Misc.	9	4	5
	Douglas	519	301	218		Total	1,046	477	569
	Misc.	4	2	2					
	Total	831	453	378	13.	Ashland	65	21	44
						Bayfield	407	174	233
3.	Ashland	285*	199	86		Sawyer	1,117	520	597
	Bayfield	820	419	401		Misc.	9	4	5
	Total	1,105	618	487		Total	1,598	719	879
4.	Douglas	436	250	186	14.	Ashland	554	252	302
						Price	244	98	146
5.	Bayfield	810	378	432		Sawyer	170	81	89
						Misc.	6	5	1
6.	Ashland	256	110	146		Total	974	436	538
	Bayfield	194	91	103					
	Misc.	3	2	1	15.	Barron	65	32	33
	Total	453	203	250		Burnett	273	116	157
						Polk	328	154	174
7.	Ashland	400	225	175		Washburn	25	14	11
	Iron	125	68	57		Misc.	3	1	2
	Misc.	3	2	1		Total	694	317	377
	Total	528	295	233					
					16.	Barron	21	12	9
8.	Burnett	288	160	128		Burnett	43	24	19
	Douglas	607	295	312		Polk	375	184	191
	Washburn	313	135	178		Misc.	4	-	4
	Misc.	2	1	1		Total	443	220	223
	Total	1,210	581	619					
					17.	Barron	202	91	111
9.	Bayfield	490	223	267		Rusk	29	14	15
	Douglas	834	393	441		Washburn	58	24	34
	Sawyer	76	32	44		Misc.	10	7	3
	Washburn	159	83	76		Total	299	136	163
	Misc.	19	4	15					
	Total	1,570	735	843	18.	Rusk	372	192	180
						Sawyer	157	89	68
10.	Burnett	842	396	446		Misc.	14	6	8
	Polk	205	88	117		Total	543	287	256
	Misc.	5	1	4					
	Total	1,052	485	567	19.	Rusk	284	132	152
						Sawyer	970	389	581
11.	Burnett	759	346	413		Misc.	8	3	5
	Washburn	312	134	178		Total	1,262	524	738
	Misc.	1	-	1					
	Total	1,072	480	592					

* Represents Apostle Island Kill.

1960 Deer Harvest by Unit and County within Management Unit (continued)

Unit	County	Total	Reg. Lic.	Party Permit	Unit	County	Total	Reg. Lic.	Party Permit
20.	Price	779	401	378	31.	Lincoln	37	12	25
	Rusk	11	-	11		Oneida	1,123	409	714
	Sawyer	227	81	146		Price	143	72	71
	Misc.	12	10	2		Vilas	31	13	18
	Total	1,029	492	537		Misc.	2	1	1
						Total	1,336	507	829
21.	Polk	266	124	142					
	Misc.	13	5	8	32.	Lincoln	1,333	582	751
	Total	279	129	150		Price	114	72	42
						Taylor	105	59	46
22.	Barron	81	43	38		Misc.	3	3	-
	Dunn	80	28	52		Total	1,555	716	839
	Misc.	9	3	6					
	Total	170	74	96	33.	Lincoln	18	6	12
						Marathon	33	16	17
23.	Barron	10	-	10		Misc.	11	4	7
	Chippewa	220	96	124		Total	62	26	36
	Rusk	224	116	108					
	Misc.	15	12	3	34.	Iron	168	75	93
	Total	469	224	245		Vilas	665	251	414
						Misc.	4	1	3
24.	Chippewa	83	45	38		Total	837	327	510
	Rusk	490	241	249					
	Taylor	46	20	26	35.	Forest	89	33	56
	Misc.	7	2	5		Vilas	1,170	457	713
	Total	626	308	318		Misc.	5	2	3
						Total	1,264	492	772
25.	Price	-	689	618					
	Rusk	-	96	106	36.	Oneida	347	128	219
	Taylor	-	62	77		Vilas	1,055	374	681
	Misc.	-	2	-		Misc.	1	-	1
	Total	-	849	801		Total	1,403	502	901
26.	Taylor	1,104	524	580	37.	Oneida	1,107	444	663
27.	Taylor	358	160	198		Misc.	12	4	8
	Misc.	24	9	15		Total	1,119	448	671
	Total	382	169	213					
					38.	Forest	21	13	8
28.	Ashland	253	121	132		Oneida	589	282	307
	Iron	194	107	87		Misc.	25	12	13
	Misc.	16	10	6		Total	635	307	328
	Total	463	238	225	39.	Florence	20	8	12
29.	Ashland	61	24	37		Forest	514	220	294
	Iron	375	159	216		Oneida	82	37	45
	Price	240	88	152		Vilas	30	9	21
	Vilas	137	58	79		Total	646	274	372
	Misc.	5	4	1	40.	Florence	442	162	280
	Total	818	333	485		Forest	60	27	33
30.	Price	955	422	533		Total	502	189	313
					41.	Marinette	588	239	349

Unit	County	Total	Reg. Lic.	Party Permit	Unit	County	Total	Reg. Lic.	Party Permit
42.	Langlade	573	289	284	51.	Marinette	426	246	180
	Lincoln	160	82	78		Oconto	436	200	236
	Oneida	43	25	18		Misc.	7	7	-
	Misc.	1	1	-		Total	869	453	416
	Total	777	397	380					
					52.	Lincoln	669	283	386
43.	Forest	16	6	10		Oneida	67	28	39
	Langlade	516	233	283		Misc.	4	3	1
	Oneida	85	38	47		Total	740	314	426
	Misc.	1	-	1	53.	Adams	197	197	-
	Total	618	277	341		Juneau	93	93	-
						Waushara	13	13	-
44.	Forest	515	218	297		Wood	327	327	-
	Langlade	200	78	122		Misc.	4	4	-
	Oconto	200	60	140		Total	634	634	-
	Misc.	4	3	1					
	Total	919	359	560	54.	Adams	233	233	-
						Juneau	239	239	-
45.	Forest	-	213	291		Marquette	19	19	-
	Marinette	-	387	591		Monroe	12	12	-
	Oconto	-	65	104		Misc.	3	3	-
	Misc.	-	1	-		Total	506	506	-
	Total	-	666	986					
					55.	Clark	345	345	-
46.	Langlade	53	28	25		Jackson	1,338	1,338	-
	Lincoln	107	41	66		Monroe	339	339	-
	Marathon	438	163	275		Misc.	13	13	-
	Shawano	31	9	22		Total	2,035	2,035	-
	Misc.	4	1	3					
	Total	633	242	391	56.	Clark	8	8	-
						Jackson	14	14	-
47.	Shawano	707	249	458		Juneau	184	184	-
	Misc.	7	3	4		Monroe	97	97	-
	Total	714	252	462		Wood	322	322	-
						Misc.	2	2	-
48.	Langlade	149	67	82		Total	627	627	-
	Oconto	314	136	178					
	Shawano	133	47	86	57.	Clark	39	39	-
	Misc.	1	-	1		Marathon	67	65	2
	Total	597	250	347		Portage	77	77	-
						Wood	107	107	-
49.	Forest	24	24	-		Misc.	3	3	-
	Marinette	1,576	615	961		Total	293	291	2
	Oconto	727	255	472					
	Misc.	4	3	1	58.	Clark	339	339	-
	Total	2,331	897	1,434		Chippewa	2	-	2
						Eau Claire	231	231	-
50.	Florence	387	135	252		Misc.	16	16	-
	Marinette	82	43	39		Total	588	586	2
	Misc.	8	8	-					
	Total	477	186	291					

Unit	County	Total	Reg. Lic.	Party Permit	Unit	County	Total	Reg. Lic.	Party Permit
59.	Chippewa	228	103	125	65.	Portage	140	140	-
	Clark	10	10	-		Waupaca	168	168	-
	Dunn	469	141	328		Waushara	65	65	-
	Eau Claire	167	167	-		Misc.	3	3	-
	Jackson	274	274	-		Total	376	376	-
	La Crosse	311	311	-					
	Monroe	17	17	-	66.	Waupaca	123	123	-
	Pepin	92	92	-		Waushara	200	200	-
	Trempealeau	309	309	-		Winnebago	36	36	-
	Misc.	17	12	5		Misc.	5	5	-
	Total	1,894	1,436	458		Total	364	364	-
60.	Dunn	138	54	84	67.	Green Lake	87	87	-
	Pepin	30	30	-		Marquette	240	240	-
	Pierce	136	136	-		Waushara	105	105	-
	St. Croix	178	79	99		Misc.	13	13	-
	Misc.	20	19	1		Total	445	445	-
	Total	502	318	184					
					68.	Columbia	18	18	-
61.	Buffalo	2,034	2,034	-		Dodge	23	23	-
	La Crosse	18	18	-		Fond du Lac	32	32	-
	Pepin	243	243	-		Green Lake	42	42	-
	Pierce	231	231	-		Misc.	22	22	-
	Trempealeau	667	667	-		Total	137	137	-
	Misc.	2	2	-					
	Total	3,195	3,195	-	69.	Fond du Lac	28	28	-
						Ozaukee	13	13	-
62.	Marathon	129	122	7		Sheboygan	79	79	-
	Portage	132	132	-		Washington	9	9	-
	Shawano	288	283	5		Misc.	7	7	-
	Waupaca	411	411	-		Total	136	136	-
	Misc.	5	5	-					
	Total	965	953	12	70.	Adams	-	72	-
						Columbia	-	228	-
63.	Brown	40	20	20		Dane	-	8	-
	Oconto	261	100	161		Iowa	-	54	-
	Outagamie	291	291	-		Juneau	-	30	-
	Shawano	181	154	27		Sauk	-	157	-
	Waupaca	126	126	-		Misc.	-	17	-
	Winnebago	12	12	-		Total	-	566	-
	Misc.	4	4	-					
	Total	915	707	208	71.	Grant	101	101	-
						Iowa	51	51	-
64.	Brown	22	21	1		Misc.	1	1	-
	Calumet	46	46	-		Total	153	153	-
	Door	72	72	-					
	Kewaunee	52	52	-	72.	La Crosse	96	96	-
	Manitowoc	108	108	-		Monroe	157	157	-
	Misc.	8	8	-		Richland	31	31	-
	Total	308	307	1		Vernon	101	101	-
						Misc.	7	7	-
						Total	392	392	-

1960 Deer Harvest by Unit and County within Management Unit (continued)

Unit	County	Total	Reg. Lic.	Party Permit
73.	Grant	330	330	-
	Misc.	4	4	-
	Total	334	334	-
74.	Crawford	345	345	-
	La Crosse	5	5	-
	Vernon	133	133	-
	Total	483	483	-
75.	Dane	7	7	-
	Green	33	33	-
	Iowa	41	41	-
	Lafayette	57	57	-
	Misc.	6	6	-
	Total	144	144	-
76.	Dodge	36	36	-
	Jefferson	69	69	-
	Washington	10	10	-
	Waukesha	60	60	-
	Misc.	32	32	-
	Total	207	207	-
77.	Green	18	18	-
	Kenosha	7	7	-
	Racine	7	7	-
	Rock	12	12	-
	Walworth	32	32	-
	Misc.	5	5	-
	Total	81	81	-
Un- known	Misc.	347	225	122

STATE TOTALS

61,005 35,490 25,515

THE 1961 SEASON

Counties	Kill Regular License	Notes
Adams	709	
Ashland	926	**71 Counties Open**
Barron	250	
Bayfield	1,612	A nine-day spike buck season state-wide, including Madeline Island.
Brown	61	
Buffalo	514	Definition of a spike buck: One whose antler is not less than three inches in length.
Burnett	1,270	
Calumet	108	
Chippewa	360	
Clark	1,467	Except the following areas:
Columbia	422	
Crawford	100	(1) Southeast Block
Dane	46	
Dodge	71	A 2-day either sex season in 8 counties: Green, Jefferson, Kenosha,
Door	83	Lafayette, Racine, Rock, Walworth and
Douglas	1,570	Waukesha, November 18 and 19. Shotgun
Dunn	257	only. Kill: Antlered deer - 249, antler-
Eau Claire	807	less - 356 - total: 605.
Florence	367	
Fond du Lac	101	A 44-day either sex season on the
Forest	562	Apostle Islands, except Madeline, October
Grant	170	14 - November 26.
Green	125	
Green Lake	234	A nine-day spike buck season in the
Iowa	196	Necedah National Wildlife Refuge,
Iron	414	November 18 - November 26. Estimated
Jackson	2,524	10 hunters per square mile. Kill - 149.
Jefferson	78	
Juneau	1,103	Milwaukee County closed.
Kenosha	10	
Kewaunee	53	Percent of license purchasers successful:
La Crosse	259	
Lafayette	207	Resident Big Game 10.0
Langlade	698	Voluntary Sportsmen 13.0
Lincoln	1,061	Nonresident Big Game 22.0
Manitowoc	183	
Marathon	594	Party Permit deer hunting discontin-
Marinette	1,523	ued for two years by Legislative action.
Marquette	390	
Milwaukee	C	The Conservation Congress approved
Menominee	-	the basic proposals of the Joint Board of
Monroe	1,035	the Conservation Department, i.e , a
Oconto	836	nine-day spike buck season, statewide,
Oneida	1,336	a 44-day either sex season in the Apostle
Outagamie	452	Islands and the elimination of the Managed
Ozaukee	16	Gun Hunt at Horicon for the year 1961.
Pepin	127	The Conservation Commission concurred.
Pierce	155	
Polk	603	

(continued on following page)

THE 1961 SEASON

Counties	Kill Regular License	Notes
Portage	642	
Price	1,869	
Racine	11	
Richland	78	
Rock	52	
Rusk	758	
St. Croix	115	
Sauk	192	
Sawyer	1,251	
Shawano	830	
Sheboygan	109	
Taylor	735	
Trempealeau	400	
Vernon	149	
Vilas	1,184	
Walworth	28	
Washburn	1,000	
Washington	28	
Waukesha	94	
Waupaca	1,197	
Waushara	647	
Winnebago	122	
Wood	1,236	
Total	38,772	

License Sales

Resident Big Game License Sales	174,504
Voluntary Sportsmen's License Sales	130,898
Nonresident Big Game License Sales	2,461
Total	307,863

Summary of the Kill by Age and Sex

| Type of License | Total Kill | Antlered | | | Antlerless | | |
		Forked Buck	Spike Buck	% Spike Buck	Adult Doe	Fawn Buck	Fawn Doe
Regular License	38,772	33,320	5,044	13.1	246	91	71

1961 DEER GUN HARVEST

By
Unit and County within Management Unit

Unit	County	Total	Unit	County	Total	Unit	County	Total
1.	Douglas	220	13.	Ashland	21	22.	Barron	73
				Bayfield	197		Chippewa	3
2.	Bayfield	182		Sawyer	560		Dunn	39
	Douglas	342		Misc.	1		Polk	10
	Total	524		Total	779		St. Croix	3
							Misc.	1
3.	Ashland*	150	14.	Ashland	237		Total	129
	Bayfield	479		Price	88			
	Total	629		Sawyer	72	23.	Barron	8
				Misc.	1		Chippewa	103
4.	Douglas	320		Total	398		Rusk	129
							Total	240
5.	Bayfield	358	15.	Barron	22			
				Burnett	185	24.	Chippewa	78
6.	Ashland	139		Polk	168		Rusk	166
	Bayfield	132		Washburn	34		Taylor	37
	Misc.	1		Total	409		Misc.	1
	Total	272					Total	282
			16.	Barron	6			
7.	Ashland	256		Burnett	35	25.	Price	692
	Iron	104		Polk	200		Rusk	64
	Misc.	3		Misc.	1		Taylor	75
	Total	363		Total	242		Misc.	1
							Total	832
8.	Burnett	177	17.	Barron	131	26.	Taylor	447
	Douglas	354		Rusk	6			
	Washburn	111		Washburn	52	27.	Clark	4
	Total	642		Misc.	1		Taylor	107
				Total	190		Misc.	2
9.	Bayfield	260					Total	113
	Douglas	328	18.	Rusk	223			
	Sawyer	49		Sawyer	105	28.	Ashland	92
	Washburn	94		Misc.	12		Iron	110
	Total	731		Total	340		Misc.	2
							Total	204
10.	Burnett	517	19.	Rusk	152			
	Polk	91		Sawyer	324	29.	Ashland	27
	Misc.	1		Misc.	3		Iron	124
	Total	609		Total	479		Oneida	3
							Price	89
11.	Burnett	353	20.	Price	401		Vilas	67
	Washburn	139		Rusk	10		Misc.	2
	Misc.	1		Sawyer	70		Total	312
	Total	493		Misc.	3			
				Total	484	30.	Price	452
12.	Sawyer	70						
	Washburn	566	21.	Polk	130	31.	Lincoln	5
	Misc.	1		St. Croix	8		Oneida	445
	Total	637		Misc.	2		Price	68
				Total	140		Vilas	9
							Misc.	1
							Total	528

* Apostle Islands Harvest.

1961 Deer Gun Harvest by Unit and County within Management Unit (continued)

Unit	County	Total	Unit	County	Total	Unit	County	Total
32.	Lincoln	661	43.	Forest	14	53.	Adams	309
	Price	63		Langlade	234		Juneau	157
	Taylor	59		Oneida	36		Portage	5
	Misc.	1		Misc.	1		Waushara	18
	Total	784		Total	285		Wood	510
							Misc.	3
33.	Lincoln	11	44.	Forest	144		Total	1,002
	Marathon	22		Langlade	46			
	Taylor	6		Oconto	60	54.	Adams	339
	Misc.	1		Total	250		Juneau	369
	Total	40					Marquette	31
			45.	Forest	128		Monroe	27
34.	Iron	73		Marinette	432		Waushara	4
	Vilas	224		Oconto	31		Misc.	7
	Misc.	1		Total	591		Total	777
	Total	298						
			46.	Langlade	28	55.	Clark	587
35.	Forest	38		Lincoln	53		Jackson	2,085
	Vilas	400		Marathon	186		Monroe	527
	Misc.	1		Shawano	2		Misc.	8
	Total	439		Total	269		Total	3,207
36.	Oneida	120	47.	Langlade	3	56.	Clark	3
	Vilas	459		Shawano	225		Jackson	16
	Total	579		Total	228		Juneau	489
							Monroe	129
37.	Lincoln	2	48.	Langlade	42		Wood	482
	Oneida	375		Oconto	126		Total	1,119
	Total	377		Shawano	36			
38.	Forest	17		Misc.	1	57.	Adams	1
	Langlade	1		Total	205		Clark	79
	Oneida	302					Marathon	185
	Vilas	7	49.	Marinette	465		Portage	239
	Total	327		Oconto	334		Waushara	1
				Total	799		Wood	237
39.	Florence	7					Misc.	6
	Forest	197	50.	Florence	179		Total	748
	Oneida	26		Marinette	83			
	Vilas	17		Total	262	58.	Chippewa	15
	Misc.	3					Clark	781
	Total	250	51.	Marinette	252		Eau Claire	427
40.	Florence	181		Oconto	172		Misc.	7
	Forest	24		Misc.	1		Total	1,230
	Total	205		Total	425			
						59.	Chippewa	161
41.	Marinette	291	52.	Langlade	2		Clark	7
				Lincoln	275		Dunn	154
42.	Langlade	340		Oneida	17		Eau Claire	376
	Lincoln	54		Misc.	1		Jackson	388
	Oneida	10		Total	295		La Crosse	167
	Total	404					Monroe	38
							Pepin	38
							Taylor	12
							Trempealeau	130
							Misc.	1
							Total	1,472

Unit	County	Total	Unit	County	Total	Unit	County	Total
60.	Dunn	63	67.	Columbia	24	73.	Crawford	3
	Pepin	7		Green Lake	68		Grant	104
	Pierce	54		Marquette	335		Misc.	1
	St. Croix	103		Waushara	208		Total	108
	Misc.	2		Misc.	7			
	Total	229		Total	642	74.	Crawford	96
							La Crosse	1
61.	Buffalo	504	68.	Columbia	15		Vernon	93
	La Crosse	9		Dodge	23		Misc.	2
	Pepin	80		Fond du Lac	47		Total	192
	Pierce	101		Green Lake	163			
	Trempealeau	269		Waushara	9	75.	Dane	3
	Misc.	4		Winnebago	13		Grant	4
	Total	967		Misc.	4		Green	61
				Total	274		Iowa	36
62.	Marathon	200					Lafayette	172
	Portage	68	69.	Calumet	10		Total	276
	Shawano	347		Fond du Lac	53			
	Waupaca	507		Manitowoc	9	76.	Columbia	3
	Misc.	8		Ozaukee	16		Dane	15
	Total	1,130		Sheboygan	109		Dodge	47
				Washington	17		Jefferson	78
63.	Brown	31		Misc.	3		Washington	11
	Oconto	112		Total	217		Waukesha	84
	Outagamie	443					Total	238
	Shawano	214	70.	Adams	50			
	Waupaca	188		Columbia	375	77.	Green	64
	Winnebago	6		Dane	28		Kenosha	10
	Misc.	2		Iowa	85		Racine	11
	Total	996		Juneau	66		Rock	52
				Marquette	16		Walworth	28
64.	Brown	30		Richland	6		Waukesha	10
	Calumet	98		Sauk	185		Total	175
	Door	83		Misc.	2			
	Kewaunee	53		Total	813	Unknown --------		94
	Manitowoc	169						
	Misc.	1	71.	Grant	61	STATE TOTAL		38,772
	Total	434		Iowa	73			
				Lafayette	35			
65.	Portage	327		Sauk	5			
	Waupaca	257		Misc.	1			
	Waushara	95		Total	175			
	Misc.	3						
	Total	682	72.	Crawford	1			
				Juneau	11			
66.	Waupaca	227		La Crosse	80			
	Waushara	307		Monroe	305			
	Winnebago	103		Richland	71			
	Misc.	3		Sauk	1			
	Total	640		Vernon	55			
				Total	524			

THE 1962 SEASON

Counties	Regular License	Notes
Adams	806	
Ashland	1,086	71 Open Counties.
Barron	229	
Bayfield	1,891	A nine-day spike buck season in
Brown	78	53 counties, or parts of counties north of
Buffalo	2,465	Highway 60, including Madeline Island.
Burnett	1,307	Definition of a spike buck: One
Calumet	155	whose antler is not less than three inches
Chippewa	258	in length.
Clark	1,249	
Columbia	502	Except in the following areas:
Crawford	381	
Dane	152	(1) Southern Zone - south of Highway 60
Dodge	172	
Door	82	A two-day either sex season in Craw-
Douglas	1,684	ford, Dane*, Grant, Green*, Iowa, Jef-
Dunn	292	ferson*, Kenosha*, Lafayette*, Racine*,
Eau Claire	651	Rock*, Walworth*, and Waukesha* counties
Florence	451	and small portions of Columbia, Dodge*,
Fond du Lac	137	Ozaukee* and Washington* counties.
Forest	902	
Grant	508	* Shotgun only.
Green	85	
Green Lake	264	(2) Mississippi River Zone
Iowa	524	
Iron	530	A split season providing a two-day
Jackson	2,394	either sex season, Nov. 17 and Nov. 18,
Jefferson	100	followed by a five-day spike buck season,
Juneau	1,172	Nov. 19-Nov. 23, in Buffalo*, La Crosse**,
Kenosha	8	Pepin*, Pierce*, Trempealeau** and Vernon**
Kewaunee	94	counties.
La Crosse	545	
Lafayette	165	* Shotgun only
Langlade	691	** Shotgun - Nov. 17-Nov. 18.
Lincoln	1,009	Rifle - Nov. 19-Nov. 23
Manitowoc	256	
Marathon	570	Apostle Islands
Marinette	1,671	
Marquette	493	A 42-day either sex season in the
Menominee	--	Apostle Islands (except Madeline Island) -
Milwaukee	C	Oct. 15-Nov. 25. Harvest - 93 deer.
Monroe	997	Necedah National Wildlife Refuge
Oconto	881	
Oneida	1,742	A nine-day spike buck season, Nov. 17-
Outagamie	548	Nov. 25. 33,500 acres or 85% of the refuge
Ozaukee	23	was open. 26 hunters per square mile -
Pepin	511	harvest - 135.
Pierce	478	
Polk	690	Milwaukee County was closed.
Portage	614	

(continued on following page)

THE 1962 SEASON (continued)

Counties	Regular License	Notes
Price	1,700	The Conservation Congress supported the Conservation Department recommendation for a two-day either sex season south of Highway 60, a two-day either sex season, followed by a five-day spike buck season in the Mississippi River Zone and a nine-day spike buck season for the remainder of the state. The Conservation Commission concurred.
Racine	13	
Richland	126	
Rock	68	
Rusk	707	
St. Croix	106	
Sauk	262	
Sawyer	1,235	
Shawano	928	
Sheboygan	133	
Taylor	583	
Trempealeau	1,145	
Vernon	215	
Vilas	1,680	
Walworth	66	
Washburn	1,005	
Washington	58	
Waukesha	95	
Waupaca	1,234	
Waushara	718	
Winnebago	148	
Wood	1,117	
TOTAL	**45,835**	

License Sales

Resident Big Game	170,278
Voluntary Sportsmen	158,518
Nonresident Big Game	2,239
TOTAL	331,035

Total Harvest by Age and Sex

Type of License	Total	Antlered			Antlerless			Unknown
		Forked Buck	Spike Buck	% Spike Buck	Adult Doe	Buck Fawn	Doe Fawn	
Regular License	45,835	31,967	9,083	22.1	2,626	1,211	888	60

Leading Buck Harvest Counties

Rank	County	Harvest	Rank	County	Harvest
1.	Jackson	2,394	6.	Vilas	1,680
2.	Bayfield	1,891	7.	Marinette	1,671
3.	Oneida	1,742	8.	Burnett	1,307
4.	Price	1,700	9.	Clark	1,249
5.	Douglas	1,684	10.	Sawyer	1,235
				TOTAL	16,553*

* 40.3% of total buck harvest

1962 DEER GUN HARVEST

By
Management Unit and County within Unit

Unit	County	Total	Unit	County	Total	Unit	County	Total
1.	Douglas	186	14.	Ashland	237	24.	Chippewa	32
				Price	107		Rusk	165
2.	Bayfield	249		Sawyer	48		Taylor	41
	Douglas	447		Total	392		Total	238
	Total	696						
			15.	Barron	21	25.	Price	533
3.	Ashland*	200		Burnett	203		Rusk	67
	Bayfield	570		Polk	170		Taylor	50
	Total	770		Washburn	22		Total	650
				Total	416			
4.	Douglas	317				26.	Taylor	347
			16.	Barron	6			
5.	Bayfield	424		Burnett	25	27.	Clark	5
				Polk	220		Taylor	76
6.	Ashland	136		Total	251		Total	81
	Bayfield	136						
	Total	272	17.	Barron	121	28.	Ashland	133
				Rusk	9		Iron	145
7.	Ashland	330		Washburn	61		Total	278
	Iron	110		Total	191			
	Total	440				29.	Ashland	33
			18.	Barron	4		Iron	175
8.	Burnett	196		Rusk	203		Oneida	6
	Douglas	350		Sawyer	96		Price	114
	Washburn	128		Total	303		Vilas	95
	Total	674					Total	423
			19.	Rusk	147			
9.	Bayfield	309		Sawyer	304	30.	Price	465
	Douglas	382		Total	451			
	Sawyer	63				31.	Lincoln	7
	Washburn	90	20.	Price	359		Oneida	551
	Total	844		Rusk	5		Price	64
				Sawyer	55		Vilas	2
10.	Burnett	464		Total	419		Total	624
	Polk	131						
	Total	595	21.	Polk	155	32.	Lincoln	558
				St. Croix	4		Price	40
11.	Burnett	419		Total	159		Taylor	50
	Washburn	140					Total	648
	Total	559	22.	Barron	75			
				Chippewa	5	33.	Lincoln	14
12.	Sawyer	76		Dunn	38		Marathon	19
	Washburn	564		Polk	13		Taylor	3
	Total	640		St. Croix	2		Total	36
				Total	133			
13.	Ashland	17				34.	Iron	96
	Bayfield	201	23.	Barron	5		Vilas	269
	Sawyer	590		Chippewa	103		Total	365
	Total	808		Rusk	112			
				Total	220	35.	Forest	67
							Vilas	670
							Total	737

1962 Deer Gun Harvest by Management Unit and County within Unit (continued)

Unit	County	Total	Unit	County	Total	Unit	County	Total
36.	Oneida	207	48.	Langlade	45	58.	Chippewa	15
	Vilas	610		Oconto	103		Clark	626
	Total	817		Shawano	34		Eau Claire	370
				Total	182		Trempealeau	2
37.	Oneida	494					Total	1,013
			49.	Marinette	552			
38.	Forest	30		Oconto	335	59.	Buffalo	6
	Langlade	5		Total	857		Chippewa	102
	Lincoln	3					Clark	3
	Oneida	325	50.	Florence	206		Dunn	197
	Vilas	11		Forest	1		Eau Claire	274
	Total	374		Marinette	81		Jackson	419
				Total	288		La Crosse	414
39.	Forest	322					Monroe	40
	Oneida	60	51.	Marinette	267		Pepin	141
	Vilas	23		Oconto	192		Taylor	16
	Total	405		Total	459		Trempealeau	356
							Total	1,968
40.	Florence	244	52.	Lincoln	313			
	Forest	37		Oneida	28	60.	Dunn	62
	Total	281		Total	341		Pepin	6
							Pierce	141
41.	Marinette	266	53.	Adams	354		St. Croix	100
				Juneau	208		Total	309
42.	Lincoln	82		Portage	6			
	Langlade	276		Waushara	13	61.	Buffalo	2,444
	Oneida	13		Wood	554		La Crosse	28
	Total	371		Total	1,135		Pepin	687
							Trempealeau	763
43.	Forest	15	54.	Adams	361		Total	3,922
	Langlade	240		Juneau	419			
	Oneida	55		Marquette	29	62.	Marathon	226
	Total	310		Monroe	23		Portage	153
				Waushara	9		Shawano	431
44.	Forest	227		Total	841		Waupaca	578
	Langlade	81					Total	1,387
	Oconto	75	55.	Clark	548			
	Total	383		Jackson	1,938	63.	Brown	16
				Monroe	571		Calumet	1
45.	Forest	203		Total	3,057		Oconto	122
	Marinette	530					Outagamie	545
	Oconto	54	56.	Clark	7		Shawano	217
	Total	787		Jackson	25		Waupaca	226
				Juneau	477		Winnebago	15
46.	Langlade	32		Monroe	89		Total	1,142
	Lincoln	54		Wood	363			
	Marathon	168		Total	961	64.	Brown	62
	Shawano	12					Calumet	149
	Total	266	57.	Adams	3		Door	82
				Clark	55		Kewaunee	92
47.	Langlade	10		Marathon	157		Manitowoc	252
	Shawano	241		Portage	189		Total	637
	Total	251		Waushara	2			
				Wood	195			
				Total	607			

Unit	County	Total	Unit	County	Total	Unit	County	Total
65.	Portage	267	72.	La Crosse	94			
	Waupaca	227		Monroe	200			
	Waushara	105		Crawford	5			
	Total	599		Juneau	3			
				Monroe	68			
66.	Waupaca	559		Richland	105			
	Waushara	5		Sauk	3			
	Winnebago	116		Vernon	69			
	Total	680		Total	547			
67.	Columbia	61	73.	Crawford	60			
	Green Lake	104		Grant	336			
	Marquette	424		Total	396			
	Waushara	217						
	Total	806	74.	Crawford	314			
				La Crosse	8			
68.	Columbia	19		Vernon	146			
	Dodge	38		Total	468			
	Fond du Lac	51						
	Green Lake	159	75.	Dane	19			
	Waushara	25		Grant	30			
	Winnebago	17		Green	45			
	Total	309		Iowa	76			
				Lafayette	160			
69.	Calumet	6		Total	330			
	Dodge	3						
	Fond du Lac	83	76.	Columbia	4			
	Manitowoc	4		Dane	41			
	Ozaukee	23		Dodge	130			
	Sheboygan	133		Jefferson	89			
	Washington	31		Rock	3			
	Total	283		Walworth	1			
				Washington	27			
70.	Adams	79		Waukesha	88			
	Columbia	422		Total	383			
	Dane	90						
	Dodge	1	77.	Dane	1			
	Iowa	294		Green	40			
	Juneau	57		Jefferson	12			
	Marquette	32		Kenosha	8			
	Richland	16		Racine	12			
	Sauk	254		Rock	65			
	Total	1,245		Walworth	60			
				Waukesha	7			
71.	Crawford	1		Total	205			
	Grant	142						
	Iowa	154	Unit Unknown -----		111			
	Lafayette	8						
	Richland	1						
	Sauk	4	STATE TOTAL		45,835			
	Total	310						

- 149 -

Annual Registered Deer Gun Harvest in Open Counties (continued)
1955-1964

THE 1963 SEASON

Counties	Total	Kill Regular License	Party Permit	Notes
Adams	1,448	1,016	432	71 Open Counties.
Ashland	1,241	1,115	126	
Barron	337	337	-	A nine-day spike buck season in
Bayfield	2,661	2,455	206	northern and central counties including
Brown	75	75	-	Madeline Island Nov. 23-Dec. 1.
Buffalo	2,415	2,415	-	Definition of a spike buck: One
Burnett	1,481	1,481	-	whose antlers are not less than three
Calumet	568	568	-	inches in length.
Chippewa	288	284	4	Except the following areas:
Clark	2,471	1,741	730	
Columbia	625	625	-	(1) Eastern Zone - shotgun only
Crawford	505	505	-	A two-day either sex shotgun only
Dane	310	310	-	season in Calumet, Dodge, Fond du Lac,
Dodge	353	353	-	Manitowoc, Ozaukee, Sheboygan and
Door	102	102	-	Washington Counties, Nov. 23-Nov. 24,
Douglas	2,393	2,035	358	followed by a seven day spike buck
Dunn	1,264	1,264	-	season, Nov. 25-Dec. 1.
Eau Claire	1,132	886	246	(2) Mississippi River Zone
Florence	638	638	-	
Fond du Lac	564	564	-	A split season which provided for a
Forest	1,059	1,059	-	two-day either sex season in Buffalo*,
Grant	850	850	-	Dunn*, La Crosse**, Pepin*, Pierce*,
Green	161	161	-	Trempealeau** and portions of Eau
Green Lake	360	360	-	Claire**, Jackson**, Monroe** and
Iowa	285	285	-	Vernon counties, Nov. 23 and Nov. 24,
Iron	479	479	-	followed by a seven-day spike buck
Jackson	5,062	3,805	1,257	season, Nov. 25 - Dec. 1.
Jefferson	173	173	-	
Juneau	1,791	1,320	471	* Shotgun only.
Kenosha	4	4	-	** Shotgun - Nov. 23-Nov. 24.
Kewaunee	99	99	-	Rifle season - Nov. 25-Dec. 1.
La Crosse	719	719	-	
Lafayette	286	286	-	(3) Southern Zone
Langlade	810	810	-	A two-day either sex season in
Lincoln	1,277	1,277	-	Crawford, Dane*, Grant, Green*, Jef-
Manitowoc	1,217	1,217	-	ferson*, Kenosha*, Lafayette*, Racine*,
Marathon	765	765	-	Rock*, Walworth* and Waukesha* Counties,
Marinette	2,040	2,040	-	Nov. 23-Nov. 24.
Marquette	662	632	30	* Shotgun only.
Menominee	5	5	-	
Milwaukee	(c)	-	-	A 48-day either sex season on the
Monroe	1,441	1,252	189	Apostle Islands, except Madeline
Oconto	1,042	1,042	-	Island, Oct. 15-Dec. 1. Harvest - 93.
Oneida	2,188	2,188	-	Necedah National Wildlife Area
Outagamie	707	707	-	A nine-day spike buck and party
Ozaukee	99	99	-	permit season - Nov. 23-Dec. 1. (In
Pepin	533	533	-	variable quota party permit area I.)
Pierce	649	649	-	Harvest - 193 (regular license - 130,
Polk	718	718	-	party permit 63).
Portage	865	865	-	

(continued on following page)

		Kill		
Counties	Total	Regular License	Party Permit	Notes

THE 1963 SEASON (continued)

Counties	Total	Regular License	Party Permit	Notes
Price	2,042	1,990	-	
Racine	19	19	-	
Richland	149	149	-	
Rock	106	106	-	
Rusk	887	887	-	
St. Croix	129	129	-	
Sauk	308	308	-	
Sawyer	1,656	1,600	56	
Shawano	1,120	1,120	-	
Sheboygan	588	588	-	
Taylor	690	690	-	
Trempealeau	1,452	1,452	-	
Vernon	500	500	-	
Vilas	1,996	1,996	-	
Walworth	107	107	-	
Washburn	1,229	1,229	-	
Washington	205	205	-	
Waukesha	127	127	-	
Waupaca	1,416	1,416	-	
Waushara	903	888	15	
Winnebago	192	192	-	
Wood	1,982	1,641	341	
TOTAL	65,020	60,507	4,513	

Notes:

Sandhill Wildlife Demonstration Area - Wood County.

A four-day either sex season by permit, Nov. 23-Nov. 26. Harvest - 163.

Areas Under the Variable Quota Party Permit System

Party permit provided that a party of four or more hunters could take a deer of either sex in certain areas for management purposes, Nov. 23-Dec. 1*. Section 29.107 - Wisconsin Conservation Laws.

Area	Mgt. Unit	Harvest	Permits Issued	Hunter Success(%)
E.	2,4	564	831	67.9
F.	14	234	404	57.9
G.	58	665	738	70.1
H.	55,56	2,249	2,580	87.2
I.	53,54	801	1,025	78.1
TOTAL		4,513	5,578	80.9

Conservation Congress approved the nine-day spike buck season, Nov. 23-Dec. 1 and endorsed the variable quota management plan. The Conservation Commission concurred.

License Sales

Resident Big Game	165,296
Voluntary Sportsmen	192,308
Nonresident Big Game	2,948
Total	360,552

Total Harvest by Age and Sex

Type of License	Total Harvest	Antlered			Antlerless			
		Forked Buck	Spike Buck	% Spike Buck	Adult Doe	Fawn Buck	Fawn Doe	Unknown
Regular	60,507	40,965	9,694	19.1	5,821	2,141	1,886	-
Party Permit	4,513	34	127	78.9	2,862	806	684	-
Total	65,020	40,999	9,821	19.3	8,683	2,947	2,570	-

* The program provided for the issuance of 25% of the permits at County Clerk offices in the quota areas on a first-come, first-served basis. County Clerks issued 1,361 permits out of an alloted 1,400.

Four thousand two hundred permits were to be issued from the Madison office, selected by IBM from the valid applications. From a total of 7,863 on-time applications, 894 were rejected for various reasons. From the 6,969 valid applications, 4,217 permits, drawn by IBM, were issued.

1963 DEER GUN HARVEST

By
Management Unit and County within Unit

Unit	County	Total	Reg. Lic.	Party Permit
1.	Douglas	236	236	--
	Total	236	236	--
2.	Bayfield	594	388	206
	Douglas	712	550	162
	Total	1,306	938	368
3.	Bayfield	709	709	--
	Ashland*	167	167	--
	Total	876	876	--
4.	Douglas	568	372	196
	Total	568	372	196
5.	Bayfield	552	552	--
	Total	552	552	--
6.	Ashland	132	132	--
	Bayfield	170	170	--
	Total	302	302	--
7.	Ashland	317	317	--
	Iron	103	103	--
	Total	420	420	--
8.	Burnett	240	240	--
	Douglas	403	403	--
	Washburn	172	172	--
	Total	815	815	--
9.	Bayfield	334	334	--
	Douglas	474	474	--
	Sawyer	51	51	--
	Washburn	102	102	--
	Total	961	961	--
10.	Burnett	533	533	--
	Polk	121	121	--
	Total	654	654	--
11.	Burnett	444	444	--
	Washburn	156	156	--
	Total	600	600	--
12.	Sawyer	83	83	--
	Washburn	697	697	--
	Total	780	780	--
13.	Ashland	24	24	--
	Bayfield	302	302	--
	Sawyer	733	733	--
	Total	1,059	1,059	--
14.	Ashland	418	292	126
	Price	180	128	52
	Sawyer	171	115	56
	Total	769	535	234
15.	Barron	30	30	--
	Burnett	230	230	--
	Polk	192	192	--
	Washburn	28	28	--
	Total	480	480	--
16.	Barron	14	14	--
	Burnett	34	34	--
	Polk	241	241	--
	Total	289	289	--
17.	Barron	173	173	--
	Rusk	7	7	--
	Washburn	74	74	--
	Total	254	254	--
18.	Rusk	245	245	--
	Sawyer	122	122	--
	Total	367	367	--
19.	Rusk	235	235	--
	Sawyer	401	401	--
	Total	636	636	--
20.	Price	429	429	--
	Rusk	11	11	--
	Sawyer	95	95	--
	Total	535	535	--
21.	Polk	149	149	--
	St. Croix	7	7	--
	Total	156	156	--

* Includes deer taken during regular gun season on the Apostle Islands.

Management Unit and County within Unit - continued.

Unit	County	Total	Reg. Lic.	Party Permit	Unit	County	Total	Reg. Lic.	Party Permit
22.	Barron	101	101	--	33.	Lincoln	15	15	--
	Chippewa	5	5	--		Marathon	36	36	--
	Dunn	162	162	--		Taylor	1	1	--
	Polk	15	15	--		Total	52	52	--
	St. Croix	2	2	--					
	Total	285	285	--	34.	Iron	57	57	--
						Vilas	303	303	--
23.	Barron	19	19	--		Total	360	360	--
	Chippewa	113	113	--					
	Rusk	155	155	--	35.	Forest	82	82	--
	Total	287	287	--		Vilas	724	724	--
						Total	806	806	--
24.	Chippewa	36	36	--					
	Rusk	159	159	--	36.	Oneida	219	219	--
	Taylor	36	36	--		Vilas	789	789	--
	Total	231	231	--		Total	1,008	1,008	--
25.	Price	597	597	--	37.	Lincoln	1	1	--
	Rusk	75	75	--		Oneida	642	642	--
	Taylor	69	69	--		Total	643	643	--
	Total	741	741	--					
					38.	Forest	25	25	--
26.	Taylor	454	454	--		Langlade	8	8	--
	Total	454	454	--		Oneida	396	396	--
						Vilas	10	10	--
27.	Clark	9	9	--		Total	439	439	--
	Taylor	54	54	--					
	Total	63	63	--	39.	Forest	372	372	--
						Oneida	73	73	--
28.	Ashland	158	158	--		Vilas	32	32	--
	Iron	146	146	--		Total	477	477	--
	Total	304	304	--					
					40.	Florence	319	319	--
29.	Ashland	25	25	--		Forest	46	46	--
	Iron	173	173	--		Total	365	365	--
	Price	155	155	--					
	Vilas	133	133	--	41.	Marinette	375	375	--
	Total	486	486	--		Total	375	375	--
30.	Price	580	580	--	42.	Langlade	331	331	--
	Total	580	580	--		Lincoln	73	73	--
						Oneida	16	16	--
31.	Lincoln	3	3	--		Total	420	420	--
	Oneida	769	769	--					
	Price	56	56	--	43.	Forest	12	12	--
	Vilas	5	5	--		Langlade	246	246	--
	Total	833	833	--		Oneida	33	33	--
						Total	291	291	--
32.	Lincoln	762	762	--					
	Price	45	45	--	44.	Forest	266	266	--
	Taylor	66	66	--		Langlade	90	90	--
	Total	873	873	--		Oconto	110	110	--
						Total	466	466	--

Management Unit and County within Unit - continued.

Unit	County	Total	Reg. Lic.	Party Permit	Unit	County	Total	Reg. Lic.	Party Permit
45.	Forest	251	251	--	56.	Clark	14	11	3
	Marinette	649	649	--		Jackson	17	9	8
	Oconto	58	58	--		Juneau	803	541	262
	Total	958	958	--		Monroe	161	130	31
						Wood	966	736	230
46.	Langlade	52	52	--		Total	1,961	1,427	534
	Lincoln	73	73	--					
	Marathon	252	252	--	57.	Adams	1	1	--
	Shawano	11	11	--		Clark	89	89	--
	Total	388	388	--		Marathon	156	156	--
						Portage	230	230	--
47.	Langlade	17	17	--		Waushara	5	5	--
	Shawano	305	305	--		Wood	278	278	--
	Menominee	1	1	--		Total	759	759	--
	Total	323	323	--					
					58.	Chippewa	27	23	4
48.	Langlade	66	66	--		Clark	1,327	912	415
	Oconto	139	139	--		Eau Claire	709	463	246
	Shawano	43	43	--		Total	2,063	1,398	665
	Menominee	4	4	--					
	Total	252	252	--	59.	Chippewa	107	107	--
						Clark	4	4	--
49.	Marinette	605	605	--		Dunn	813	813	--
	Oconto	379	379	--		Eau Claire	423	423	--
	Total	984	984	--		Jackson	1,459	1,459	--
						La Crosse	570	570	--
50.	Florence	319	319	--		Monroe	159	159	--
	Forest	5	5	--		Pepin	225	225	--
	Marinette	126	126	--		Taylor	10	10	--
	Total	450	450	--		Trempealeau	435	435	--
						Total	4,205	4,205	--
51.	Marinette	285	285	--					
	Oconto	221	221	--	60.	Dunn	289	289	--
	Total	506	506	--		Pepin	14	14	--
						Pierce	131	131	--
52.	Lincoln	350	350	--		St. Croix	120	120	--
	Oneida	40	40	--		Total	554	554	--
	Total	390	390	--					
					61.	Buffalo	2,415	2,415	--
53.	Adams	680	457	223		La Crosse	29	29	--
	Juneau	312	241	71		Pepin	294	294	--
	Waushara	31	21	10		Pierce	518	518	--
	Wood	738	627	111		Trempealeau	1,017	1,017	--
	Total	1,761	1,346	415		Total	4,273	4,273	--
54.	Adams	721	512	209	62.	Marathon	321	321	--
	Juneau	597	459	138		Portage	159	159	--
	Marquette	86	56	30		Shawano	493	493	--
	Monroe	48	44	4		Waupaca	646	646	--
	Waushara	11	6	5		Total	1,619	1,619	--
	Total	1,463	1,077	386					
55.	Clark	1,028	716	312					
	Jackson	3,588	2,339	1,249					
	Monroe	748	594	154					
	Total	5,364	3,649	1,715					

Management Unit and County within Unit - continued.

Unit	County	Total	Reg. Lic.	Party Permit
63.	Brown	23	23	--
	Calumet	1	1	--
	Oconto	135	135	--
	Outagamie	706	706	--
	Shawano	268	268	--
	Waupaca	321	321	--
	Winnebago	24	24	--
	Total	1,478	1,478	--
64.	Brown	52	52	--
	Calumet	537	537	--
	Door	102	102	--
	Kewaunee	99	99	--
	Manitowoc	1,186	1,186	--
	Outagamie	1	1	--
	Total	1,977	1,977	--
65.	Portage	470	470	--
	Waupaca	252	252	--
	Waushara	122	122	--
	Total	844	844	--
66.	Portage	6	6	--
	Waupaca	197	197	--
	Waushara	444	444	--
	Winnebago	148	148	--
	Total	795	795	--
67.	Columbia	24	24	--
	Green Lake	156	156	--
	Marquette	539	539	--
	Waushara	287	287	--
	Total	1,006	1,006	--
68.	Columbia	10	10	--
	Dodge	73	73	--
	Fond du Lac	267	267	--
	Green Lake	204	204	--
	Waushara	3	3	--
	Winnebago	20	20	--
	Total	577	577	--
69.	Calumet	30	30	--
	Dodge	1	1	--
	Fond du Lac	297	297	--
	Manitowoc	31	31	--
	Ozaukee	99	99	--
	Sheboygan	588	588	--
	Washington	151	151	--
	Total	1,197	1,197	--
70.	Adams	47	47	--
	Columbia	591	591	--
	Dane	183	183	--
	Iowa	147	147	--
	Juneau	66	66	--
	Marquette	37	37	--
	Richland	9	9	--
	Sauk	303	303	--
	Total	1,383	1,383	--
71.	Grant	337	337	--
	Iowa	88	88	--
	Lafayette	6	6	--
	Richland	4	4	--
	Sauk	3	3	--
	Total	438	438	--
72.	Crawford	8	8	--
	Juneau	10	10	--
	La Crosse	120	120	--
	Monroe	325	325	--
	Richland	136	136	--
	Sauk	2	2	--
	Vernon	94	94	--
	Total	695	695	--
73.	Crawford	3	3	--
	Grant	475	475	--
	Total	478	478	--
74.	Crawford	494	494	--
	Vernon	406	406	--
	Total	900	900	--
75.	Dane	34	34	--
	Grant	38	38	--
	Green	76	76	--
	Iowa	50	50	--
	Lafayette	280	280	--
	Total	478	478	--
76.	Dane	93	93	--
	Dodge	279	279	--
	Green	9	9	--
	Jefferson	173	173	--
	Rock	3	3	--
	Washington	54	54	--
	Waukesha	116	116	--
	Total	727	727	--
77.	Green	76	76	--
	Kenosha	4	4	--
	Racine	19	19	--
	Rock	103	103	--
	Walworth	107	107	--
	Waukesha	11	11	--
	Total	320	320	--
	Grand Total	65,020	60,507	4,513

THE 1964 SEASON

Counties	Total Harvest	Kill Reg. Lic.	Party Permit	Notes
Adams	2,244	1,386	858	
Ashland	1,820	1,403	417	71 Open Counties.
Barron	373	373	-	
Bayfield	4,844	3,248	1,596	A nine-day spike buck season in
Brown	122	108	14	northern, central and eastern coun-
Buffalo	2,683	2,683	-	ties, including Madeline Island,
Burnett	2,826	1,904	922	Nov. 21-Nov. 29.
Calumet	100	100	-	Except the following areas:
Chippewa	381	371	10	
Clark	3,015	1,888	1,127	(1) Southern Zone
Columbia	943	906	37	A three-day either sex season,
Crawford	688	688	-	Nov. 21-Nov. 23 in Crawford, Dane*,
Dane	484	484	-	Grant, Green*, Jefferson*, Kenosha*,
Dodge	360	360	-	Lafayette*, Racine*, Rock*, Walworth*,
Door	103	103	-	Washington* and Waukesha* Counties
Douglas	3,770	2,504	1,266	* Shotgun only.
Dunn	1,011	1,011	-	
Eau Claire	1,446	1,033	413	(2) Mississippi River Zone
Florence	1,038	844	194	A split season which provided for
Fond du Lac	194	194	-	a two-day either sex season, Nov. 21-
Forest	1,635	1,383	252	Nov. 22, followed by a seven-day spike
Grant	1,093	1,093	-	buck season, Nov. 23-Nov. 29, in
Green	252	252	-	Buffalo*, Dunn*, La Crosse**, Pepin*,
Green Lake	663	575	88	Pierce*, St. Croix*, Trempealeau**,
Iowa	300	300	-	and portions of Eau Claire**,
Iron	576	576	-	Jackson**, Monroe** and Vernon Counties
Jackson	6,745	4,617	2,128	* Shotgun only
Jefferson	260	260	-	** Shotgun only Nov. 21-22; Rifle
Juneau	2,549	1,612	937	season, Nov. 23 - Nov. 29.
Kenosha	16	16	-	
Kewaunee	110	110	-	Horicon Managed Deer Hunt
La Crosse	795	795	-	A two-day either sex season by
Lafayette	341	341	-	permit, Nov. 30-Dec. 1. Number of
Langlade	1,116	1,116	-	permits not to exceed 250 at any one
Lincoln	2,087	1,715	372	time. Fee - $1.00. 655 hunters.
Manitowoc	218	218	-	Harvest - 213.
Marathon	1,448	1,260	188	
Marinette	2,621	2,621	-	Necedah National Wildlife Refuge
Marquette	1,152	874	278	A nine-day spike buck and party
Menominee	16	16	-	permit season, Nov. 21-Nov. 29.
Milwaukee	C	-	-	Harvest - 177 (regular license - 109,
Monroe	1,851	1,435	416	party permit - 68).
Oconto	1,393	1,331	62	
Oneida	3,316	2,772	544	A 46-day either sex season on the
Outagamie	1,404	1,022	382	Apostle Islands, except Madeline
Ozaukee	35	35	-	Island, Oct. 15-Nov. 29. Harvest - 85.
Pepin	470	470	-	Sandhill Wildlife Demonstration Area
Pierce	565	565	-	A two-day either sex season,
Polk	936	877	59	Nov. 21- Nov. 22, by permit. Harvest -
Portage	1,600	1,298	302	150.
Price	3,912	2,788	1,124	

(continued on following page)

THE 1964 SEASON (continued)

Counties	Total Harvest	Kill Reg. Lic.	Party Permit
Racine	27	27	-
Richland	190	190	-
Rock	173	173	-
Rusk	1,451	1,183	268
St. Croix	625	625	-
Sauk	455	455	-
Sawyer	3,574	2,280	1,294
Shawano	1,833	1,464	369
Sheboygan	175	175	-
Taylor	1,085	991	94
Trempealeau	1,336	1,336	-
Vernon	644	644	-
Vilas	2,928	2,388	540
Walworth	148	148	-
Washburn	2,588	1,610	978
Washington	338	338	-
Waukesha	213	213	-
Waupaca	2,849	2,091	758
Waushara	1,702	1,323	379
Winnebago	322	260	62
Wood	2,869	2,040	829
Total	93,445	73,888	19,557

License Sales

Resident Big Game	164,167
Voluntary Sportsmen	218,450
Nonresident Big Game	3,902
Total	386,519

Notes

Area under the Variable Quota Party Permit System*, Nov. 21 - Nov. 29.

Mgt. Unit	Harvest	Permits Issued	Hunter Success(%)
2,4	977	1,359	71.9
3	277	462	60.0
5	236	300	78.7
10	258	311	83.0
8,11	1,298	1,617	80.3
9,12	1,655	2,215	74.7
13,14	1,451	2,045	71.0
19,20	1,012	1,355	74.5
25	561	815	68.8
30	254	365	69.6
31	280	345	81.2
32	396	465	85.2
35	287	350	82.0
36	323	375	86.1
37	185	230	80.4
39,40	470	775	60.6
53,54	1,814	2,200	82.5
55,56	3,985	4,495	88.7
58	975	1,090	89.4
62	862	1,110	77.7
63	835	1,045	80.0
65	381	420	90.7
66	356	395	90.1
67	429	470	91.3
Total	19,557	24,609	79.5

The Conservation Congress at its county meetings voted in favor of the seasons as outlined above The Conservation Commission concurred.

Total Harvest by Age and Sex

Type of License	Total Harvest	Antlered Forked Buck	Spike Buck	% Spike Buck	Antlerless Adult Doe	Fawn Buck	Fawn Doe	Unknown
Reg. License	73,888	52,628	11,645	18.1	5,375	2,216	2,024	-
Party Permit	19,557	186	593	76.1	12,794	3,181	2,550	253
Total	93,445	52,814	12,238	18.8	18,169	5,397	4,574	253

* Party Permit provided that a party of 4 or more hunters could take a deer of either sex in certain areas for management purposes. Section 29.107 Wisconsin Conservation Laws.

The variable quota Party Permit program provided for the issuance of 25% of the permits at the offices of County Clerks in the quota areas on a first-come, first-served basis. County Clerks issued 5,571 permits out of an alloted 7,135.

From the 16,684 valid applications received at the Madison office, 14,465 permits were selected by IBM.

Because allotments were not filled in some areas, 4,573 permits were issued over the counter at the Madison office. 3,929 permits remained unsold.

1964 DEER GUN HARVEST

By
Management Unit and County within Unit

Unit	County	Total	Reg. Lic.	Party Permit	Unit	County	Total	Reg. Lic.	Party Permit
1.	Douglas	290	290	--	14.	Ashland	751	383	368
						Price	281	163	118
2.	Bayfield	971	556	415		Sawyer	255	142	113
	Douglas	970	651	319		Total	1,287	688	599
	Total	1,941	1,207	734					
					15.	Barron	33	33	--
3.	Ashland*	229	229	--		Burnett	210	210	--
	Bayfield	1,174	897	277		Polk	227	227	--
	Total	1,403	1,126	277		Washburn	20	20	--
						Total	490	490	--
4.	Douglas	687	444	243					
					16.	Barron	22	22	--
5.	Bayfield	1,024	788	236		Burnett	44	44	--
						Polk	266	266	--
6.	Ashland	157	157	--		Total	332	332	--
	Bayfield	155	155	--					
	Total	312	312	--	17.	Barron	193	193	--
						Rusk	19	19	--
7.	Ashland	393	393	--		Washburn	88	88	--
	Iron	112	112	--		Total	300	300	--
	Total	505	505	--					
					18.	Rusk	288	288	--
8.	Burnett	595	371	224		Sawyer	125	125	--
	Douglas	728	443	285		Total	413	413	--
	Washburn	332	198	134					
	Total	1,655	1,012	643	19.	Rusk	517	335	182
						Sawyer	1,128	716	412
9.	Bayfield	811	429	382		Total	1,645	1,051	594
	Douglas	1,095	676	419					
	Sawyer	194	125	69	20.	Price	973	644	329
	Washburn	320	192	128		Rusk	23	20	3
	Total	2,420	1,422	998		Sawyer	231	145	86
						Total	1,227	809	418
10.	Burnett	790	591	199					
	Polk	225	166	59	21.	Polk	205	205	--
	Total	1,015	757	258		St. Croix	14	14	--
						Total	219	219	--
11.	Burnett	1,187	688	499					
	Washburn	384	228	156	22.	Barron	101	101	--
	Total	1,571	916	655		Chippewa	12	12	--
						Dunn	129	129	--
12.	Sawyer	230	133	97		Polk	13	13	--
	Washburn	1,444	884	560		St. Croix	10	10	--
	Total	1,674	1,017	657		Total	265	265	--
13.	Ashland	96	47	49	23.	Barron	24	24	--
	Bayfield	715	429	286		Chippewa	147	147	--
	Sawyer	1,411	894	517		Rusk	166	166	--
	Total	2,222	1,370	852		Total	337	337	--

* Represents Apostle Island harvest.

1964 Deer Gun Harvest by Management Unit and County within Unit - continued

Unit	County	Total	Reg. Lic.	Party Permit	Unit	County	Total	Reg. Lic.	Party Permit
24.	Chippewa	46	46	--	36.	Oneida	287	223	64
	Rusk	225	225	--		Vilas	1,238	979	259
	Taylor	44	44	--		Total	1,525	1,202	323
	Total	315	315	--					
					37.	Lincoln	2	2	--
25.	Price	1,347	944	403		Oneida	1,038	853	185
	Rusk	213	130	83		Total	1,040	855	185
	Taylor	216	141	75					
	Total	1,776	1,215	561	38.	Forest	23	23	--
						Langlade	10	10	--
26.	Taylor	598	598	--		Lincoln	7	7	--
						Oneida	462	462	--
27.	Clark	21	21	--		Vilas	16	16	--
	Taylor	73	73	--		Total	518	518	--
	Total	94	94	--					
					39.	Florence	31	23	8
28.	Ashland	157	157	--		Forest	754	550	204
	Iron	173	173	--		Oneida	124	92	32
	Total	330	330	--		Vilas	41	29	12
						Total	950	694	256
29.	Ashland	31	31	--					
	Iron	195	195	--	40.	Florence	670	484	186
	Oneida	2	2	--		Forest	97	69	28
	Price	160	160	--		Total	767	553	214
	Vilas	124	124	--					
	Total	512	512	--	41.	Marinette	459	459	--
30.	Price	1,012	758	254	42.	Langlade	486	486	--
						Lincoln	86	86	--
31.	Lincoln	6	6	--		Oneida	32	32	--
	Oneida	1,283	1,020	263		Total	604	604	--
	Price	78	63	15					
	Vilas	19	17	2	43.	Forest	26	26	--
	Total	1,386	1,106	280		Langlade	364	364	--
						Oneida	47	47	--
32.	Lincoln	1,433	1,061	372		Total	437	437	--
	Price	61	56	5					
	Taylor	146	127	19	44.	Forest	316	316	--
	Total	1,640	1,244	396		Langlade	111	111	--
						Oconto	128	128	--
33.	Lincoln	18	18	--		Total	555	555	--
	Marathon	60	60	--					
	Taylor	2	2	--	45.	Forest	315	315	--
	Total	80	80	--		Marinette	858	858	--
						Oconto	81	81	--
34.	Iron	96	96	--		Total	1,254	1,254	--
	Vilas	285	285	--					
	Total	381	381	--	46.	Langlade	59	59	--
						Lincoln	80	80	--
35.	Forest	104	84	20		Marathon	396	396	--
	Vilas	1,205	938	267		Total	535	535	--
	Total	1,309	1,022	287					

Unit	County	Total	Reg. Lic.	Party Permit	Unit	County	Total	Reg. Lic.	Party Permit
47.	Langlade	16	16	--	57.	Clark	85	85	--
	Shawano	324	324	--		Marathon	276	276	--
	Total	340	340	--		Portage	266	266	--
48.	Langlade	70	70	--		Waushara	5	5	--
	Menominee	16	16	--		Wood	339	339	--
	Oconto	160	160	--		Total	971	971	--
	Shawano	47	47	--	58.	Chippewa	42	32	10
	Total	293	293	--		Clark	1,392	840	552
49.	Marinette	785	785	--		Eau Claire	949	536	413
	Oconto	449	449	--		Total	2,383	1,408	975
	Total	1,234	1,234	--	59.	Buffalo	24	24	--
50.	Florence	337	337	--		Chippewa	134	134	--
	Marinette	170	170	--		Clark	14	14	--
	Total	507	507	--		Dunn	636	636	--
51.	Marinette	349	349	--		Eau Claire	497	497	--
	Oconto	191	191	--		Jackson	1,864	1,864	--
	Total	540	540	--		La Crosse	633	633	--
52.	Lincoln	455	455	--		Monroe	165	165	--
	Oneida	41	41	--		Pepin	234	234	--
	Total	496	496	--		Taylor	6	6	--
53.	Adams	1,028	597	431		Trempealeau	415	415	--
	Juneau	565	342	223		Total	4,622	4,622	--
	Portage	17	17	--	60.	Dunn	246	246	--
	Waushara	15	10	5		Pepin	14	14	--
	Wood	1,199	817	382		Pierce	155	155	--
	Total	2,824	1,783	1,041		St. Croix	601	601	--
54.	Adams	1,116	689	427		Total	1,016	1,016	--
	Juneau	888	598	290	61.	Buffalo	2,659	2,659	--
	Marquette	140	93	47		La Crosse	19	19	--
	Monroe	34	29	5		Pepin	222	222	--
	Waushara	14	10	4		Pierce	410	410	--
	Total	2,192	1,419	773		Trempealeau	921	921	--
55.	Clark	1,480	911	569		Total	4,231	4,231	--
	Jackson	4,767	2,686	2,081	62.	Marathon	716	528	188
	Monroe	1,126	794	332		Portage	507	372	135
	Total	7,373	4,391	2,982		Shawano	865	666	199
56.	Clark	23	17	6		Waupaca	1,097	757	340
	Jackson	114	67	47		Total	3,185	2,323	862
	Juneau	1,010	586	424	63.	Brown	57	43	14
	Monroe	250	171	79		Oconto	384	322	62
	Wood	1,331	884	447		Outagamie	1,396	1,014	382
	Total	2,728	1,725	1,003		Shawano	597	427	170
						Waupaca	695	508	187
						Winnebago	69	49	20
						Total	3,198	2,363	835

Unit	County	Total	Reg. Lic.	Party Permit	Unit	County	Total	Reg. Lic.	Party Permit
64.	Brown	65	65	--	71.	Grant	467	467	--
	Calumet	84	84	--		Iowa	113	113	--
	Door	103	103	--		Lafayette	26	26	--
	Kewaunee	110	110	--		Richland	3	3	--
	Manitowoc	209	209	--		Sauk	8	8	--
	Outagamie	8	8	--		Total	617	617	--
	Total	579	579	--					
					72.	Crawford	62	62	--
65.	Portage	810	643	167		Juneau	17	17	--
	Waupaca	560	431	129		La Crosse	135	135	--
	Waushara	284	199	85		Monroe	276	276	--
	Total	1,654	1,273	381		Richland	169	169	--
						Sauk	2	2	--
66.	Waupaca	497	395	102		Vernon	227	227	--
	Waushara	874	662	212		Total	888	888	--
	Winnebago	233	191	42					
	Total	1,604	1,248	356	73.	Grant	590	590	--
67.	Columbia	147	110	37	74.	Crawford	626	626	--
	Green Lake	295	207	88		La Crosse	8	8	--
	Marquette	979	748	231		Vernon	417	417	--
	Waushara	508	435	73		Total	1,051	1,051	--
	Total	1,929	1,500	429					
					75.	Dane	42	42	--
68.	Columbia	58	58	--		Grant	36	36	--
	Dodge	260	260	--		Green	114	114	--
	Fond du Lac	92	92	--		Iowa	57	57	--
	Green Lake	368	368	--		Lafayette	315	315	--
	Waushara	2	2	--		Total	564	564	--
	Winnebago	20	20	--					
	Total	800	800	--	76.	Columbia	4	4	--
						Dane	227	227	--
69.	Calumet	16	16	--		Dodge	100	100	--
	Fond du Lac	102	102	--		Green	8	8	--
	Manitowoc	9	9	--		Jefferson	259	259	--
	Ozaukee	35	35	--		Rock	13	13	--
	Sheboygan	175	175	--		Washington	116	116	--
	Washington	222	222	--		Waukesha	199	199	--
	Total	559	559	--		Total	926	926	--
70.	Adams	100	100	--	77.	Dane	9	9	--
	Columbia	734	734	--		Green	130	130	--
	Dane	206	206	--		Jefferson	1	1	--
	Iowa	130	130	--		Kenosha	16	16	--
	Juneau	69	69	--		Racine	27	27	--
	Marquette	33	33	--		Rock	160	160	--
	Richland	18	18	--		Walworth	148	148	--
	Sauk	445	445	--		Waukesha	14	14	--
	Total	1,735	1,735	--		Total	505	505	--

STATE TOTAL   93,445   73,888   19,557

County	Years Open	Average Annual Kill	Total Kill
Adams	18	945	17,017
Ashland . . .	21	2,041	42,869
Barron. . . .	21	186	3,899
Bayfield. . .	21	3,812	80,047
Buffalo . . .	12	404	4,847
Burnett . . .	21	1,753	36,817
Chippewa. . .	21	299	6,268
Clark	20	1,847	36,939
Columbia. . .	14	462	6,473
Crawford. . .	9	95	855
Dane.	6	151	904
Dodge	4	77	306
Door.	5	167	836
Douglas . . .	21	2,695	56,605
Dunn.	7	403	2,819
Eau Claire. .	20	889	17,775
Florence. . .	21	1,853	38,907
Fond du Lac .	2	41	82
Forest. . . .	21	2,649	55,624
Grant	10	114	1,142
Green Lake. .	6	300	1,802
Iowa.	12	89	1,063
Iron.	21	1,236	25,964
Jackson . . .	19	3,000	56,991
Juneau. . . .	19	1,534	29,154
La Crosse . .	12	260	3,123
Langlade. . .	21	1,007	21,140
Lincoln . . .	21	1,239	26,028
Marathon. . .	20	290	5,801
Marinette . .	21	3,250	68,241
Marquette . .	10	583	5,830
Monroe. . . .	19	804	15,275
Oconto. . . .	21	1,548	32,515
Oneida. . . .	21	3,347	70,296
Outagamie . .	4	355	1,421
Pepin	8	134	1,071
Pierce. . . .	6	264	1,586
Polk.	21	913	19,172
Portage . . .	12	384	4,612
Price	21	2,749	57,737
Richland. . .	11	36	395
Rusk.	21	1,199	25,189
St. Croix . .	9	180	1,624
Sauk.	12	278	3,337
Sawyer. . . .	21	3,075	64,575
Shawano . . .	18	294	5,285
Taylor. . . .	21	978	20,542
Trempealeau .	12	250	3,000
Vernon. . . .	4	121	484
Vilas	21	4,721	99,136
Washburn. . .	21	1,181	24,791
Washington. .	1	14	14
Waupaca . . .	6	996	5,978
Waushara. . .	11	552	6,068
Winnebago . .	1	32	32
Wood.	19	1,381	26,230
Misc. . . .	-	-	6,186

COUNTIES CLOSED
TO DEER GUN HUNTING
FROM 1932 TO 1954
INCLUSIVE

1. Brown	9. Milwaukee
2. Calumet	10. Ozaukee
3. Green	11. Racine
4. Jefferson	12. Rock
5. Kenosha	13. Sheboygan
6. Kewaunee	14. Walworth
7. Lafayette	15. Waukesha
8. Manitowoc	

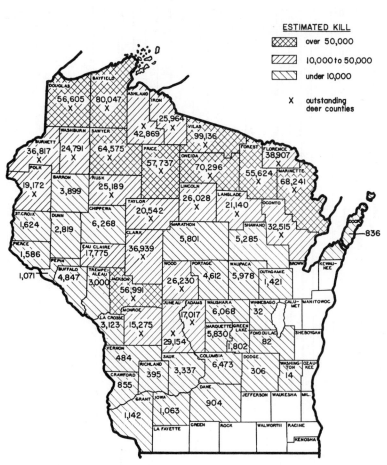

WISCONSIN DEER KILL COUNTIES
1932 - 1954

ESTIMATED KILL

over 50,000

10,000 to 50,000

under 10,000

X   outstanding
     deer counties

THE RANK OF COUNTIES HAVING THE HEAVIEST ESTIMATED DEER KILL
FOR A TWENTY-ONE YEAR PERIOD

YEAR	1932	34	36	37	38	39	40	41	42	43	44	45	46	47	48	49	50	51	52	53	54	Total Kill
Vilas	4	3	1	1	1	1	1	1	1	1	2	3	1	4	4	2	1	7	15	1	1	99,136
Bayfield	3	2	2	2	1	2	1	1	1	4	1	1	3	2	3	4	3	2	7	8	13	80,047
Oneida	6	4	4	3	2	3	4	2	4	4	4	8	6	8	5	5	4	4	6	5	7	70,296
Marinette	11	10	10	9	9	7	7	6	7	6	4	2	5	3	1	5	2	4	3	3	3	68,241
Sawyer	1	1	3	4	3	4	3	3	3	2	6	10	12	10	8	11	9	8	10	12	9	64,575
Price	2	6	5	5	5	5	5	5	5	5	13	14	10	12	6	12	10	3	9	4	5	57,737
Jackson	-	-	11	11	13	9	13	12	9	17	7	4	4	5	2	6	5	13	2	2	4	56,991
Douglas	10	9	7	7	8	6	6	8	6		5	5	7	7	7	8	8	5	5	9	6	56,665
Forest	8	7	8	8	6	8	10	9	11	9	8	6	9	6	9	10	6	6	1	6	2	55,624
Ashland	5	5	6	6	7	9	9	7	8	10	9	13	14	13	21	18	13	12	14	11	14	42,869
Florence	12	12	11	13	11	10	12	10	10	12	10	9	20	15	20	12	11	9	11	17	8	38,907
Clark	-	-	16	17	17	18	18	18	13	21	12	7	8	9	11	6	7	18	25	10	15	36,939
Burnett	17	17	13	10	12	11	8	13	12	8	13	15	13	16	13	16	14	10	20	21	16	36,817
Oconto	18	20	20	22	20	17	20	17	16	13	16	16	16	11	10	14	12	11	12	16	11	32,515
Juneau	-	-	19	21	21	22	25	24	20	24	17	11	3	1	14	9	16	21	28	14	10	29,154
TOTAL																						826,453

NOTE: The above table shows a comparative increase in kill in Clark, Douglas, Jackson, Juneau, Marinette, and Oconto Counties during the 21-year period.
The comparative decrease in kill in the remaining nine counties is not as great as the comparative increase in kill in the above-named counties.

In Juneau County, the rank increased the greatest in the years 1946 and 1947 when controlled hunting was carried on in the Necedah National Wildlife Refuge. The next year (1948) Juneau County, with its normal harvest, dropped back to 14th place.

Statewide closed seasons prevailed in 1933 and 1935.

The heaviest deer kill counties accounted for 72% of the total state kill (1,152,719) during the 21 open seasons.

REGISTERED AVERAGE ANNUAL DEER GUN KILL
1955-1964 Inclusive

County	Years Open	Average Annual Harvest	Total Harvest
Adams. . . .	10	1,272	12,725
Ashland. . .	10	1,546	15,462
Barron . . .	10	322	3,217
Bayfield . .	10	2,676	26,761
Brown. . . .	10	86	855
Buffalo. . .	10	1,868	18,683
Burnett. . .	10	1,787	17,875
Calumet. . .	10	143	1,434
Chippewa . .	10	389	3,886
Clark. . . .	10	1,689	16,891
Columbia . .	10	656	6,561
Crawford . .	10	349	3,491
Dane	10	180	1,797
Dodge. . . .	10	155	1,546
Door	10	104	1,043
Douglas. . .	10	2,206	22,061
Dunn	10	686	6,863
Eau Claire .	10	952	9,520
Florence . .	10	1,166	11,656
Fond du Lac.	10	160	1,599
Forest . . .	10	2,074	20,744
Grant. . . .	10	469	4,694
Green. . . .	5	135	674
Green Lake .	10	388	3,878
Iowa	10	267	2,667
Iron	10	713	7,130
Jackson. . .	10	3,449	34,489
Jefferson. .	10	132	1,316
Juneau . . .	10	1,445	14,448
Kenosha. . .	6	12	71
Kewaunee . .	10	99	994
La Crosse. .	10	598	5,980
Lafayette. .	8	148	1,180
Langlade . .	10	1,174	11,743
Lincoln. . .	10	1,664	16,641
Manitowoc. .	10	332	3,323
Marathon . .	10	725	7,251
Marinette. .	10	3,061	30,613
Marquette. .	10	763	7,633
Menominee. .	4*	5	21
Monroe . . .	10	1,061	10,609
Oconto . . .	10	1,660	16,601
Oneida . . .	10	3,089	30,893
Outagamie. .	10	697	6,966
Ozaukee. . .	10	28	283
Pepin. . . .	10	368	3,683
Pierce . . .	10	404	4,045
Polk	10	881	8,815
Portage. . .	10	824	8,239
Price. . . .	10	2,948	29,481

COUNTIES CLOSED
TO DEER GUN HUNTING
FROM 1955 TO 1964
INCLUSIVE

Milwaukee - 10 years, 1955-1964
Green and Racine - 5 years -
  1955-1959
Kenosha - 4 years - 1955-1958
Walworth - 3 years - 1956-1958
Rock - 3 years - 1955-1957
Lafayette - 2 years - 1955+1959

* Menominee County formed in 1961.

- 165 -

Registered Average Annual Deer Gun Kill - continued
1955-1964 Inclusive

County	Years Open	Average Annual Harvest	Total Harvest
Racine. . . .	5	15	77
Richland. . .	10	101	1,006
Rock.	7	89	621
Rusk.	10	1,254	12,538
St. Croix . .	10	230	2,302
Sauk.	10	319	3,186
Sawyer. . . .	10	2,426	24,258
Shawano . . .	10	1,136	11,362
Sheboygan . .	10	160	1,595
Taylor. . . .	10	1,006	10,057
Trempealeau .	10	935	9,346
Vernon. . . .	10	322	3,223
Vilas	10	2,501	25,011
Walworth. . .	7	80	557
Washburn. . .	10	1,535	15,349
Washington. .	10	115	1,150
Waukesha. . .	10	110	1,099
Waupaca . . .	10	1,455	14,548
Waushara. . .	10	1,069	10,689
Winnebago . .	10	166	1,656
Wood.	10	1,493	14,933

Wisconsin Deer Kill Counties
1955 - 1964

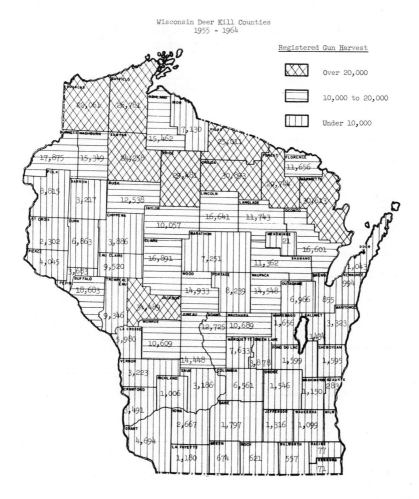

Registered Gun Harvest

|⬚| Over 20,000

|▭| 10,000 to 20,000

|▥| Under 10,000

THE RANK OF COUNTIES HAVING THE HIGHEST REGISTERED
GUN KILL FOR A TEN YEAR PERIOD
1955-1964

Year	1955	56	57	58	59	60	61	62	63	64	Total Kill
Jackson	6	1	1	1	24	17	1	2	1	1	34,489
Oneida	4	3	3	2	1	3	7	4	6	6	30,893
Marinette	1	2	2	3	3	2	5	8	8	15	30,613
Price	3	5	7	4	2	1	2	5	7	3	29,481
Bayfield	10	7	5	9	6	5	3	3	2	2	26,761
Vilas	8	4	4	5	7	4	12	7	10	8	25,011
Sawyer	11	8	9	7	4	6	9	11	12	5	24,258
Douglas	9	9	13	11	8	7	4	6	5	4	22,061
Forest	7	6	6	6	5	14	29	22	25	24	20,744
Buffalo	2	29	16	18	13	11	30	1	4	14	18,683
Burnett	14	13	15	19	9	9	8	9	13	13	17,875
Clark	18	10	10	10	30	25	6	10	3	7	16,891
Lincoln	12	15	14	14	17	8	14	17	18	19	16,641
Oconto	15	11	8	8	12	10	18	22	26	30	16,601
Ashland	13	12	19	21	11	13	17	16	20	22	15,462
TOTAL											346,464

COMPARISON OF 10 LEADING COUNTIES DURING
LIBERAL SEASON YEARS OF 1943, 1949, 1950, and 1951

	1943				1949	
Rank	County	Kill		Rank	County	Kill
1	Vilas	16,756		1	Jackson	16,263
2	Sawyer	11,271		2	Vilas	14,773
3	Oneida	10,251		3	Marinette	9,597
4	Bayfield	9,941		4	Bayfield	8,981
5	Price	7,588		5	Oneida	8,583
6	Marinette	6,879		6	Clark	8,359
7	Douglas	6,705		7	Wood	7,399
8	Burnett	5,776		8	Douglas	7,367
9	Forest	5,539		9	Juneau	7,086
10	Ashland	4,889		10	Forest	6,781
TOTAL		85,595		TOTAL		95,189
% OF STATE TOTAL KILL		66.7%		% OF STATE TOTAL KILL		59.8%
TOTAL STATE KILL (all counties)		128,296		TOTAL STATE KILL (all counties)		159,112

	1950				1951	
Rank	County	Kill		Rank	County	Kill
1	Vilas	16,558		1	Marinette	8,979
2	Marinette	12,262		2	Bayfield	7,695
3	Bayfield	10,785		3	Price	7,057
4	Oneida	10,520		4	Oneida	6,730
5	Jackson	8,878		5	Douglas	6,622
6	Forest	8,540		6	Forest	6,376
7	Clark	8,489		7	Vilas	6,030
8	Douglas	7,863		8	Sawyer	5,514
9	Sawyer	7,559		9	Florence	4,768
10	Price	7,168		10	Burnett	4,741
TOTAL		98,622		TOTAL		64,512
% OF STATE TOTAL KILL		58.7%		% OF STATE TOTAL KILL		49.8%
TOTAL STATE KILL (all counties)		167,911		TOTAL STATE KILL (all counties)		129,475

COMPARISON OF 10 LEADING COUNTIES DURING
THE LIBERAL (PARTY PERMIT) SEASON YEARS
OF 1957, 1958, 1959, 1960, 1963 AND 1964

	1957			1958			1959	
Rank	County	Kill	Rank	County	Kill	Rank	County	Kill
1	Jackson	4,998	1	Jackson	5,824	1	Oneida	5,962
2	Marinette	4,475	2	Oneida	5,585	2	Price	5,851
3	Oneida	3,775	3	Marinette	5,351	3	Marinette	5,631
4	Vilas	3,480	4	Price	4,207	4	Sawyer	5,570
5	Bayfield	3,280	5	Vilas	4,136	5	Forest	4,730
6	Forest	3,219	6	Forest	3,815	6	Bayfield	4,132
7	Price	2,843	7	Sawyer	3,549	7	Vilas	3,402
8	Oconto	2,370	8	Oconto	3,075	8	Douglas	3,213
9	Sawyer	2,337	9	Bayfield	2,936	9	Burnett	3,108
10	Clark	2,079	10	Clark	2,785	10	Florence	3,098
TOTAL		32,856	TOTAL		41,263	TOTAL		44,697

% OF STATE TOTAL KILL	48.2%	% OF STATE TOTAL KILL	43.3%	% OF STATE TOTAL KILL	42.3%

TOTAL STATE KILL (all counties)	68,138	TOTAL STATE KILL (all counties)	95,234	TOTAL STATE KILL (all counties)	105,596

	1960			1963			1964	
Rank	County	Kill	Rank	County	Kill	Rank	County	Kill
1	Price	3,816	1	Jackson	5,062	1	Jackson	6,745
2	Marinette	3,651	2	Bayfield	2,661	2	Bayfield	4,844
3	Oneida	3,487	3	Clark	2,471	3	Price	3,912
4	Vilas	3,123	4	Buffalo	2,415	4	Douglas	3,770
5	Bayfield	3,045	5	Douglas	2,393	5	Sawyer	3,574
6	Sawyer	2,844	6	Oneida	2,188	6	Oneida	3,316
7	Douglas	2,737	7	Price	2,042	7	Clark	3,015
8	Lincoln	2,357	8	Marinette	2,040	8	Vilas	2,928
9	Burnett	2,222	9	Vilas	1,996	9	Wood	2,869
10	Oconto	2,126	10	Wood	1,982	10	Waupaca	2,849
TOTAL		29,409			25,250			37,822

% OF STATE TOTAL KILL	47.5%	% OF STATE TOTAL KILL	38.8%	% OF STATE TOTAL KILL	40.5%

TOTAL STATE KILL (all counties)	61,005	TOTAL STATE KILL (all counties)	65,020	TOTAL STATE KILL (all counties)	93,445

UNIT HARVEST PER SQUARE MILE OF DEER RANGE
1957-1964

Deer Mgt. Units	Gross Area Sq. Miles	Net Deer Range	% of Gross Area in Deer Range	Deer Harvest per sq. mile of Deer Range		
				1957	1958*	1959
1.	229.7	186.7	81.3	0.7	2.0	2.5
2.	568.5	526.5	92.6	1.6	2.0	2.3
3.	577.9**	546.3	94.5	3.2	1.3	1.9
4.	346.2	338.9	97.9	1.3	1.1	1.7
5.	248.5	230.9	92.9	1.7	4.0	4.9
6.	342.8	267.2	77.9	1.6	2.4	4.1
7.	444.3	376.7	84.8	0.8	1.4	1.9
8.	394.7	367.7	93.2	1.9	4.1	3.9
9.	466.6	437.9	93.8	2.6	3.2	4.6
10.	389.1	319.7	82.2	3.1	3.0	4.4
11.	343.0	272.6	79.5	2.5	3.9	4.8
12.	538.5	499.9	92.8	1.2	2.2	3.2
13.	819.2	752.0	91.8	1.3	2.2	3.3
14.	442.0	413.1	93.5	1.9	2.9	4.1
15.	507.1	309.0	60.9	1.7	2.2	2.5
16.	495.8	251.3	50.7	1.5	2.4	1.9
17.	454.6	215.6	47.4	1.3	1.0	1.6
18.	400.1	341.0	85.2	1.1	2.4	3.2
19.	427.1	379.8	88.9	2.6	4.3	9.2
20.	405.3	347.8	85.8	2.3	4.4	5.5
21.	458.5	130.6	28.5	2.0		2.8
22.	564.9	210.1	37.2	0.7		1.0
23.	510.3	339.1	66.5	1.0		1.7
24.	334.0	230.3	69.9	1.2		2.4
25.	462.2	389.4	84.2	2.1	2.8	3.7
26.	414.7	341.0	82.2	1.7	2.5	3.5
27.	537.3	227.8	42.4			1.0
28.	477.3	453.2	95.0	1.0	1.7	1.9
29.	549.9	451.9	82.2	2.2	2.3	3.5
30.	333.1	284.6	85.4	2.9	5.4	6.9
31.	450.3	392.1	87.1	3.5	4.8	9.1
32.	603.5	489.8	81.2	2.5	3.0	3.5
33.	455.7	126.2	27.7	0.7		0.4
34.	305.0	259.0	84.9	2.6	4.1	3.3
35.	461.1	410.9	89.1	4.5	3.7	5.0
36.	329.1	269.8	82.0	5.2	8.7	2.1
37.	267.7	231.5	86.5	4.9	8.5	2.5
38.	435.8	388.5	89.1	2.2	3.0	3.8
39.	436.0	402.5	92.3	3.2	4.4	5.7
40.	335.7	323.1	96.2	3.4	4.5	6.7
41.	203.2	184.9	91.0	3.9	4.6	3.7
42.	368.4	295.5	80.2	2.2	2.6	3.3
43.	376.2	335.8	89.3	2.4	2.2	2.3
44.	423.0	363.1	85.8	3.6	5.5	4.8

Unit Harvest Per Square Mile of Deer Range (continued)
1957-1964

Deer Mgt. Units	Gross Area Sq. Miles	Net Deer Range	% of Gross Area in Deer Range	Deer Harvest per sq. mile of Deer Range		
				1957	1958*	1959
45.	593.6	567.5	95.6	4.3	4.5	4.3
46.	467.7	246.9	52.8	0.9		2.4
47.	300.1	261.0	87.0	0.5		2.3
48.	374.1	281.2	75.2	1.5		2.7
49.	467.7	393.0	84.0	5.6	6.9	8.2
50.	352.1	338.8	96.2	2.8	4.7	5.8
51.	750.2	333.2	44.4	2.4	2.8	2.7
52.	276.1	187.6	67.9	3.6	4.9	4.8
53.	621.7	380.1	61.1	4.6		5.3
54.	649.1	365.5	56.3	3.5		3.3
55.	942.8	736.2	78.1	7.6		2.9
56.	371.1	317.2	85.5	8.1		3.0
57.	1,667.5	532.9	32.0	1.1		2.5
58.	644.3	441.6	68.5	2.4		2.5
59.	2,837.5	1,212.0	42.7	1.5		2.2
60.	1,187.9	280.0	23.6	1.7		2.0
61.	1,551.5	703.9	45.4	3.9		6.4
62.	1,066.7	674.3	63.2	1.1		3.8
63.	1,586.6	792.9	50.0	1.1		4.2
64.	1,975.2	425.4	21.5	0.6		2.8
65.	566.7	231.3	40.8	2.1		6.2
66.	566.8	169.2	29.8	2.8		10.7
67.	717.2	178.5	24.9	4.2		16.7
68.	1,136.9	178.2	15.7	0.5		3.5
69.	1,063.6	259.1	24.4	0.6		2.6
70.	2,534.5	1,042.4	41.1	0.7		3.2
71.	891.2	239.3	26.8	0.6		1.3
72.	1,967.4	898.0	45.6	0.7		0.9
73.	599.7	135.4	22.6	1.9		3.5
74.	920.7	412.8	44.8	1.5		1.9
75.	1,339.2	344.8	25.7	0.2		0.3
76.	2,263.4	415.9	18.4	0.2		2.8
77.	2,629.2	341.1	13.0	7.0		1.1

* The 1958 harvest shows kill in a limited number of management units in 20 northern counties.
** Does not include Apostle Island data.

UNIT HARVEST PER SQUARE MILE OF DEER RANGE
1957-1964

Deer Mgt. Unit	Gross Area Sq. Miles	Net Deer Range	% of Gross Area in Deer Range	Deer Harvest Per Sq. Mile of Deer Range				
				1960	1961	1962	1963	1964
1.	229.7	186.7	81.3	1.3	1.2	1.0	1.3	1.6
2.	568.5	526.5	92.6	1.6	1.0	1.3	2.5	3.7
3.	577.9*	546.3	94.5	2.0	.9	1.0	1.5	2.6
4.	346.2	338.9	97.9	1.3	.9	.9	1.7	2.0
5.	248.5	230.9	92.9	3.5	1.6	1.8	2.2	4.4
6.	342.8	267.2	77.9	1.7	1.0	1.0	.9	1.2
7.	444.3	376.7	84.8	1.4	1.0	1.2	1.1	1.3
8.	394.7	367.7	93.2	3.3	1.7	1.8	2.2	4.5
9.	466.6	437.9	93.8	3.6	1.7	1.9	2.2	5.5
10.	389.1	319.7	82.2	3.3	1.9	1.9	2.0	3.2
11.	343.0	272.6	79.5	3.9	1.8	2.0	2.2	5.8
12.	538.5	499.9	92.8	2.1	1.3	1.3	1.6	3.3
13.	819.2	752.0	91.8	2.1	1.0	1.1	1.4	2.9
14.	442.0	413.1	93.5	2.4	1.0	1.0	1.9	3.1
15.	507.1	309.0	60.0	2.2	1.3	1.3	1.6	1.6
16.	495.8	251.3	50.7	1.8	1.0	1.0	1.1	1.3
17.	454.6	215.6	47.4	1.4	.9	.9	1.2	1.4
18.	400.1	341.0	85.2	1.6	1.0	.9	1.1	1.2
19.	427.1	379.8	88.9	3.3	1.3	1.2	1.7	4.3
20.	405.3	347.8	85.8	3.0	1.4	1.2	1.5	3.5
21.	458.5	130.6	28.5	2.1	1.1	1.2	1.2	1.7
22.	564.9	210.1	37.2	.8	.6	.6	1.4	1.3
23.	510.3	339.1	66.5	1.4	.7	.6	.8	1.0
24.	334.0	230.3	69.9	2.7	1.2	1.0	1.0	1.4
25.	462.2	389.4	84.2	4.2	2.1	1.7	1.9	4.6
26.	414.7	341.0	82.2	3.2	1.3	1.0	1.3	1.8
27.	537.3	227.8	42.4	1.7	.5	.4	.3	.4
28.	477.3	453.2	95.0	1.0	.5	.6	.7	.7
29.	549.9	451.9	82.2	1.8	.7	.9	1.1	1.1
30.	333.1	284.6	85.4	3.4	1.6	1.6	2.0	3.6
31.	450.3	392.1	87.1	3.4	1.3	1.6	2.1	3.5
32.	603.5	489.8	81.2	3.2	1.6	1.3	1.8	3.3
33.	455.7	126.2	27.7	.5	.3	.3	.4	.6
34.	305.0	259.0	84.9	3.2	.8	1.4	1.4	1.5
35.	461.1	410.9	89.1	3.1	1.1	1.8	2.0	3.2
36.	329.1	269.8	82.0	5.2	2.1	3.0	3.7	5.7
37.	267.7	231.5	86.5	4.8	1.6	2.1	2.8	4.5
38.	435.8	388.5	89.1	1.6	.8	1.0	1.1	1.3
39.	436.0	402.5	92.3	1.6	.6	1.0	1.2	2.3
40.	335.7	323.1	96.2	1.6	.6	.9	1.1	2.4
41.	203.2	184.9	91.0	3.2	1.6	1.4	2.0	2.5
42.	368.4	295.5	80.2	2.6	1.4	1.3	1.4	2.0
43.	376.2	335.8	89.3	1.8	.8	.9	.9	1.3
44.	423.0	363.1	85.8	2.5	.7	1.0	1.3	1.5
45.	593.6	567.5	95.6	2.9	1.0	1.4	1.7	2.2
46.	467.7	246.9	52.8	2.6	1.1	1.1	1.6	2.2
47.	300.1	261.0	87.0	2.7	.9	1.0	1.2	1.3
48.	374.1	281.2	75.2	2.1	.7	.6	.9	1.0
49.	467.7	393.0	84.0	5.9	2.0	2.2	2.5	3.1
50.	352.1	338.8	96.2	1.4	.8	.9	1.3	1.5

* Does not include Apostle Islands data.

- 173 -

Unit Harvest Per Square Mile of Deer Range (continued)
1957-1964

Deer Mgt. Units	Gross Area Sq. Miles	Net Deer Range	% of Gross Area in Deer Range	Deer Harvest per sq. mile of Deer Range				
				1960	1961	1962	1963	1964
51.	750.2	333.2	44.4	2.6	1.3	1.4	1.5	1.6
52.	276.1	187.6	67.9	3.9	1.6	1.8	2.1	2.6
53.	621.7	380.1	61.1	1.7	2.6	3.0	4.6	7.4
54.	649.1	365.5	56.3	1.4	2.1	2.3	4.1	6.0
55.	942.8	736.2	78.1	2.8	4.4	4.2	7.3	10.1
56.	371.1	317.2	85.5	2.0	3.5	3.0	6.2	8.6
57.	1,667.5	532.9	32.0	.5	1.4	1.1	1.4	1.8
58.	644.3	441.6	68.5	1.3	2.8	2.3	4.7	5.4
59.	2,837.5	1,212.0	42.7	1.6	1.2	1.6	3.5	3.8
60.	1,187.9	280.0	23.6	1.8	.8	1.1	2.0	3.6
61.	1,551.5	703.9	45.4	4.5	1.4	5.6	6.1	6.0
62.	1,066.7	674.3	63.2	1.4	1.7	2.0	2.4	4.7
63.	1,586.6	792.9	50.0	1.2	1.3	1.4	1.9	4.0
64.	1,975.2	425.4	21.5	.7	1.0	1.5	4.6	1.4
65.	566.7	231.3	40.8	1.6	2.9	2.6	3.7	7.1
66.	566.8	169.2	29.8	2.2	3.8	4.0	4.7	9.5
67.	717.2	178.5	24.9	2.5	3.6	4.5	5.6	10.8
68.	1,136.9	178.2	15.7	.8	1.5	1.7	3.2	4.5
69.	1,063.6	259.1	24.4	.5	.8	1.1	4.6	2.2
70.	2,534.5	1,042.4	41.1	.5	.8	1.2	1.3	1.7
71.	891.2	239.3	26.8	.6	.7	1.3	1.8	2.6
72.	1,967.4	898.0	45.6	.4	.6	.6	.8	1.0
73.	599.7	135.4	22.6	2.5	.8	2.9	3.5	4.4
74.	920.7	412.8	44.8	1.2	.5	1.1	2.2	2.5
75.	1,339.2	344.8	25.7	.4	.8	1.0	1.4	1.6
76.	2,263.4	415.9	18.4	.5	.6	.9	1.7	2.2
77.	2,629.2	341.1	13.0	.2	.5	.6	.9	1.5

DEER HARVEST BY DAY

1953-1962

Percent of Deer Taken Daily

Year	1st Day	2nd Day	3rd Day	4th Day	5th Day	6th Day	7th Day	8th Day	9th Day	Misc.
1953	46.4	22.3	10.7	8.3	5.4	3.1	4.0	-	-	-
1954	42.3	21.1	8.7	5.7	6.8	8.9**	6.4	-	-	-
1955	39.0	25.4	8.2	7.4	3.8	4.7**	3.5	5.2	2.8	-
1956	37.7	21.8	8.7	5.1	4.7	6.1**	3.9	5.6	4.9	-
1957	39.8	20.3	7.8	3.6	4.8	3.9	4.1	10.1	5.5	-
1958	43.2	18.8	4.9	4.0	4.7	3.7	2.6	6.9	4.9	*
1959	17.3	11.2	3.6	1.5	1.6	1.0	.7	No. zone -	Nov. 14-20	
	24.9	13.9	3.4	2.5	2.2	4.3**	2.8	So. zone -	Nov. 21-27	
1960	38.7	22.8	7.4	4.7	3.9	6.1	4.9	6.2	4.6	.7
1961	42.0	20.2	6.6	4.5	4.4	7.0**	4.5	6.4	4.0	.4
1962	45.2	21.0	5.5	4.3	3.8	6.5**	4.0	5.7	3.7	.3
Total Avg.	37.9	19.9	6.9	4.7	4.2	5.0	3.8	6.5	4.3	.5

* .3 and .4 percent of the total season kill were registered on the opening
two days, Nov. 24, 25, of the extended season north of Highway 8.

** Thanksgiving Day.

PERCENT OF DEER TAKEN 1ST 2 DAYS
1953-1962

Year		Percent	Type of Season
1953		69.0	Forked Horn Buck
1954		63.0	Forked Horn Buck
1955		64.0	Forked Horn Buck
1956		59.0	Spike Buck
1957		60.0	Spike Buck & Party Permit
1958		62.0	Spike Buck & Party Permit
1959		67.0	Spike Buck & Party Permit
1960		61.0	Spike Buck & Party Permit
1961		62.0	Spike Buck
1962		66.2	Spike Buck - Either sex in
	Average	63.3	some areas

APOSTLE ISLAND DEER KILL
1955-1964

Island	Square Miles	1955	56	57	58	59	60	61	62	63	64
Madeline	22	76	82	96	59	208	147	60	107	126	144
Madeline*		1	3	7	5	11	5	3	9	8	27
Basswood	3.1	13	26	16	10	8	12	13	17	11	16
Basswood*		--	--	--	--	--	--	--	--	--	--
Bear	2.8	38	28	31	26	8	20	9	12	6	9
Bear*		1	--	--	--	--	--	--	--	--	--
Cat	2.2	--	--	--	2	1	3	--	5	9	10
Cat*		--	--	--	--	--	--	--	--	--	--
Hermit	1.5	13	10	11	2	5	15	--	3	3	7
Hermit*		--	--	--	--	--	--	--	--	--	--
Ironwood	1.0	1	8	6	4	1	4	7	3	5	--
Ironwood*		--	--	--	--	--	--	--	--	--	--
Manitou	2.5	38	8	12	13	18	37	13	2	--	--
Manitou*		--	--	--	--	--	--	--	--	--	--
Michigan	3.0	--	5	--	1	1	6	--	4	8	13
Michigan*		--	--	--	--	--	--	--	--	--	--
Oak	8.0	10	11	6	5	1	6	17	15	7	1
Oak*		--	--	--	--	--	--	--	--	--	--
Otter	2.6	7	8	8	6	--	6	14	10	12	6
Otter*		--	--	--	--	--	--	--	--	--	--
Rocky	2.2	30	45	6	22	8	5	7	11	15	9
Rocky*		28	9	--	--	--	--	--	--	--	--
S. Twin	0.8	1	10	13	2	1	--	--	--	5	4
S. Twin*		--	--	2	--	--	--	--	--	--	--
Stockton	16.5	74	50	12	2	2	24	10	11	4	10
Stockton*		--	--	--	--	--	--	--	--	--	--
Long	--	--	--	--	--	--	--	--	--	1	--
Long*		--	--	--	--	--	--	--	--	--	--
Outer	2.6	--	--	--	--	--	--	--	--	1	--
Outer*		--	--	--	--	--	--	--	--	--	--
Unknown	--	--	--	1	--	--	--	--	--	6	--
Unknown*	--	--	--	--	--	--	--	--	--	--	--
Total		331	303	227	159	273	290	153	209	227	256

* Bow and arrow deer kill.

DEER HUNTING, AUTOMOBILE AND ILLEGAL SEIZURE KILL
1953-1964

Year	Registered Gun Harvest	Registered Bow and Arrow	Automobile	Illegal Seizures	Total
1953	15,880	355	790	744	17,769
1954	19,877	743	1,093	976	22,689
1955	35,060	1,131	1,472	1,702	39,365
1956	35,562	1,267	2,137	1,592	40,558
1957	68,138	1,753	2,470	918	73,279
1958	95,234	1,885	3,172	706	100,997
1959	105,596	1,320	2,980	1,277	111,123
1960	61,005	1,091	3,046	518	65,660
1961	38,772	1,167	3,756	1,206	44,901
1962	45,835	1,625	4,483	995	52,938
1963	65,020	2,194	5,995	1,096	74,305
1964	93,445	3,164	8,107	1,057	105,773

WEIGHT				SPREAD			
Dressed Weight	County	Year	Hunter	Greatest Spread	County	Year	Hunter
321½#	Bayfield	1938	Richard Kay	30 7/8"	Walworth	1963	Arlene Grube
315	Juneau	1938	Fay Hammersley, Jr.	30 1/2	Vilas	1910	Robert Hunter
303	Burnett	1939	Clint Norine	30 7/16	Marquette	1952	John O'Connell
301	Ashland	1937	John Pohl	28 1/4	St. Croix	1944	W. A. Sais
300	Rusk	1939	Anton Evitch	27 1/2	Rock	1963	Louis Schumaker
300	Sawyer	1941	Edwin Dumke	27 1/4	Iron	1952	Fred Brehm
				26 7/8	Iowa	1952	Glen Potterton
				26 5/8	Dunn	1961	Ed. Stark

DEER WEIGHTS

Season	Hunter and Address	County of Kill	Mgt. Unit	Dressed Scale Weight	Live Weight (Est.)
1910	Robert Hunter, Galesville	Vilas		256#	323
1924	Robert Hogue, Hayward	Sawyer		386	488
1936	Bert Wageneus, Grantsburg	Burnett		285**	360
1937	John Pohl, Ashland	Ashland		301*	380
	Emil Senn, Fountain City	Taylor		294*	371
	Hugo Gould, Barron	Burnett		266	336
	Ellsworth Koth, Tomahawk	Lincoln		257**	324
	Truman Munson, Beloit	Monroe		250*	316
	F. Jensen & G. Knutson, Frederic	Polk		248*	313
	W. H. Kraemer, Wausau	Marathon		247**	311
	H. O. Hogan, Madison	Washburn		245*	309
1938	Richard Kay, Washburn	Bayfield		321½*	406
	Fay Hammersley, Jr., Madison	Juneau		315*	398
	Arvid Erkilla, Brule	Bayfield		290*	366
	Charles Fish, Tomahawk	Lincoln		275*	347
	George Thomas, Birchwood	Sawyer		275*	347
	Warren Eanfil, Evansville	Oneida		275	347
	M. K. Fields, Plainfield	Oneida		247	311
	James Zifke, Sun Prairie	Iron		245	309
	Charles Cators, Minocqua	Oneida		245	309

* Verified weights.
** Excluding hide, head and feet.
*** Excluding hide, head and legs.

Deer Weights - continued

Season	Hunter and Address	County of Kill	Mgt. Unit	Dressed Scale Weight	Live Weight (Est.)
1939	Clint Norine, Frederic	Burnett		303*	383
	Anton Evitch, Birchwood	Rusk		300*	379
	Herman Paphal, Merrill	Marinette		297*	375
	Lyle Harman, Black River Falls	Jackson		275*	347
	Toivo Dahl, Hurley	Iron		271*	342
	O. H. Lemke, Spread Eagle	Florence		270*	341
	Edwin Harninen, Marengo	Ashland		265*	335
	Rudolph Fluegel, Milwaukee	Barron		260*	328
	L. H. Clayton, Madison	Sawyer		252*	318
	A. M. Sanford, Plover	Price		250*	316
	Don Mattson, St. Croix Falls	Polk		250*	316
1941	Arnhold Peter, Mercer	Iron		378	478
	Edwin Dumke, Ojibwa	Sawyer		300*	379
	John Fehr, Jr., Gleason	--		285*	360
	Ed. Klemens, Kenosha	Forest		280*	353
	Fred Kleckner, Glen Flora	Rusk		270*	341
	Oscar Nelmark, Highbridge	Ashland		265*	335
	Ed. Lindloff, Delavan	Sauk		260*	328
	T. F. Sutrick, Abrams	Oconto		260*	328
	O. E. Larson, Eau Claire	Marinette		256*	323
	Alex A. Olah, Westboro	Taylor		255*	321
	Clint Norine, Frederic	Burnett		252*	318
	Ed. Young, Woodruff	Vilas		251*	317
	Geo. Roeben, Osceola	Polk		250*	316
	William Ortman, Wyocena	Taylor		250*	316
	Joe Tober, Jr., Marengo	Bayfield		250*	316
	Berlie Stokes, Eau Claire	Eau Claire		250*	316
	Cloyse Mishler, Kempster	Langlade		250*	316
	Geo. Wellerman, Delavan	Langlade		250*	316
	Gordon Kern, Waukesha	Oneida		250*	316
	Ray Thara, Hayward	Sawyer		250*	316
1950	Car Kill	Buffalo		264	334
1951	Donald Coisman, Neenah	Waupaca		270	341
	Ed. Ferber, Menomonie	Dunn		265*	335
	Rev. Geo. J. Zwadzich, Greendale	Douglas		240***	303
1952	Gary Wagner	Waupaca		276	349
	A. W. Johnson, West Bend	Forest		266*	336
	LaVerne Lipke, Pine River	Waupaca		262*	331
	Fred Richardson, Janesville	Sawyer		241*	304
1953	Car Kill	Lincoln		228	288
1954	Edward Mazel, Rice Lake	Washburn		251*	317
	John Meyer, Bangor	La Crosse		240*	303
	Ralph Truman Smith, Madison	Florence		240*	303

*Verified weights.
**Excluding hide, head and feet.
***Excluding hide, head and legs.

Deer Weights - continued

Season	Hunter and Address	County of Kill	Mgt. Unit	Dressed Scale Weight	Live Weight (Est.)
1958	Gary Andrus, Eau Claire	Jackson	55	255*	321
	Howard B.Witt, Corpus Christi, Tex.	Ashland	78	250*	316
	Earl Alm, Monticello	Lafayette	75	240*	303
1959	John Miner, Menomonie	Dunn	59	253	319
	Timoteo Tigerina, Watertown	Vilas	--	253*	319
	Marlowe Myers, Superior	Douglas	1	252	318
	Alton Kiel, Monroe	Vilas	29	250*	316
	Ronald Myers, Arcadia	Trempealeau	61	245*	309
	Jerrold Wald, Alma	Buffalo	4	240*	303
	Francis W. Murphy, Portage	Bayfield	3	237½*	299
	Barney Kasmarek, Rhinelander	Oneida	38	237*	299
	Stanley Hundt, Bangor	La Crosse	--	235*	297
	Melvin Peters	Shawano	63	230*	290
	Gene Mower, Chippewa Falls	Douglas	8	229	289
	Paul Petit, Winter	Sawyer	--	225½*	284
1960	Does				
	Marvin Schultz, Milton	Rock	27	152*	191
	Kenneth Jackelin, Alma	Buffalo	61	140*	175
	Glenn Kappelin, Two Rivers	Oconto	45	137*	172
	Aldine Bahler, Sheboygan	Oconto	51	128¼*	161
	Bucks				
	Ulrick Redit, Jr., Alma	Buffalo	61	247½*	312
	Cycil Wright, Alma	Buffalo	61	247*	311
1961	Does				
	Charles Huber, Black River Falls	Grant	--	175*	220
	Rodney Nord, Hudson	St. Croix	60	160*	201
	Joseph Wendels, Fond du Lac	Vilas	35	138*	173
	C. Markwig, Oshkosh	Vilas	36	135*	169
	Tom Larson, Racine	Ashland	--	134*	168
	Dr. Don E. Willard, Madison	Grant	73	133	167
	Car Kill (fawn), Madison	Dane	76	81*	101
	Bucks				
	Paul Stasek, Owen	Washburn	--	248*	313
	Arthur J. Mellon, Milwaukee	Marathon	--	235	297
	Kenneth Gusick, Coleman	Oconto	49	228*	288
	J. Peter Haupt, Milwaukee	Oconto	46	226*	285
	Howard Kins, Mondovi	Ashland	3	225*	284
	Edward Zalesky, Haugen	Burnett	10	225	284
	Bernard Louis, Cazenovia	Richland	72	225	284
	Harvey Klabunde, Two Rivers	Iron	28	225*	284
1962	Does				
	Charles A. Weisbecker, St. Anne, Ill. (B. & A.)	Vilas	--	173*	217
	James N. Mayer, Chippewa Falls	Buffalo	61	155*	195
	Bucks				
	Robert Bauer, Campbellsport	Fond du Lac	--	240*	303

*Verified weights.
**Excluding hide, head and feet.
***Excluding hide, head and legs.

Deer Weights - continued

Season	Hunter and Address	County of Kill	Mgt. Unit	Dressed Scale Weight	Live Weight (Est.)
1963	**Does**				
	Jack W. Beisse, Chicago, Ill.	Price	20	151*	190
	Bucks				
	Carl Kleven, Herbster	Bayfield	3	244*	308
	Joseph Sukala, Baraboo	Price	20	230*	290
1964	**Does**				
	Duane Jensen, Viroqua	Crawford	74	167	210
	Calvin Lindley, St. Croix Falls	Burnett	16	160	201
	Confiscated	Iowa	71	142½*	179
	Arlene Fremmerer, Appleton	Shawano	62	141*	177
	Richard Arpke, Sheboygan Falls	Outagamie	63	139	175
	Confiscated	Sauk	71	135*	169
	George Hendricks	Crawford	74	126	158
	Confiscated	Iowa	70	125*	157
	Bucks				
	Lloyd Beesecker, Bagley	Grant	73	258	326
	Joyce Johnson, Maple (B. & A.)	Douglas	2	240	303
	W. E. Thurow, Tomah	--	--	220	277

* Verified weights.
** Excluding hide, head and feet.
*** Excluding hide, head and legs.

NOTE: The above list of record deer weights is based upon information
derived from available hunters' reports and questionnaires. Deer
weighing less than 225 pounds (dressed weight) are not included in this
table. Undoubtedly other large deer have been taken and not reported here
because of lack of authentic data. At the present time, 200-pound bucks
are not often bagged. Legal bucks weighing less than 100 pounds are common
today; however, real heavy deer are taken in the Mississippi River counties
and other agricultural areas where the deer population is light and food
conditions generally are good. Bucks (25) averaging 160 pounds, and does
(118) averaging 116 pounds, were taken in the open counties bordering the
Mississippi during the 1948 season.

The relationship of the live weight of deer to the dressed weight is
always of interest to hunters and game technicians. In establishing the
estimated live weight of a deer, 25% of the total dressed weight should
be added.

The following formula also may be used in calculating the live weight
from the dressed weight; this formula was prepared by Walter E. Scott and
Lowell Woodbury, both of the Wisconsin Conservation Department, from weights
taken in the field during the 1939 deer season: "The live weight equals
1.20 times the dressed weight, plus 12.5 pounds".

Formula used on preceding table: dressed weight minus 1.5 pounds
times 1.27.

RECORD DEER ANTLERS

Year	Hunter	County	Greatest Spread	Length of Main Beam Left	Length of Main Beam Right	Circumference of Main Beam	Diameter	No. of Points
1898	Phillip Schlegal** Owner	Sawyer	22"*	25"	25"	L. 3 3/8" R. 5"	1.6	18
1910	Robert Hunter Galesville	Vilas	30½	30	29½	L. 5½ R. 5½	1.8	12
1915	Joe Froelich**	Vilas	--	25 1/8	25 5/8	--	--	10
1928	Phillip Schlegal** Owner	--	22¼	27 3/8	27 3/4	L. 4 3/8 R. 4 5/8	1.5	14
1930	John Grumann**	Forest	--	24	23½	--	--	11
1932	Alan Bourg** Winter	Sawyer	25 3/4*	--	24½	R. 5¼	1.7	14
	W. H. Rudolph	Sawyer	22½	27 3/4	28¼	L. 5 R. 4 3/4	1.6	12
1934	Earl Holt**	Bayfield	25½*	23½	25¼	L. 6¼ R. 6	2.0	29
	Ernest Zeroth** Minong	Washburn	22*	27	27	L. 6½ R. 6	2.1	22
1937	Homer Pearson** Almena	Burnett	25½*	27 5/8	27	L. 6 1/8 R. 6	1.9	36
1938	Merlin Davis Elkhorn	Sawyer	25½	24¼	26½	5	1.6	12
	Fay Hammersley, Jr. Madison	Juneau	24	29	27½	5½	1.8	19

Record Deer Antlers - continued

Year	Hunter	County	Greatest Spread	Length of Main Beam		Circumference of Main Beam	Diameter	No. of Points
				Left	Right			
1938	Arnold Erkila Brule	Bayfield	24"	25"	25"	5¼"	1.7	8
	M. K. Field Plainfield	Oneida	22 3/4	28	28	7	2.2	11
	Luke A. Banke Stevens Point	Iron	22½	24 7/8	26 3/4	4 3/4	1.5	8
	Ashley Rhodes Whitewater	Sawyer	22¼	--	--	L. 5 / R. 5¼	1.7	16
1939	Frank Stedl Menchalville	Oneida	26½	--	--	L. 5 **3/8** / R. 5 3/4	1.83	19
1940	Clarence Huebschen West Allis	Burnett	22½	23½	23½	L. 5¼ / R. 5 1/8	1.7	10
1944	W. A. Sais New Richmond	St. Croix	28¼	--	--	6½	2.1	--
	Jerry Kruz Port Edwards	Wood	26¼	24	24	L. 4 1/8 / R. 5	1.6	9
1945	Erskine Auel Beetown	Grant	24½	--	--	--	--	10
1947	George Bierstaker Pembine	Marinette	24½	--	--	--	--	24
1952	John O'Connell Appleton	Marquette	30 7/16*	--	--	--	--	12
	Fred Brehm Milwaukee	Iron	27¼*	--	--	--	--	13

Record Deer Antlers - continued

Year	Hunter	County	Greatest Spread	Length of Main Beam Left	Length of Main Beam Right	Circumference of Main Beam	Diameter	No. of Points
1952	Glen Potterton, Mineral Point	Iowa	26 7/8"	23 3/4"	22½"	5¼"	1.7	8
	Arthur Pare, Columbus	Florence	25*	--	--	--	--	10
	Gary Wagner, Fond du Lac	Waupaca	24	--	--	--	--	21
1954	Gene Ritzer, Eagle River	Oneida	25½*	23½	24	5 3/4	1.8	4
1958	Don Erickson, Racine	Ashland	25¼	--	--	--	--	--
	Gary Andrus, Eau Claire	Jackson	23½	--	--	--	--	12
1959	Eugene Morvitz, Eastman	Crawford	24 7/8	28 3/4	27 3/4	5	1.6	18
	Thomas Glass, Milton Junction	Rock	24½*	23	23¼	6¼	2.0	20
	Norman Retzlaff, Catawba	Price	24¼*	20	19 7/8	5½	1.8	18
	Marlowe Myers, Superior	Douglas	24*	22½	21½	5	1.6	12
	John Fliss, Jr., Hatley	Marathon	22 3/4*	23¼	19 3/4	5¼	1.7	12
	Walter Vetterkind, New Auburn	Taylor	23 3/4*	20¼	22 3/4	4 3/8	1.4	9

Record Deer Antlers - continued

Year	Hunter	County	Greatest Spread	Length of Main Beam		Circumference of Main Beam	Diameter	No. of Points
				Left	Right			
1959	William Taylor Hawkins	Rusk	22 3/4"*	23½"	--	--	--	10
	George Mudgett Gilman	Taylor	22½*	22¼	22¼"	5½"	1.75	12
	Francis W. Murphy	Bayfield	22 3/8*	22½	23¼	6½	2.1	20
	Robert W. Lohrey Wausau	Vilas	22¼	25 3/8	25½	5 5/8	1.8	17
	Robert Johnson Green Bay	Forest	22 1/8*	21½	21 1/8	5 7/8	1.87	10
	Cyril Van Camp Green Bay	Florence	22	--	--	3	1.0	10
	Wilford Trokjar Hawkins	Rusk	22*	23 3/4	--	--	--	8
	John Holte	Ashland	22*	24	25	5¼	1.7	10
1960	John Keel, Jr. Burnett	Dodge	25¼	24 3/4	22 1/8	4 3/4	1.5	9
	William Hartz Elkhorn	Bayfield	25 1/8	20¼	20	5	1.6	9
	Ralph Duellman Fountain City	Buffalo	25*	23½	25	5½	1.75	11
	Ralph Klimek Independence	Trempealeau	24*	27	28¼	--	--	12

Record Deer Antlers - continued

Year	Hunter	County	Greatest Spread	Length of Main Beam Left	Length of Main Beam Right	Circumference of Main Beam	Diameter	No. of Points
1960	Rawley Metz, Jr. Shullsburg	Lafayette	24"*	24½"	24¼"	4 3/4"	1.5	11
	Otto Kolbe Marathon	Oneida	23½*	22	21 3/4	5 3/4	1.83	8
	George Krug Curtiss	Price	23 3/8*	--	--	4 3/4	1.5	10
	Walter Zimmerman New Glarus	Green	23 3/8*	22½	23 3/4	5 3/8	1.7	13
	Richard Laier Hayward	Washburn	23	--	--	--	--	13
	Ulrik Redit Alma	Buffalo	22½*	26½	25	6½	2.1	8
	W. P. Kuklinski Milwaukee	Oneida	22½	25	24½	5 3/4	1.83	14
	H. W. Lauritzen Madison	Sawyer	22 3/8	--	--		--	10
	Frank Keifenheim St. Cloud	Fond du Lac	22¼	25½	25½	5	1.6	12
1961	Ed. Stark Menomonie	Dunn	26 5/8*	25 1/8	26¼	5	1.6	10
	Paul Stazek Owen	Washburn	26¼	27 3/4	27	5½	1.75	12
	Car Kill (James Bell) Dodge	Dodge	25*	21½	24	5½	1.75	9

Record Deer Antlers - continued

Year	Hunter	County	Greatest Spread	Length of Main Beam Left	Length of Main Beam Right	Circumference of Main Beam	Diameter	No. of Points
1961	Stephen Horn Fond du Lac	Florence	24½"	24½"	24 5/8"	5 5/8"	1.8	11
	Ronald Pyka Milwaukee	Buffalo	24¼*	21¼	22	5	1.6	14
	John Schutte Ashland	Ashland	24 1/8*	25	25¼	5 3/4	1.83	9
	Arthur Mellon Milwaukee	Marathon	24	23	23	6	1.9	11
	Odin Semingson Eleva	Buffalo	24	25½	25	6	1.9	12
	Martin Wepner Marion	Waupaca	23½	24¼	24	6	1.9	11
	Gene Irish Ladysmith	Rusk	23¼*	--	--	5 3/4	1.83	8
	Kenneth Cusick Coleman	Oconto	22 7/8	23	22½	5 3/8	1.7	10
	Howard Kins Naples	Ashland	22	24	24	6	1.9	9
	Elmer Sann Wausau	Forest	22*	21	22½	4½	1.4	8
	Anthony Buss Eland	Marathon	22*	20	20½	4½	1.4	10

Record Deer Antlers - continued

Year	Hunter	County	Greatest Spread	Length of Main Beam		Circumference of Main Beam	Diameter	No. of Points
				Left	Right			
1962	Frank Kulus Superior	Douglas	27½"*	24½"	24 3/4"	5 3/4"	1.8	10
	Jack Baer Galesville	Trempealeau	23 7/8*	24½	24½	4 3/4	1.5	11
	George Schauer Summit Lake	Langlade	23 7/8*	19½	19 5/8	5½	1.7	8
	Alphonse Bauer Eau Claire	Eau Claire	23½*	21½	22½	6½	2.1	13
	Ray Wozney Cudahy	Trempealeau	23¼*	21¼	22 3/8	5	1.6	15
	Keith McNelly Spencer	Taylor	22¼*	23	22	5	1.6	10
1963	Arlene Grube Whitewater	Walworth	30 7/8*	23 5/8	24 1/8	5	1.6	9
	Louis Schumaker Janesville	Rock	27½*	22½	24 5/8	6 3/4	2.1	10
	Ronald Gleiter Alma	Buffalo	24¼*	23	25	5 7/8	1.8	9
	Melvin Plank Mondovi	Buffalo	23 3/4*	25¼	23½	5 3/4	1.8	21
	Joseph Sokala Baraboo	Price	22½*	--	--	--	--	10

Record Deer Antlers - continued

Year	Hunter	County	Greatest Spread	Length of Main Beam		Circumference of Main Beam	Diameter	No. of Points
				Left	Right			
1964	Joseph Maffesante Montreal	Iron	22 3/4"	20 3/4"	23"	5"	1.6	6
	Lester Johnson Downsville	Bayfield	22¼*	22 5/8	22¼	5 5/16	1.7	10
	James Johnson Chaseburg	Vernon	22¼**	20¼	20¼	4	1.3	8
	Robert Secor Hurley	Iron	22 1/8*	25½	24¼	5 3/8	1.7	9
	Joyce Johnson Maple (B. & A.)	Douglas	22	22½	22 3/4	5½	1.75	13

* Verified reports.

** Listed by Boone and Crokett Club.

PART TWO

BOW AND ARROW DEER HUNTING

Year	Season		Number of Open Counties	Actual Kill	Number of Bowmen*	Chronology
	Length	Type				
1934	Nov. 24-Nov. 28 5 days	One buck not less than one year old.	2 Columbia Sauk	1	40	Hunting with bow and arrow permitted for first time in (1931). Special deer tag required (1934-1940).
1935	No open season.					
1936	Oct. 25-Oct. 31 7 days	Forked-horn buck only.	2 Columbia Sauk	1	111	
1937	Oct. 9-Oct. 28 20 days	Forked-horn buck only.	4	None	134	
1938	Oct. 8-Nov. 6 30 days	Forked-horn buck only.	8	1	330	Turkey season in Adams and Sauk Counties. 380 bowmen. Reported kill - 57.
1939	Oct. 14-Nov. 12 30 days	Forked-horn buck only.	14	6	600	Bow hunting for migratory waterfowl permitted.
1940	Oct. 1-Oct. 31 31 days	Forked-horn buck only.	38	5	1,200	
1941	Oct. 4-Nov. 2 30 days	One buck one year of age or older.	48	18	2,232	Wisconsin Bow Hunters Association organized. Nonresident license required; fee: $5.00
1942	Oct. 10-Nov. 10 32 days	Forked-horn buck only.	51	15	1,520	Minimum requirement for hunting bow was one with pull of 40 lbs. First bow and arrow bear season in 51 counties.

* Bow hunters were required to register 1934 through 1944.

Bow and Arrow Deer Hunting Seasons (continued)
1934-1964

Year	Season Length	Season Type	Number of Open Counties	Actual Kill	Number of Bowmen	Chronology
1943	Oct. 2-Nov. 12 42 days	Any deer	51	76	2,495	
1944	Oct. 7-Nov. 19 44 days	Any deer	49	78	2,043	
1945	Sept. 29-Nov. 12 45 days	Any deer	50	160	3,500* (est.)	Law required that 50% of clothing be red. Nonresident license sales: 388. First opening of Necedah Refuge.
1946	Sept. 28-Nov. 11 45 days	Deer of either sex one year of age or older.	49	256	6,000 (est.)	Use of crossbows for hunting deer or bear prohibited. Nonresident license sales: 763.
1947	Sept. 27-Nov. 11 46 days	Any deer	50	368	10,000 (est.)	A strung bow in car prohibited (1947-1951). Nonresident license sales: 1,112.
1948	Sept. 25-Nov. 7 44 days	Any deer	49	279	10,000 (est.)	Because of critical fire situation, emergency action taken whereby large number of northern counties were closed, Oct. 30 to Nov. 4 (noon). First bow and arrow pheasant season in Milwaukee County. Nonresident license sales: 1,284.

* Since 1945 the number of resident bowmen is unknown since the purchaser of a deer tag may hunt with a rifle, shotgun or bow and arrow.

- 194 -

Bow and Arrow Deer Hunting Seasons (continued)
1934-1964

Year	Season Length	Season Type	Number of Open Counties	Actual Kill	Number of Bowmen	Chronology
1949	Sept. 24-Nov. 7 45 days	Any deer	Entire State	551	12,000 (est.)	Nonresident license sales: 1,621.
1950	Sept. 23-Nov. 6 45 days	Any deer	Entire State	383	12,000-15,000 (est.)	Nonresident license sales: 2,401. First bow and arrow Hungarian partridge season in Milwaukee County.
1951	Sept. 22 at 1.00 p.m. to Nov. 11 50½ days	Any deer	Entire State	188	10,000-15,000 (est.)	Wearing of red or orange clothing no longer required. Resident big game license required. Cost including tag: $2.50 Nonresident license fee increased from $5.00 to $10.00 Nonresident license sales: 1,337.
1952	Sept. 27-Nov. 16 51 days	Any deer	Entire State	126	8,000-10,000 (est.)	Minimum bow pull reduced from 40 to 30 pounds. Seven out of ten successful hunters belonged to an archery club. 12-point buck weighting 262 lbs. dressed, bagged in Waupaca County. Nonresident license sales: 1,016. A strung bow or a bow not enclosed within a carrying case prohibited (1952-).

Bow and Arrow Deer Hunting Seasons (continued)
1934-1964

Year	Season		Number of Open Counties	Actual Kill	Number of Bowmen	Chronology
	Length	Type				
1953	Sept. 26-Nov. 15 51 days Dec. 5-Dec. 18 14 days	Any deer Any deer	Entire State Horicon Marsh, Necedah Refuge, Kewaunee and Manitowoc Counties.	182 $\frac{173}{355}$	15,000 (est.)	First December bow season. First opening of federal portion of Horicon Marsh. Nine deer per sq. mile. No bow hunting accidents occurred (1934-1953). Nonresident license sales: 1,169. Kill in Horicon Marsh Wildlife area: 9 deer per sq. mile in the federal or northern portion.

Year	Season		Number of Open Counties	Actual Kill	Number of Bowmen	Chronology
	Length	Type				
1954	Sept. 25-Nov. 14 51 days Dec. 4-Dec. 19 16 days	Any deer Any deer	Entire State Calumet, Crawford, Dane, Dodge, Fond du Lac, Juneau, Kenosha, La Crosse, Manitowoc, Richland, Sheboygan, Vernon, and Wood Counties.	436 307 743	15,000+	Federal portion of Horicon Marsh closed to bow hunting. Apostle Islands open during early season. 92 deer taken on six of 12 islands. Necedah Refuge had kill of 334, of which 292 were taken during December season. First bow hunting accidents occurred; three hunters injured. Nonresident lisence sales: 1,370. Deer were arrow-killed in 61 counties (1934-).

Bow and Arrow Deer Hunting Seasons (continued)
1934-1964

Year	Season		Number of Open Counties	Actual Kill	Number of Bowmen	Chronology
	Length	Type				
1955	Sept. 24-Nov. 13 51 days	Any deer	All counties	461		Kill in Apostle Islands - 30. Average bow pull of 919 hunters - 52 lbs.
	Dec. 10-Jan. 1 23 days	Any deer south of Highway 64				Federal portion of Horicon Marsh National Wildlife Refuge closed Dec. 20. Kill - 221.
	Dec. 10-Jan. 1 23 days	Any deer	Horicon National Wildlife Refuge	670 1,131		Four out of five violations occurred on this area.
1956	Sept. 22-Nov. 11 51 days	Any deer	All counties	747	25,000 (est.)	Horicon National Wildlife Refuge opened. 750 permits available. Kill - 32.
	Dec. 15-Jan. 13 30 days	Any deer	South of Highway 64	520 1,267		Green and Rock Counties registered first bow and arrow kills, closed to gun hunting since 1906.
1957	Sept. 21-Nov. 12 53 days	Any deer	All counties	830	25,000 (est.)	Horicon National Wildlife Refuge managed hunt by permit, Dec. 14 and 15. Kill - 46.
	Dec. 14-Jan. 12 30 days	Any deer	South of Highway 64	923 1,753		Largest state Kill: Necedah National Wildlife Refuge - 900. Resident big game license - $4.00 (1957-1960).
1958	Sept. 20-Nov. 11 53 days	Any deer	All counties	1,164	25,000 (est.)	Women registered 150 deer. Horicon National Wildlife Refuge Managed deer hunt Dec. 20 and 21. 1,329 permits issued. Kill - 26.
	Dec. 13-Jan. 11 30 days	Any deer	South of Highway 64	721 1,885 in 65 counties		

Bow and Arrow Deer Hunting Seasons (continued)
1934-1964

Year	Season		Number of Open Counties	Actual Kill	Number of Bowmen	Chronology
	Length	Type				
1959	Sept. 19-Nov. 10 53 days	Any deer	All counties	936		Seven out of ten deer were taken on the opening 2 days of the season. Federal portion of Horicon National Wildlife Refuge closed to bow hunting.
	Dec. 5-Dec. 31 27 days	Any deer	All counties	384 1,320 in 66 counties		
1960	Sept. 17-Nov. 15 60 days	Any deer	All counties	642	25,000 (est.)	Horicon National Wildlife Refuge (federal portion) managed deer hunt by permit, Nov. 28 and 29. Number of hunters - 527. Kill - 21. Bow hunting by permit at Barksdale fenced enclosure (1,200 acres). Kill - 120.
	Dec. 3-Dec. 31 29 days	Any deer	All counties	449 1,091 in 58 counties		
1961	Sept. 23-Nov. 14 53 days	Any deer	All counties	694		Resident big game license: $5.00. (1961-).
	Dec. 2-Dec. 31 30 days	Any deer	All counties	473 1,167 in 62 counties		
1962	Sept. 22-Nov. 13 53 days	Any deer	All counties	977		One-third of the total state kill was registered in Juneau and Vilas Counties. Bow hunting was permitted at Barkdale enclosure in December. Kill - 32. Bow hunting on an unrestricted basis on the Horicon National Wildlife Refuge in December.
	Dec. 1-Dec. 31 31 days	Any deer	All counties	648 1,625 in 68 counties		

Bow and Arrow Deer Hunting Seasons (continued)
1934-1964

Year	Season		Number of Open Counties	Actual Kill	Number of Bowmen	Chronology
	Length	Type				
1963	Sept. 21-Nov. 23 60 days	Any deer	All counties	1,528		Largest bow and arrow bear kill-121. Bow hunting on an unrestricted basis at Horican National Wildlife Refuge in December. First Sandhill Wildlife Demonstration Area managed hunt. Number of permits-231. Kill - 1. Seven out of ten deer taken during the early season. One out of five deer taken by Wisconsin Bow Hunters Association membership: 4,011.
	Dec. 7-Dec. 31 25 days	Any deer	All counties	666 2,194 in 68 counties		
1964	Sept. 26-Nov. 17 53 days	Any deer	All counties	2,491	46,000 (est.)	Thirtieth annual bow and arrow deer season. 20,207 arrow-shot deer have been registered. (1934-1964). Deer have been killed in all counties except Milwaukee.
	Dec. 5-Dec. 31 27 days	Any deer	All counties	673 3,164 in 68 counties		

BOW AND ARROW DEER HUNTING FACTS
1934-1954

Year	Bucks	Does	Total	Kill by Residents	Kill by Nonresidents	Ave. Distance of Shot	
						Number	Yards
1934	1	Closed	1	-	1		
1935	Closed	Closed	-	-	-		
1936	1	-	1	1	-		
1937	-	Closed	-	-	-		
1938	1	.	1	1	-		
1939	6	Closed	6	6	-	6	21.2
1940	5	Closed	5	5	-	4	23.2
1941	18	Closed	18	10	8	8	16.7
1942	15	Closed	15	13	2	14	27.6
1943	32	44	76	55	21	-	-
1944			78				
1945	70	90	160	104	56	115	28.2
1946	118	138	256	202	54	225	27.8
1947	196	172	368	289	79	317	27.8
1948	120	159	279	215	64	257	26.7
1949	237	314	551	426	125	498	27.7
1950	157	226	383	259	124	213	28.8
1951	78	110	188	129	59	170	29.0
1952	65	61	126	105	21	113	29.3
1953	177	178	355	296	59	291	26.3
1954	335	408	743	643	100	633	25.7
TOTALS	1,632	1,900	3,610	2,759 (78.1%)	773 (21.9%)	2,864	27.3

Year	Ave. Distance Recovered			Average Bow Pull		Running Shots	Standing Shots
	Number	Yards		Number	Pounds		
1939	6	243.0		6	62.0	3	3
1940	5	141.0		5	55.8	2	3
1941	6	318.0		7	55.9	7	1
1942	14	437.0		14	59.1	7	7
1943	-	-		-	-	-	-
1944	-	-		-	-	-	-
1945	114	103.3		114	56.5	42	70
1946	-	-		227	55.8	107	117
1947	-	-		318	56.6	128	187
1948	255	129.8		-	-	95	184
1949	472	165.9		-	-	164	330
1950	193	150.5		-	-	96	287
1951	156	183.7		-	-	39	149
1952	107	198.1		-	-	35	91
1953	289	261.7		271	54.9	113	176
1954	610	279.9		601	53.0	320	312
TOTALS	2,227	206.0		1,563	54.8	1,158 (37.7%)	1,917 (62.3%)

REGISTERED BOW AND ARROW DEER KILL
BY AGE AND SEX
1955-1964

Year	Total Harvest	Antlered		Antlerless			
		Forked Buck	Spike Buck	Adult Doe	Fawn Doe	Fawn Buck	Unknown
1955	461	117	20	166	65	89	4
	670*	146	24	273	92	112	23
	1,131	263	44	439	157	201	27
1956	747	115	62	254	132	155	29
	520*	86	38	175	94	113	14
	1,267	201	100	429	226	268	43
1957	830	162	73	292	122	172	9
	923*	167	40	292	212	210	2
	1,753	329	113	584	334	382	11
1958	1,164	196	108	366	202	288	4
	721*	123	46	255	139	146	12
	1,885	319	154	621	341	434	16
1959	936	124	85	317	190	218	2
	384*	38	38	129	100	77	2
	1,320	162	123	446	290	295	4
1960	642	100	60	245	111	122	4
	449*	50	26	164	92	115	2
	1,091	150	86	409	203	237	6
1961	694	127	45	242	111	166	3
	473*	53	26	191	100	100	3
	1,167	180	71	433	211	266	6
1962	977	147	82	368	163	209	8
	648*	79	34	238	122	164	11
	1,625	226	116	606	285	373	19
1963	1,528	269	120	602	258	278	1
	666*	81	33	256	139	153	4
	2,194	350	153	858	397	431	5
1964	2,491	437	169	865	479	527	14
	673*	86	19	261	145	158	4
	3,164	523	188	1,126	624	685	18

*Deer taken during late season in December.

LEADING BOW AND ARROW DEER HARVEST COUNTIES
1955-1959

County	Total Harvest	Percent of State Harvest	1955	1956	1957	1958	1959
Juneau*	2,885	39.2	367	472	900	814	332
Vilas	866	11.8	134	186	199	166	181
Dodge	467	6.3	315	39	61	45	7
Oneida	337	4.6	25	63	70	94	85
Forest	176	2.4	15	45	33	37	46
Iron	170	2.3	22	34	23	45	46
Marinette	160	2.2	10	24	37	55	34
Waupaca	152	2.1	13	25	26	47	41
Burnett	150	2.0	16	32	35	34	33
Buffalo	136	1.8	5	16	30	36	49
Total	5,499		922	936	1,414	1,373	854
State Harvest	7,356		1,131	1,267	1,753	1,885	1,320
Percent of State Harvest	74.7		81.5	73.9	80.7	72.8	64.7

1960-1964

County	Total Harvest	Percent of State Harvest	1960	1961	1962	1963	1964
Juneau*	1,563	16.9	221	246	315	346	435
Vilas	1,249	13.5	137	120	210	318	464
Oneida	459	5.0	35	39	81	122	182
Waupaca	445	4.8	44	62	51	111	177
Bayfield	336	3.6	129	12	53	36	106
Shawano	313	3.4	28	45	46	72	122
Jackson	300	3.2	22	44	48	75	111
Burnett	253	2.7	20	34	43	62	94
Sawyer	241	2.6	12	27	31	55	116
Outagamie	240	2.6	14	34	45	50	97
Total	5,399		662	663	923	1,247	1,904
State Harvest	9,241		1,091	1,167	1,625	2,194	3,164
Percent of State Harvest	58.4		60.6	56.8	56.8	56.8	60.2

* The Necedah National Wildlife Refuge harvest is recorded as the Juneau
  County kill, since this area and adjacent lands account for almost the
  entire harvest.

NECEDAH NATIONAL WILDLIFE REFUGE
BOW AND ARROW DEER HARVEST
40,000 Acres in Juneau County

Year	Total	Antlered		Antlerless			Unknown	No. of Bowmen
		Forked Buck	Spike Buck	Adult Doe	Fawn Doe	Fawn Buck		(Estimated)
1945	61	--	--	--	--	--	--	2,000
1946	129	--	--	--	--	--	--	3,900
1947	111	35	10	32	10	24	--	3,000
1948	18	2	6	4	1	4	1	--
1949	18	3	2	6	3	4	--	400
1950	19	3	1	4	5	5	1	--
1951	10	2	--	8	--	--	--	--
1952	38	7	1	15	5	10	--	500-1,000
1953·	17	4	--	6	3	3	1	--
	48*	13	--	17	8	10	--	2,000
	65	17	--	23	11	13	1	
1954	42	14	3	11	9	5	--	--
	292*	54	7	130	44	47	10	3,000+
	334	68	10	141	53	52	10	
1955	61	15	2	21	6	17	--	4,000
	306*	47	2	143	53	59	2	5,000
	367	62	4	164	59	76	2	
1956	93	27	6	25	20	15	--	4,000-5,000
	379*	59	32	140	66	76	6	6,000-7,000
	472	86	38	165	86	91	6	
1957	130	33	18	47	15	17	--	3,500-4,000
	770*	131	33	252	177	176	1	6,500+
	900	164	51	299	192	193	1	
1958	248	65	26	81	36	40	--	7,000
	566*	95	36	210	105	109	11	3,500-4,000
	814	160	62	291	141	149	11	
1959	67	9	15	22	10	11	--	5,000
	265*	28	35	92	62	46	2	3,000-3,500
	332	37	50	114	72	57	2	
1960	14	2	2	7	2	1	--	2,000
	207*	16	11	95	41	44	--	4,000
	221	18	13	102	43	45	--	
1961	27	7	3	8	4	5	--	1,200
	219*	22	11	91	41	53	1	5,000
	246	29	14	99	45	58	1	
1962	33	5	2	8	9	9	--	3,000
	282*	34	17	112	50	64	5	4,000-5,000
	315	39	19	120	59	73	5	

Necedah National Wildlife Refuge - continued

| Year | Total | Antlered | | Antlerless | | | Unknown | No. of Bowmen (Estimated) |
		Forked Buck	Spike Buck	Adult Doe	Fawn Doe	Fawn Buck		
1963	44	6	3	13	13	9	--	2,500
	302*	33	15	132	53	65	4	6,000
	346	39	18	145	66	74	4	
1964	83	11	5	23	20	21	3	2,000
	352*	46	6	138	79	80	3	5,000
	435	57	11	161	99	101	6	

* Deer killed during the late December season when the entire refuge was open.
  At least 95% of the deer were taken on the opening two days.

UNRECOVERED WOUNDED DEER AND DEAD DEER*

Year	Arrow-Wounded Deer	Deer Found Dead Later	Annual Legal Kill	Season— Number of Days
1945	14	5	160	45
1946	35	22	256	45
1947	35	10	368	46
1948	30	5	279	44
1949	35	9	551	45
1950	24	9	383	45
1951	21	7	188	50½
1952	20	9	126	51
1953	24	13	355	65
1954	76	25	743	67
1955	97	43	1,131	74
1956	60	20	1,267	81
1957	48	21	1,753	83
1958	70	32	1,885	83
1959	130	53	1,320	80
1960	103	46	1,091	89
1961	69	24	1,167	83
1962	139	40	1,625	84
1963	94	53	2,194	85
1964	226	87	3,164	80

*   The number of unrecovered wounded deer and dead deer found later is based
    on reports of conservation wardens who investigate bow hunting in all
    open counties.

BOW AND ARROW HUNTING VIOLATIONS
1955-1964

Year	Total Number of Violations	MAJOR VIOLATIONS			
		Transporting Strung Bow in Automobile	Shining Wild Animals	Hunting After Hours	Hunting in closed Areas
1955	100	37	6	5	14
1956	93	22	28	2	13
1957	96	33	11	7	1
1958	91	33	19	17	3
1959	116	54	21	16	2
1960	83	17	34	12	1
1961	70	11	27	8	8
1962	93	28	16	14	11
1963	154	40	77	14	8
1964	227	75	69	33	13
Total	1,123	350	308	128	74

BOW AND ARROW DEER HUNTING ACCIDENTS
1934-1964

Year	County	Fatality	Injury	Cause of Accident
1934-53	None			
1954	Juneau	None	1	Deflected arrow.
	Vilas	None	1	Self-inflicted. Stumbled and fell.
	Eau Claire	None	1	" " " "
	Total		3	
1955	Ashland	None	1	Self-inflicted.
1956	Oconto	None	1	Victim out of sight of shooter.
1957	Jackson	None	1	Unknown.
	Jackson	None	1	Pierced hand by arrow held by partner.
	Juneau	None	1	Self-inflicted.
	Juneau	None	1	Victim covered by shooter swinging on game.
	Juneau	None	1	Victim out of sight of shooter.
	Juneau	None	1	" " " " " "
	Total		6	
1958	Juneau	None	1	Victim mistaken for game.
	Oneida	None	1	Self-inflicted. Stumbled and fell.
	Dodge	None	1	Self-inflicted. Pierced by arrow while swinging on game.
	Total		3	
1959	Vilas	None	1	Self-inflicted.
	Juneau	None	1	"
	Total		2	
1960	Juneau	None	1	Self-inflicted.
	Marathon	None	1	"
	Shawano	None	1	"
	Total		3	
1962	Waupaca	None	1	Victim covered by shooter swinging on game.
	Waupaca	None	1	Deflected arrow.
	Total		2	
1963	Juneau	None	1	Mistaken for deer.
1964		None	1	Self-inflicted.
			1	"
	Total		2	

NONRESIDENT BOW HUNTERS

Year	License Sales	Number of Deer Taken	Percent of Licensees Successful	Percent of Total Harvest Taken
1955	2,022	142	7.0	12.6
1956	3,017	231	7.7	18.2
1957	3,343	260	7.8	14.8
1958	4,225	326	7.7	17.2
1959	4,510	283	6.3	21.4
1960	3,939	216	5.5	20.0
1961	3,796	206	5.4	17.7
1962	4,289	266	6.2	16.3
1963	4,892	426	8.8	19.4
1964	6,356	664	10.4	21.0

Counties having no bow and arrow kill

LITERATURE RELATING TO WISCONSIN DEER

Although in recent years there has been an increasing amount of literature dealing with the white-tailed deer, the following bibliography is
limited to deer in Wisconsin. The appended references are presented in
alphabetical order with the aim of presenting a complete list of all known
source material pertinent to Wisconsin deer management and a large number
of publications having historical significance.

LITERATURE RELATING TO WISCONSIN DEER

Anonymous. 1900. Information Concerning Game; Seasons, Shipment and Sale. Circ. 31, U. S. Dept. Agric., Washingtor.

.... 1901a. The Evolution of Wisconsin. The Wisconsin Blue Book. Madison, pp. 115-116.

.... 1901b. Indians in Wisconsin. The Wisconsin Blue Book. Madison, p. 500.

.... 1901c. Population of Wisconsin. The Wisconsin Blue Book. Madison, pp. 490-492.

.... 1911. Census Statistics Relatin' to Population and Agriculture. The Wisconsin Blue Book. Madi on, pp. 48-121.

.... 1917. Fish, Game and State Parl :. The Wisconsin Blue Book. Madison, pp. 445-446.

.... 1919a. The One Buck Law. Wis. Conservationist 1(1):13.

.... 1919b. That Buck Law. Wis. Conservationist 1(4):10.

.... 1920a. The Buck Law Has Proven Successful. Wis. Conservationist 2(6):5.

.... 1920b. Deer Conservation. Wis. Conservationist 2(2):15.

.... 1920c. One Buck Law in Favor. Wis. Conservationist 2(2):4.

.... 1920d. One Buck Law Elsewhe e. Wis. Conservationist 2(4):5.

.... 1920e. One Buck Law Now in Force. Wis. Conservationist 2(4):12.

.... 1920f. The Wisconsin Game Protective Association Resolutions. Wis. Conservationist 2(6):9.

.... 1920g. Test of One Buck Law. Wis. Conservationist 2(5):5.

.... 1920h. Twenty-five Thousand Deer Killed. Wis. Conservationist 2(1):28.

.... 1921a. Editor Thompson Approves the Buck Law. Wis. Conservationist 3(1):13.

.... 1921b. Fewer Deer Killed. Wis. Conservationist 3(1):20.

.... 1921c. Wisconsin Census Statistics. The Wisconsin Blue Book. Madison, pp. 437-502.

.... 1929. More Deer in State. Monthly Survey. Wis. Cons. Dept., July, p. 7.

.... 1932. 1932 Deer Season. Monthly Survey. Wis. Cons. Dept., Nov., p. 16.

.... 1932-1954. Game Harvest Reports Showing Annual Game Yields. Wis.
Cons. Dept. 11 pp. Mimeo.

.... 1934. Wisconsin 1934 Regional Plan Report. Wisconsin State
Plan. Board. Madison, p. 244.

.... 1934-1954. Deer Feeding Costs and Deer Yard Expenditures.
Wis. Cons. Dept. 1 p. Mimeo.

.... 1935-36--1954-55. Wisconsin Hunting and Trapping Laws and
Regulations Pamphlets. Wis. Cons. Dept.

.... 1935-38. Deer Drive Totals for the Entire State. Wis. Cons.
Dept. 6 pp. Typewritten ms.

.... 1936a. Deer Survive. Wis. Cons. Bull. 1(3):4.

.... 1936b. More Deer Refuges Necessary. Wis. Sportsman 1(1):4.

.... 1936c. New Deer Food. Wis. Cons. Bull. 1(4):4.

.... 1937a. Wisconsin Archers - Bow and Arrow Hunting. Wis.
Cons. Bull. 2(6):6-8.

.... 1937b. Pro and Con - The 1937 Deer Hunting Season. Wis.
Sportsman 2(1):3; 2(2):6.

.... 1937c. An Analysis of Population Growth in Wisconsin. Wis.
State Plan. Board Bull. 4. 68 pp.

.... 1937-38. Deer Hunters Air Their Views. Wis. Cons. Bull.
2,3(12,1):26-37.

.... 1938a. Deer Food Conditions. Wis. Cons. Bull. 3(4):9.

.... 1938b. Wisconsin Archers. Wis. Cons. Bull. 3(12):25-26.

.... 1938c. Clow's Deer College. Wis. Cons. Bull. 3(12):19-20.

.... 1939a. Deer Taken With Bow and Arrow. Wis. Cons. Bull.
4(11):3-4.

.... 1939b. Schedule Showing Comparative County Totals of Deer
Tags Sold During Open Deer Seasons from 1928-1938. Wis. Cons.
Dept. 3 pp. Mimeo.

.... 1940a. Record Deer Head. Wis. Cons. Bull. 5(6):63.

.... 1940b. Record Trophy for 1939. Wis. Cons. Bull. 5(1):24.

.... 1940c. Then and Now. Wis. Cons. Bull. 5(9):46.

.... 1940d. 200 Deer in 30 Minutes. Wis. Cons. Bull. 5(5):14.

.... 1941a. Hunting in 1856. Wis. Cons. Bull. 6(3):20.

.... 1941b. 1940 Record Antlers. Wis. Cons. Bull. 6(4):21.

.... 1941c. Number of Deer Tags Sold For Years 1917-1940. Wis. Cons. Dept. 1 p. Mimeo.

.... 1941d. Schedule Showing Comparative County Totals of Hunting Licenses Sold for Years 1927-1940. Wis. Cons. Dept. 2 pp. Mimeo.

.... 1942. The Bow and Arrow Season. Wis. Cons. Bull. 7(12):21.

.... 1943a. Deer Horn Collection. Wis. Cons. Bull. 8(2):17.

.... 1943b. Majority Report of the Citizens' Deer Committee to Wisconsin Conservation Commission. Wis. Cons. Bull. 8(8):19-22.

.... 1944a. Deer Protests. Wis. Cons. Bull. 9(1):16.

.... 1944b. An Open Letter to the Governor, Senators and Assemblymen. Save Wis. Deer 1(1):8.

.... 1944c. Six Points of Deer Policy. Wis. Cons. Bull. 9(11):10.

.... 1945a. Chambers Island. Wis. Cons. Bull. 10(11):3-5.

.... 1945b. Deer, Bear Damage Payments. Wis. Cons. Bull. 10(3):15.

.... 1945c. Barksdale Deer Herd. Wis. Cons. Bull. 10(4):23.

.... 1945d. Deer Parking. Save Wis. Deer. May, 1945, pp. 1,8.

.... 1945e. The 1945 Deer Survey. Wis. Cons. Dept. 17 pp. Mimeo.

.... 1945f. Record Antlers. Wis. Cons. Bull. 10(4):18; 10(5,6):12.

.... 1945g. Wildlife. A Picture of Wisconsin. Wis. State Plan. Board Bull. 16, Ch. 6, pp. 92-105.

.... 1946a. Begging Deer. Wis. Cons. Bull. 11(5):14.

.... 1946b. Deer Concentrations. Wis. Cons. Bull. 11(3):31.

.... 1946c. The Deer Debate. Wis. Cons. Bull. 11(6):10.

.... 1946d. Deer Feeding. Wis. Cons. Bull. 11(8,9):28-30.

.... 1946e. Deer Observations. Wis. Cons. Bull. 11(3):22-27.

.... 1946f. The Deer Problem. Wis. Cons. Bull. 11(7):18.

.... 1946g. Deer Season Notes. Wis. Cons. Bull. 11(1):9.

.... 1946h. The Deer Summary. Wis. Cons. Bull. 11(4):28.

.... 1946i. The 1946 Deer Survey. Wis. Cons. Dept. 21 pp. Mimeo.

.... 1946j. Deer Yard Acquisition. Wis. Cons. Bull. 11(4):16.

.... 1946k. No Feed for Deer. Wis. Cons. Bull. 11(8,9):24.

.... 1946l. Wisconsin Deer Review. Wis. Cons. Bull. 11(12):14-15.

.... 1946-1954. Reports of License Sales. Wis. Cons. Dept.
5 pp. Mimeo.

.... 1947a. Deer Hunters' Book Wis. Cons. Bull. 12(5):23-24.

.... 1947b. Deer in 1882. Wis. Cons. Bull. 12(4):5.

.... 1947c. Deer Shiners. Wis. Cons. Bull. 12(3):23.

.... 1947d. Fairchild Deer Tour. Wis. Cons. Bull. 12(4):3-4.

.... 1947e. The Flambeau and Deer. Wis. Cons. Bull. 12(2):13.

.... 1947f. Where is the Deer Feed Going? Department Gives
Detailed Report. Badger Sportsman 3(9):2.

.... 1947g. Schedule Showing Comparative County Totals of Hunting
Licenses Sold for Years 1934-1945. Wis. Cons. Dept. Mimeo.

.... 1948a. Wisconsin Deer. Mich. Dept. of Cons., Lansing,
20 pp. Mimeo.

.... 1948b. Jackson County Deer Survey. Wis. Cons. Bull.
13(5):3-4.

.... 1948c. Unanimous Report of the Wisconsin Conservation
Congress Deer Committee. Wis. Cons. Dept. 24 pp. Mimeo.

.... 1948d. Governor Rennebohm Defies Conservation Goons,
Refuses to Sign "Blood and Guts" Deer Season. Badger Sportsman
5(1):1.

.... 1948e. A Century of Wisconsin Agriculture, 1848-1948. Bull.
290. Wis. Crop Reporting Service, Madison, 119 pp.

.... 1949a. Verbatum Transcript of Statements Made to Conservation
Commission Relating to Deer Damage to Agricultural Crops in Bayfield County. Wis. Cons. Dept. 11 pp. Mimeo.

.... 1949b. Final Deer Committee Report. Wis. Cons. Dept.
8 pp. Mimeo.

.... 1949c. Report of Deer Committee to the Executive Council
of the Wisconsin Conservation Congress. Minority Report Appended.
Wis. Cons. Dept. 3 pp. Mimeo.

.... 1950a. Badger Sportsman Deer Survey Proved Herd Down 50
Percent. Badger Sportsman 6(9):1-3.

.... 1950b. 1950 Deer Hunting Season Checks. Wis. Cons. Dept.
7 pp. Mimeo.

.... 1950c. That Seven-Day Season. Badger Sportsman 7(1):1-8.

.... 1951. The 1951 Deer Hunting Season Check. Wis. Cons.
Dept. 19 pp. Mimeo.

.... 1952a. The 1952 Deer Hunting Season Check. Wis. Cons. Dept. 36 pp. Mimeo.

.... 1952b. Deer Management Policy Adopted. Wis. Cons. Bull. 17(10):17-18.

.... 1953. First Official Wisconsin Conservation Department Report of the 1953 Deer Hunting Season Check. Wis. Cons. Dept. 42 pp. Mimeo.

.... 1954a. A Report on the 1954 Deer Hunting Check by the Game Management Division of the Conservation Department. Wis. Cons. Dept. 32 pp. Mimeo.

.... 1954b. Wisconsin Agriculture in Mid-Century. Bull. 325, Wis. Crop and Livestock Reporting Service, Madison, 87 pp.

.... 1956a. Report of Committee to Study Overall Management Plan for Wisconsin Deer. Wis. Cons. Dept. 5 pp. Printed.

.... 1956b. Report of Committee to Study Overall Management Plan for Wisconsin Deer. Wis. Cons. Dept. 5 pp. Printed.

.... 1957. Deer Hunting, a Loot at 1956. Wis. Cons. Dept. Circular.

.... 1958a. Say Brother, Are You Getting Your Share? Wis. Cons. Dept. Circular.

.... 1958b. How to Age Your Deer. Wis. Cons. Dept. Circular.

.... 1959a. Forest Managers Surveyed on Deer Damage to Forests. The Conservationist, May. No. 119, p. 3.

.... 1959b. Unit Hunting. Wis. Cons. Dept. Circular.

.... 1960. Deer Registration - Useful Tool. The Conservationist, No. 129. p. 3.

.... 1961a. The Conservationist, No. 138. 8 pp.

.... 1961b. Now Deer Surveys Even More Important (Pellet Count Technique). The Conservationist, No. 139, p.5.

.... 1962a. Deer-Forest Interrelationships in Forest Land Management. Wis. Cons. Dept. 60 pp. Mimeo.

.... 1962b. A Management Plan for Wisconsin's White Tails. Wis. Cons. Dept. 7 pp. Mimeo.

.... 1963a. Deer Season 1980. Wis. Cons. Bull. 28(1):3-6.

.... 1963b. The 1963 Deer Gun Season Report. 16 pp. Appendix. 19 pp. Wis. Cons. Dept. Mimeo.

.... 1963c. The 1963 Deer Party Permit System. Wis. Cons. Dept. 9 pp. Mimeo.

.... 1963d. 1963 Deer Hunting Questionnaire. Wis. Cons. Dept.
4 pp. Mimeo.

.... 1963e. Deer Observations - Summer and Fall, 1963. Wis. Cons.
Dept. Research and Planning Division. 2 pp. Mimeo.

.... 1963f. 1963 Deer Management Unit Surveys. Wis. Cons. Dept.
Research and Planning Division. 10 pp. Mimeo.

.... 1965. Deer Observations - Summer and Fall, 1964. Wis. Cons.
Dept. Research and Planning Division. 3 pp. Mimeo.

Adams, Harry E. 1938. Deer Census and Kill Records of the Lake States.
Trans. N. A. Wildl. Conf. 3:287-295.

Aldous, Shaler E. 1947. Some Forest Wildlife Problems in the Lake
States. Wis. Cons. Bull. 12(6):3-5.

Amundson, Mrs. A. J. 1947 Deer and Cranberries. Wis. Cons. Bull.
12(6):28-29.

Barber, W. E. 1920. Commission's Statewide Hearings. Wis. Conservationist 2(4):5.

.... 1921a. The Bloodstained Trail of the White-tailed Deer in
Wisconsin. Wis. Conservationist. 3(1):1-2.

.... 1921b. Distinguishing Fawns. Wis. Conservationist. 3(5):5.

.... 1922. Deer Still Plentiful in Wisconsin. Wis.
Conservationist. 3(6):16.

.... 1924. The Work of the Conservation Commission. Wisconsin -
It's History and It's People, 1634-1924. 2:381-409.

Barger, N. R. 1944. How Was the Deer Season, 1943? Wis. Cons. Bull.
9(4):3-5.

Beale, Cottam G. and V. O. Vogl R. J. 1960. Influence of Deer on
Vegetation of the Apostle Islands. Wildl. Mgt. 24(1):60-80.

Bersing, Otis S. 1945. The Hunters' Report of the 1944 Deer Kill.
Wis. Cons. Bull. 10(10):3-11.

.... 1946a. The Bowman in Wisconsin. Wis. Cons. Bull.
11(1):15-19.

.... 1946b. The 1945 Deer Kill. Wis. Cons. Bull. 11(8,9):6-15.

.... 1947a. Bow Hunting for Deer in Wisconsin. Wis. Cons.
Bull. 12(2):10-11.

.... 1947b. The 1946 Deer Hunting Season. Wis. Cons. Bull.
12(9):4-12.

.... 1948a. Bow and Arrow Deer Hunting in Wisconsin. Archery
20(4):12-16.

.... 1948b. The 1947 Deer Season. Wis. Cons. Bull. 13(10):11-12.

.... 1948c. Controlled Deer Hunting on the Necedah Refuge. Wis. Cons. Bull. 13(8):19-22.

.... 1949a. The Deer Kill--1948 Season. Wis. Cons. Dept. 7 pp. Mimeo.

.... 1949b. The Hunters' Opinion of an Any-Deer Season. Wis. Cons. Bull. 14(9):6-9.

.... 1950a. The Deer Kill--1949 Season. Wis. Cons. Dept. 7 pp. Mimeo.

.... 1950b. 15 Years of Bow and Arrow Deer Hunting in Wisconsin. Wis. Cons. Dept. Pub. 349-50. 24 pp. (With annual supplements, 1950-1954).

.... 1950c. Controlled Hunting: What Does It Mean? Wis. Cons. Bull. 15(12):15-18.

.... 1951. The Deer Kill--1950 Season. Wis. Cons. Dept. 11 pp. Multilith.

.... 1952. The Deer Kill--1951 Season. Wis. Cons. Dept. 10 pp. Multilith.

.... 1953. The Deer Kill--1952 Season. Wis. Cons. Dept. 17 pp. Multilith.

.... 1954a. The Deer Kill--1953 Season. Wis. Cons. Dept. 18 pp. Multilith.

.... 1954b. A Report of Deer Damage Claims. Wis. Cons. Dept. 15 pp. Mimeo.

.... 1955. The Deer Kill--1954 Season. Wis. Cons. Dept. 19 pp. Multilith.

Bersing, Otis S. 1955-1964 Inclusive. Reports of Annual Bow and Arrow Deer Seasons. Wis. Cons. Dept. Mimeo.

.... 1956a. A Century of Wisconsin Deer. Wis. Cons. Dept. 184 pp.

.... 1956b. Deer and Bear Damage for 1955-56 and Comparative Summary. Wis. Cons. Dept. 15 pp. Mimeo.

.... 1958a. A Report of Deer and Bear Damage (1956-57). Wis. Cons. Dept. 5 pp. Mimeo.

.... 1958b. A Report of Deer and Bear Damage (1957-58). Wis. Cons. Dept. 9 pp. Mimeo.

.... 1959a. The Deer Season, 1958. Wis. Cons. Dept. 35 pp. Multilith.

.... 1959b. 1958-59 Deer and Bear Damage Report. Wis. Cons. Dept. 9 pp. Mimeo.

.... 1960a. The 1959 Big Game Season. Wis. Cons. Dept. 51 pp. Multilith.

.... 1960b. 1959-60 Deer and Bear Damage Report. Wis. Cons. Dept.
    4 pp. Mimeo.

.... 1961a. The 1960 Deer Gun Season. Wis. Cons. Dept. 35 pp.
    Multilith.

.... 1961b. 1960-61 Fiscal Year Deer and Bear Damage Report. Wis.
    Cons. Dept. 6 pp. Mimeo.

.... 1962a. The 1961 Big Game Seasons. Wis. Cons. Dept. 30 pp.
    Mimeo.

.... 1962b. 1961-62 Fiscal Year Deer and Bear Damage Report. Wis.
    Cons. Dept. 4 pp. Mimeo.

.... 1962c. Record Deer in Wisconsin (1898-1961). Wis. Cons. Dept.
    14 pp. Mimeo.

.... 1963a. The 1962 Big Game Seasons. Wis. Cons. Dept. 33 pp.
    Mimeo.

.... 1963b. 1962-63 Fiscal Year Deer and Bear Damage Report. Wis.
    Cons. Dept. 4 pp. Mimeo.

.... 1964. 1963-64 Fiscal Year Deer and Bear Damage Report. Wis.
    Cons. Dept. 4 pp. Mimeo.

Bersing, Otis S. and Hale, James B. 1956. The 1955 Deer Kill. Wis.
    Cons. Dept. 18 pp. Multilith.

Bersing, Otis S. and Hale, James B. 1957. The 1956 Deer Kill. Wis.
    Cons. Dept. 54 pp. Multilith.

Bersing, Otis S., Keener, John M. and Hale, James B. 1958. The 1957
    Deer Kill. Wis. Cons. Dept. 79 pp. Multilith.

Bersing, Otis S. and Thompson, D. R. 1960. Deer Hunter Polls. Wis.
    Cons. Dept. 2 pp. Mimeo.

Bersing, Otis S. and Hartman, George F. 1964. Deer Hunt '64. Wis.
    Cons. Dept. 41 pp. Mimeo.

Biennial Reports of the Wisconsin State Conservation Commission.
    1915-1954. Year and Pages: 1915-1916, 43,53-57; 1917-1918,
    15-35; 1919-1920, 5,6; 1921-1922, 5,24; 1923-1924, 17,23; 1925-
    1926, 21,22; 1927-1928, 18; 1929-1930, 13,83-96; 1931-1932,
    34-37; 1933-1934, 58-66; 1935-1936, 85-95; 1945-1946, 66-84;
    1947-1948, 49-80; 1949-1950, 20-52; 1951-1952, 51-70; 1953-1954,
    47-77; 1954-1955, 11-35; 1956-1958, 14-27; 1958-1960, 83-93;
    1960-1962, 37-44.

Bordner, John S., William W. Morris, Lamar M. Wood, and John H. Steenis.
    1933. Land Economic Inventory. Dept. of Agric. and Mkts. Bull.
    146. Madison, p. 53.

Brown, Charles R. 1923. Wisconsin Indians. Wisconsin Blue Book.
    pp. 65-69.

Brown, Dorothy Moulding. 1948. Wisconsin Indian Place-Name Legends.
    29 pp. Monograph.

Buss, Irven O. 1941. Deer Hunting in Bayfield County. Wis. Cons. Bull. 6(2):27-29.

.... 1947. Deer Hunting Records From Central Bayfield County. Wis. Cons. Bull. 12(1):5-11.

Carhart, Arthur H. 1944. Deer Feeding Fallacies. Wis. Cons. Bull. 9(10):22.

Case, Roy I. 1936. Case Defends Archery. Wis. Cons. Bull. 1(11):9-12.

Chaddock, Dr. T. T. 1939. Epithelial Papillomas Reported in Deer. Wis. Cons. Bull. 4(2):31-32.

.... 1940. Chemical Analysis of Deer Antlers. Wis. Cons. Bull. 5(6):42.

Chido, George. 1956. A Ranger's View of the Deer Season. Wis. Cons. Bull. 21(11):11.

Chizek, James. 1960. Is Your Dog a Deer Killer? Wis. Cons. Bull. 25(3):7-8.

Christensen, Earl M. 1955. A Physiosociological Study of the Winter Range of Deer of Northern Wisconsin. Univ. of Wis. Ph.D. Thesis.

.... 1959. A Historical View of the Ranges of the White-tailed Deer in Northern Wisconsin Forests. Amer. Mid. Nat. 61(1):230-238.

.... 1962. Classification of the Winter Habits of the White-tailed Deer in Northern Wisconsin Based on Forest Ordination. Ecology 43(1):134-135.

.... 1963. Herbaceous Vegetation in Lowland Winter Habitats of White-tailed Deer in Northern Wisconsin. Ecology 44(2):411-414.

Clark, D. H. 1922. Against the Buck Law. Wis. Conservationist. 3(6):11.

Clow, W. E., Sr. 1937. Half Century of Deer Hunting. Wis. Cons. Bull. 2(9):10-11.

Conway, Ralph C. 1936. Wisconsin's Refuge Program. Wis. Cons. Bull. 1(12):8-11.

.... 1940. Wisconsin Game Refuges. Wis. Cons. Bull. 5(1):35-38.

Cook, Robert S. 1958. Deer Enclosures Tell a Story. Wis. Cons. Bull. 23(11):15-17.

Cook, Robert S. and Hale, James B. 1961. Deer on the Bad River Indian Reservation. Transactions of Wildl. Mgt. Institute. Washington. pp. 448-459. Reprint.

Corbin, Duane L. 1955. How to Miss Deer. Wis. Cons. Bull. 20(6):10-12.

Cory, C. B. 1912. The Mammals of Illinois and Wisconsin. Field. Mus. Nat. Hist., Chicago. Pub. 153 Zool. series 11:64-66.

Cramer, H. T. J. 1946. Report to Commission on the 1945-46 Deer Survey. Wis. Cons. Dept. 7 pp. Mimeo.

.... 1948. Harvest of Deer in Wisconsin. Wis. Cons. Dept. 14 pp. Mimeo.

Creed, William A. 1960. For Buck Hunters Only. Wis. Cons. Bull. 25(8):18-19.

.... 1960. Tagged Deer Tell a Story. Wis. Cons. Bull. 25(9):11-12.

.... 1962. Deer Aging in '62. Wis. Cons. Dept. 10 pp. Ditto.

.... 1963a. Make Mine Big. Wis. Cons. Bull. 28(5):8.

.... 1963b. No Deer? Phooey! Wis. Cons. Bull. 28(2):10-12.

Dahlberg, B. L. 1947. Deer Management Research Project 4 R. Wis. Wildl. Research 6(3):7-15.

.... 1948. Deer Management Research Project 4 R. Wis. Wildl. Research 7(3):1-12.

.... 1948-49. Artificial Feeding of Deer. Wis. Cons. Dept. 3 pp. Mimeo.

.... 1949a. Deer Management Deer Research Project 4 R. Wis. Wildl. Research 8(1):1-16.

.... 1949b. Winter Deer Range Conditions, 1949. Wis. Cons. Bull. 14(6):21-24.

.... 1950. The Wisconsin Deer Problem and the 1949 Hunting Season. Wis. Cons. Bull. 15(4):3-7.

Dahlberg, Burton L. and Guettinger, Ralph C. 1956. The White-tailed Deer in Wisconsin. Tech. Wildl. Bull. No. 14. Wis. Cons. Dept. 282 pp.

DeBoer, Stanley G. 1947. The Deer Damage to Forest Reproduction Survey. Wis. Cons. Bull. 12(10):3-23.

.... 1952. Feed 'Em - With An Axe! Wis. Cons. Bull. 17(3):3-11.

.... 1953. And the Browse Came Back. Wis. Cons. Bull. 18(1):3-10.

.... 1956. Probable Results Under Various Types of Deer Seasons. Forest and Farm Ranges Illustrated. Wis. Cons. Dept. 4 pp. Printed.

.... 1957. Waste in the Woods. Wis. Cons. Bull. 22(10):10-14.

.... 1958. Less Waste in the Woods. Wis. Cons. Bull. 23(10):13-17.

.... 1959. Dead Deer Transect, Necedah Wildlife Refuge. Wis. Cons. Dept. 4 pp. Mimeo.

.... 1960a. 1960 Deer Hunting Pressure - West Central Area. Wis. Cons. Dept. 4 pp. Mimeo.

.... 1960b. Deer Management's New Allies - "The Farm Herds and the Cash Register". Wis. Cons. Dept. 11 pp. Mimeo.

.... 1964. A Report on the Managed Deer Hunt, 1963. Sandhill Wildlife Demonstration Area, Wood County, Wisconsin. Wis. Cons. Dept. 9 pp. Mimeo.

.... 1965a. The 1964 Managed Deer Hunt. Sandhill Wildlife Demonstration Area, Wood County, Wisconsin. Wis. Cons. Dept. 5 pp. Mimeo.

.... 1965b. Let's Look at Deer Kill - '64 - Deer Kill - '65. Wis. Cons. Dept. 6 pp. Mimeo.

Devine, Barney. 1937-38. They'd Rather Be Wrong. Wis. Cons. Bull. 2,3(12,1):37-43.

Doll, Arthur D. and Creed, William A. 1961 Deer Mathematics. Wis. Cons. Bull. 26(5):14-15.

Dornson, James P. 1920. Our Deer Hunt at Scott's Landing (Oneida County). Wis. Conservationist 2(4):15.

Ebling, Walter H. 1929. The Development of Agriculture in Wisconsin. The Wisconsin Blue Book. pp. 51-74.

Espeseth, Edmund C. 1953. Early Vilas County - Cradle of an Industry. Wis. Mag. of Hist. 37(1):27-34, 51-54.

Evans, E. F. 1941. Eulogy of a Pet Deer. Wis. Cons. Bull. 6(1):26-28.

Feeney, W. S. 1942a. Deer Management Research Project. Wis. Wildl. Research 5 R. 1(4):1-9.

.... 1942b. Famine Stalks the Deer. Wis. Cons. Bull. 7(9):8-10.

.... 1943a. Wisconsin Deer Today and Tomorrow. Wis. Cons. Bull. 8(8):11-19.

.... 1943b. A Brief Outline of the Findings of the Wisconsin Deer Research Project for the Winter of 1942-43. Wis. Cons. Dept. 3 pp. Mimeo.

.... 1944. The Present Status of Wisconsin's Deer Herd and Deer Range. Wis. Cons. Bull. 9(6):4-5.

.... 1946. Chambers Island Data. Wis. Cons. Bull. 11(1):6-9.

Fine, I. V. and Werner, E. E. 1960. Economic Significance of Hunters in Wisconsin. Univ. of Wis. 11 pp. Mimeo.

Fite, Emerson David. 1923. History of the United States. Henry Holt & Co. New York. 603 pp.

Forest Land Use In Wisconsin. 1932. Report of the Committee on Land Use and Forestry, Executive Office, Madison. 156 pp.

Forest and Stream. 1882-1917. Forest and Stream Publishing Co., New
York. 19(18):347; 19(22):427; 21(3):48; 22(25):485; 24(18):349;
25(13):246; 25(15):307; 25(20):389; 26(5):86; 26(13):246; 27(24):467;
28(3):45; 28(10):201; 28(15):325; 31(17):326; 31(25):519; 35(18):351;
35(19):375; 38(11):248; 39(11):224; 39(12):247; 40(2):29; 40(8):159;
41(15):319; 41(20):429; 41(21):453; 43(2):29; 43(14):292; 43(18):378;
43(19):402; 44(16):328; 44(18):369; 44(22):442; 45(19):403; 45(21):445;
45(23):489; 45(25):535,538; 47(12):226; 47(17):327; 47(18):345;
47(22):427; 47(23):447; 47(24):469; 49(4):67,68; 49(17):327; 49(19):336;
49(21):405,407; 49(23):448; 49(26):509; 50(5):85; 50(20):285; 51(11):208;
51(15):283,288; 51(16):302; 51(19):370; 51(20):388; 51(21):409;
51(23):447,449; 51(24):467; 51(25):486; 52(2):30; 52(19):367; 52(20):387;
52(23):446; 54(21):405; 54(23):447; 55(21):406; 55(22):429;
55(24):467,469; 55(26):507,508; 56(21):405; 56(24):465; 56(26):506; 57(3):44;
57(10):188; 57(15):286; 57(20):387; 57(21):407; 57(22):429; 59(4):67;
59(7):126; 59(11):210; 59(20):387; 59(21):408; 59(23):451; 60(2):31;
61(25):487; 62(2):27,28; 64(5):93; 64(6):116; 87(7):330.

Grange, Wallace B. 1949. The Way to Game Abundance. Charles Scribner's
Sons, New York. 365 pp.

Great Lakes Deer Group. 1964. Research for Deer Management in the Great
Lakes Region. 73 pp. Mimeo.

Grimmer, W. F. 1948. Game Management in Wisconsin. Wis. Cons. Bull.
13(6):61-66.

Guettinger, Ralph C. 1951. Sex and Age Ratio Studies of Wisconsin Deer.
Midwest Wildl. Conf. 3 pp. Mimeo.

.... 1952. Wisconsin Deer Seasons. Mich. Conservation, Lansing,
Nov.-Dec. 1952.

Habeck, James R. 1959a. The Ecology of White Cedar Swamps in Northern
Wisconsin, with Special Attention to Their Role as Winter Deer
Range. Univ. of Wis. Ph.D. Thesis. 53 pp.

.... 1959b. A Vegetational Study of the Central Wisconsin Winter
Deer Range. Jour. of Wildl. Mgt. Vol. 23:3, July, 1959. pp. 273-278.

.... 1960. Winter Deer Activity in the White Cedar Swamps of
Northern Wisconsin. Ecology Vol. 41, No. 2, April, 1960.

Habeck, James R. and Curtis, J. R. 1959. Forest Cover and Deer Population Densities in Early Northern Wisconsin. Trans. Wis. Acad. of
Science 48:49-56.

Hadland, George S. 1951. The Story of Conservation Law Enforcement.
Wis. Cons. Dept. 5 pp. Mimeo.

Hahn, Edward H. 1960. Good Forest Management - Good Deer Management.
Wis. Cons. Bull. 25(3):25-27.

Hale, James B. 1954. Deer Hunting Prospects - 1954. Wis. Cons. Bull.
19(11):3-6.

.... 1955a. Deer Hunting Checks, 1955. Wis. Cons. Dept.
20 pp. Mimeo.

.... 1955b. Some Conclusions From Wisconsin Deer Hunting Seasons
    Since 1941. Wis. Cons. Dept. 4 pp. Mimeo.

.... 1955c. Deer Hunting Prospects. Wis. Cons. Bull. 20(10):3-5.

.... 1956a. Winter Deer Range Checks for Winter of 1955-56. Wis.
    Cons. Dept. 4 pp. Mimeo.

.... 1956b. Dead Deer Check for Spring of 1956. Wis. Cons. Dept.
    4 pp. Mimeo.

.... 1956c. Dead Doe Data for 1956. Wis. Cons. Dept. 11 pp. Mimeo.

.... 1956d. Deer Hunting Checks 1956. Wis. Cons. Dept. 28 pp.
    Mimeo.

.... 1957a. Winter Deer Range Checks for Winter of 1956-57. Wis.
    Cons. Dept. 6 pp. Mimeo.

.... 1957b. Dead Doe Data for 1957. Wis. Cons. Dept. 7 pp. Mimeo.

.... 1959. Final Report on Deer Production Study. Wis. Cons. Dept.
    10 pp. Mimeo.

Hale, James B. and Thompson, D. R. 1956. Sex and Age Ratios in Wisconsin
    Deer. Wis. Cons. Dept. 3 pp. Mimeo.

Hallock, Charles. 1877. Sportsman Gazetter and General Guide. Forest
    & Stream Pub. Co., New York.

Hammerstrom, F. N., Jr. and James Blake. 1939. Winter Movements and
    Winter Foods of White-tailed Deer in Central Wisconsin. Jour.
    Mamm. 20(2):206-215.

Hartman, George F. 1965. Deer Aging in 1964. Wis. Cons. Dept. 8 pp.
    Mimeo.

Hawkinson, Stanley L. 1936. New Deer Law Praised. Wis. Cons. Bull.
    1(12):15-16.

Hein, Edward N. 1937. Wisconsin Deer. Wis. Cons. Bull. 2(10):3.

.... 1943. The Deer Debate. Wis. Cons. Bull. 8(10):9.

.... 1945a. The Deer Season. Wis. Cons. Bull. 10(2):17.

.... 1945b. The Bow Hunters. Wis. Cons. Bull. 10(11):6-7.

Hemp, Dick. 1961. Deer Herd Refutes Prophets of Doom. Wis. Cons. Bull.
    26(1):16.

Henry, W. A. 1896. Northern Wisconsin. A Handbook for the Home Seeker.
    Democrat Co., State Printer, Madison. 192 pp.

Hettrick, Harold D. 1958. Danger: Deer Crossing. Wis. Cons. Bull.
    23(3):7-9.

Hine, Ruth L. 1957. Wildlife Research Notes. Wis. Cons. Bull. 22(11):7.

.... 1962. Deer and Forests: Better Days for Both. Wis. Cons.
Bull. 27(6):13-16.

History of Northern Wisconsin, 1881. Western Historical Co, Chicago.
1,218 pp.

Hollister, N. 1908. The Last Records of Deer in Walworth County, Wisconsin.
Wis. Nat. Hist. Soc. 6(3,4):143-144.

.... 1910. A Check List of Wisconsin Mammals. Bull Wis. Nat. Hist.
Soc. 8(1):21-31.

Hopkins, Ralph C. 1939a. Measuring Deer Antlers. Wis. Cons. Bull.
4(12):36-40.

.... 1939b. Wisconsin's Large Deer of 1938. Wis. Cons. Bull.
4(10):49-51.

Hovind, Ralph G. 1953. Wildlife for the Summer Tourist. Wis. Cons.
Bull. 18(6):3-5.

.... 1957. Tourist Deer. Wis. Cons. Bull. 22(8):3-5.

Hoy, Philo R. 1878. Fauna and Flora of Wisconsin. Hist. Atlas of Wis.,
1878. pp. 153-156.

.... 1882. The Larger Wild Animals that Have Become Extinct in
Wisconsin. Trans. Wis. Acad. Sci. Arts, Letters, 5:255-257.

Hubbard, Ben. W. 1940. Wisconsin White-tailed Deer. Wis. Cons. Bull.
5(10):10-11.

.... 1941. Five Archers Get Their Deer. Wis. Cons. Bull. 6(3):31-33.

Hurd, E. S. 1962. A Dinner Bell for the White-tail. American Forests
Reprint. 5 pp.

Jackson, Hartley H. T. 1908. A Preliminary List of Wisconsin Mammals.
Bull. Wis. Nat. Hist. Soc. 6(1,2):13-14.

.... 1910. The Distribution of Certain Wisconsin Mammals. Bull.
Wis. Nat. Hist. Soc. 8(2):86-90.

.... 1938. Distribution of Wisconsin Deer. Wis. Cons. Bull.
3(6):28.

Jackson, Hugh. 1937. An Interview with Old Many Point Buck. Wis.
Sportsman 2(2):1,3.

.... 1939. Deer Research Needed Here. Wis. Sportsman. 3(8):4.

.... 1940. New Commissioner Asks Wisconsin Conservation Congress
Be Dissolved. Wis. Sportsman 5(1):1-2.

Jacobson, J. R. 1944. Deer Browse and River Flow. Wis. Cons. Bull.
9(10):9-11.

John, Lawrence R. 1959. Highway Mortality as an Index of Deer Population Changes. Jour. of Wildl. Mgt. 14(2):187-197.

Johnson, William. 1941. Deer Hunting at Brule. Wis. Cons. Bull. 6(2):43-44.

Jorgenson, Roy J. 1938. Vilas County Deer. Wis. Sportsman 2(5):7.

Kabat, Cyril. 1953. Deer Hunting Prospects - 1953. Wis. Cons. Bull. 18(10):3-8.

Kabat, Cyril, Nicholas Collias and Ralph C. Guettinger. 1953. Some Winter Habits of White-tailed Deer and the Development of Census Methods in the Flag Yard of Northern Wisconsin. Tech. Wildl. Bull. No. 7. Wis. Cons. Dept. 32 pp.

Kabat, Cyril and Ruth L. Hine. 1954. Operation Wildlife Research. Wis. Wildl. Bull. No. 2. Wis. Cons. Dept. 35 pp.

Keener, John M. 1952. The Need for Deer Range Management. Wis. Cons. Bull. 17(11):7-10.

.... 1956a. A New Deal for Deer and Hunter. Wis. Cons. Bull. 21(12):3-9.

.... 1956b. The 1956 Deer Season. Wis. Cons. Dept. 9 pp. Mimeo.

.... 1957a. A Deer Range Management Program. Wis. Cons. Dept. 9 pp. Mimeo.

.... 1957b. The 1956 Deer Season. Wis. Cons. Bull. 22(2):8-11.

.... 1957c. What About the 1957 Deer Season? Wis. Cons. Dept. 13 pp. Mimeo.

.... 1957d. Deer Range Carrying Capacity. Wis. Cons. Dept. 3 pp. Mimeo.

.... 1958. The 1958 Deer Seasons. Wis. Cons. Bull. 23(10):5-7.

.... 1959. The 1959 Big Game Seasons. Wis. Cons. Bull. 24(10):3-5.

.... 1960a. The Big Game Hunting Seasons - 1960. Wis. Cons. Bull. 25(8):10-11.

.... 1960b. Deer Season Considerations. Wis. Cons. Bull. 25(4):12-16.

.... 1961. How Many Deer? Wis. Cons. Bull. 26(3):17-19.

Keener, John M. and DeBoer, Stanley G. 1956. Probable Results Under Various Types of Deer Seasons. Wis. Cons. Dept. 4 pp. Printed.

Keener, John M. and Hale, James B. The 1957 Deer Season. Wis. Cons. Bull. 22(10):5-9.

Keener, John M. and Thompson, Donald R. 1957. The Deer Unit: Surveys and Management. Wis. Cons. Bull. 22(8):6-10.

Kingsley, A. W. 1921. Another Opponent. Wis. Conservationist. 3(6):11.

Lake, Ivan Clyde. 1931. Deer Seasons - What Does It Mean to the North?
The Wisconsin Magazine. 8(9):8-9.

Lapham, I. A. 1853. A Systematic Catalogue of the Animals of Wisconsin.
Trans. Wis. State Agric. Soc. 2:337-340.

Laubenheimer, Edward. 1920. Muskrat Farming and Deer Hunting. Wis.
Conservationist. 2(1):45.

Lawyer, George A., W. F. Bancroft, and Frank L. Earnshaw. 1917. Game
Laws for 1917. Farmers Bull. 910. U. S. Dept. Agric., Washington.

Lawyer, George A. and Frank L. Earnshaw. 1919. Game Laws for 1919.
Farmers Bull. 1077. U. S. Dept. Agric., Washington.

.... 1921. Game Laws for 1921. Farmers Bull. 1235 U. S. Dept.
Agric., Washington.

.... 1922. Game Laws for 1922. Farmers Bull. 1288 U. S. Dept.
Agric., Washington.

.... 1923. Game Laws for the Season 1923-24. Farmers Bull.
1375. U. S. Dept. Agric., Washington.

Legislative Acts Relative to Deer Seasons. 1851-1953. Year and Chapter:
1851, 171; 1859, 59; 1860, 194; 1867, 78; 1868, 66; 1869, 33; 1871,
231; 1875, 85, 139, 219; 1876, 360, 309; 1877, 148, 240, 131; 1878,
185 sec. 4564 & 4566; 1879, 40; 1880, 114, 170, 198, 277; 1881,
312; 1883, 299; 1885, 309, 351; 1887, 374, 456; 1889, 443, 367;
1891, 351; 1893, 106; 1895, 221; 1897, 188, 221; 1899, 311, 312,
258; 1901, 358; 1903, 437, 449; 1905, 436; 1907, 414, 394, 201
sec. 4560A-16-20, 4562D; 1909, 525; 1911, 124, 563; 1913, 748, 46,
578, 258; 1915, 594, 636, 102, 118; 1917, 200, 668 (creates ch. 29
of Statutes); Laws following amend ch. 29: 1919, 696; 1921, 553,
530, 328, 364; 1923, 214, 264; 1925, 450; 1927, 426; 52, 289, 93,
63; 1929, 508, 120; 1931, 428, 411, 379, 351, 121; 1933, 152;
1935, 166, 288, 335; 1937, 164; 1939, 202, 182, 226; 1941, 133,
256; 1943, 434, 345, 343; 1944-45, 14, 347, 49, 145; 1946-47, 95,
27, 232, 185, 146, 147; 1948-49, 538, 643, 477, 528, 182; 1950-51,
409, 354, 78, 108, 558; 1952-53, 295, 133, 319, 556, 129, 195;
1954-55, 67, 172, 272, 473, 542, 696.

Administrative Code Relative to Deer Seasons - 1956-1964: 10.01.

Leopold, Aldo. 1931. Report on a Game Survey of the North Central
States. Sporting Arms and Manufacturers Inst., Madison, Wis. 299 pp.

.... 1934. The Excess Deer Problem. Audubon Mag. 45(3):156-157.

.... 1940. Wisconsin Wildlife Chronology. Wis. Cons. Bull.
5(11):8-20.

.... 1943. Deer Irruptions. Wis. Cons. Bull. 8(8):3-11.

.... 1944a. What Next in Deer Policy? Wis. Cons. Bull.
9(6):3-4, 18-19.

.... 1944b. Seven Prongs of the Deer Dilemma. Wis. Cons. Dept.
1 p. Mimeo.

.... 1945. Deer, Wolves, Foxes, and Pheasants. Wis. Cons. Bull. 10(4):3-5.

.... 1946. The Deer Dilemma. Wis. Cons. Bull. 11(8-9):3-5.

.... 1947a. Mortgaging the Future Deer Herd. Wis. Cons. Bull. 12(9):3.

.... 1947b. The Ecological Conscience. Wis. Cons. Bull. 12(12):4-7.

Leopold, Aldo, Lyle K. Sowls and David L. Spencer. 1947. A Survey of Overpopulated Deer Ranges in the United States. Jour. Wildl. Mgt. 11(2):162-177.

Lindsay, Gerald E. 1939. Dear Deer. Wis. Cons. Bull. 4(3):34-36.

Livermore, Ivory. 1944. Early Deer Hunting Days. Wis. Cons. Bull. 9(10):17-19.

Loyster, Earl L. 1942. Archery Deer Season, 1941. Wis. Cons. Bull. 7(1):21-22.

.... 1943. Large Deer, Season 1941-42. Wis. Cons. Bull. 8(1):29-30.

.... 1944a. Winter Deer Food Distribution. Wis. Cons. Bull. 9(2):5.

.... 1944b. The 1943 Archery Deer Season. Wis. Cons. Bull. 9(2):17-18.

Luckenback, Orville S. 1960. Let's Have Deer Management Make Sense. Wis. Cons. Bull. 25(9):10-11.

MacArthur, Arthur R. 1960. Letter by Commissioner MacArthur on Deer Question. Wis. Cons. Dept. 3 pp. Mimeo.

MacKenzie, H. W. 1934. Information Concerning a Tentative Change in the Deer Season to an Earlier Date. Wis. Cons. Dept. 4 pp. Mimeo.

.... 1935. Information Concerning the One Buck Law. Wis. Cons. Dept. 5 pp. Mimeo.

.... 1937. To the Citizens of Wisconsin Interested in the Deer Question. Wis. Cons. Bull. 2(9):3-9.

Madison, Galen. 1961. The White-tailed Deer. Olin Mathison Chemical Corp. Cons. Dept. pp. 7-108.

Martin, F. R. and Krefting, L. W. 1953. The Necedah Refuge Deer Irruption. Jour. Wildl. Mgt. 17(2):166-176.

McCabe, Bob, and Bray, Bob. 1955. Did You Get That Deer? Wis. Cons. Bull. 24(10):6-9.

Minor, Fred T. and John Hanson. 1939. Report of Two Deer Yards in Douglas and Bayfield Counties. Wis. Cons. Bull. 4(5):18-24.

Mitchell, J. A., and Neil LeMay. 1952. Forest Fires and Forest Fire Control in Wisconsin. Wis. Cons. Dept. 75 pp.

Newspapers: Alma Blaetter, Feb. 4, 1897, Mar. 18, 1897; Arena Star, Jan. 19, 1877; Democratic Standard, Feb. 9, 1857; Dodgeville Chronicle, Dec. 23, 1870, Dec. 26, 1879, Sept. 17, 1880, April 15, 1881, Oct. 18, 1889, Oct. 13, 1893; Dodgeville Sun, June 5, 1896; Iowa County Democrat, Dec. 6, 1878, Nov. 14, 1897; Janesville Weekly Gazette, Jan 24, 1857; Janesville Daily Gazette, Jan. 22, 1866, Nov. 23, 1866; Janesville Gazette, Jan. 6,8, 1870, Nov. 15, 1870; Dec. 27 & 30, 1870, Aug. 8, 1871; Janesville Weekly Sun, Nov. 3, 1888; Mineral Point Tribune, July 25, 1855, Dec. 10, 1874, July 6, 1876, June 6, 1877; Pick and Gad, Sept. 3, 1885; Walworth County Independent, Jan. 13, 1869, April 28, 1869, Jan. 17, 1887, Oct. 3, 1889; Whitewater Gazette, Feb. 21, 1856, Nov. 26, 1856, May 17, 1871.

Oldys, Henry. 1911. The Game Market of Today. (1910). Circ. from Yearbook of U. S. Dept. Agric., Washington.

Oldys, Henry, E. E. Brewster and Frank L. Earnshaw. 1910. Game Laws for 1910. Farmers Bull. 418, U. S. Dept. Agric., Washington.

Olson, Herman F. 1956. Timber and Deer - Twin Crops of Wisconsin Forest Lands. 5 pp. Mimeo.

Olson, Herman F., Keener, John M. and Thompson, D. R. 1955. Evaluation of Deer Pellet Group Count as a Census Method. Wis. Cons. Dept. 12 pp. Mimeo.

Owen, Asa K. 1944. Urges That Present Commission Be Abolished. Save Wis. Deer. 1(6):1-4.

Palmer, T. S. 1904. Hunting Licenses. Biological Survey Bull. 19. U. S. Dept. Agric., Washington.

.... 1906a. Statistics of Hunting Licenses. Circ. 54, Bureau of Biological Survey. U. S. Dept. Agric., Washington.

.... 1906b. Game Protection in 1906. Reprint from Yearbook of U. S. Dept. Agric. for 1906. Washington.

.... 1912. Chronology and Index of the More Important Events in American Game Protection, 1776-1911. Bull. 41. U. S. Dept. Agric., Washington.

Palmer, T. S., W. F. Bancroft and Frank L. Earnshaw. 1915. Game Laws for 1915. Farmers Bull. 692. U. S. Dept. Agric., Washington.

.... 1916. Game Laws for 1916. Farmers Bull. 774. U. S. Dept. Agric., Washington.

Palmer, T. S., C. E. Brewster and Frank L. Earnshaw. 1912. Game Laws for 1912. Farmers Bull. 510. U. S. Dept. of Agric., Washington.

Palmer, T. S. and H. W. Oldys. 1900. Laws Regulating the Transportation and Sale of Game. Bull. 14. U. S. Dept. Agric., Washington.

.... 1901. Digest of Game Laws for 1901. Bull. 16. U. S. Dept. Agric., Washington.

.... 1902. Game Laws for 1902. Farmers Bull. 160. U. S. Dept.
        Agric., Washington.

.... 1904. Game Laws for 1904. Farmers Bull. 207. U. S. Dept.
        Agric., Washington.

.... 1908. Game Laws for 1908. Farmers Bull. 336. U. S. Dept.
        Agric., Washington.

.... 1911. Progress in Game Protection in 1910. Circ. 8. U. S.
        Dept. Agric., Washington.

Palmer, T. S., H. W. Oldys and Chas. Brewster. 1907. Game Laws for
        1907. Farmers Bull. 308. U. S. Dept. Agric., Washington.

.... 1909. Game Laws for 1909. Farmers Bull. 376. U. S. Dept.
        Agric., Washington.

.... 1910. Progress in Game Protection in 1909. Circ. 73. U. S.
        Dept. Agric., Washington.

Palmer, T. S., H. W. Oldys and R. W. Williams, Jr. 1903. Game Laws
        for 1903. Farmers Bull. 180. U. S. Dept. Agric., Washington.

.... 1905. Game Laws for 1905. Farmers Bull. 230. U. S. Dept.
        Agric., Washington.

Palmer, T. S. and R. W. Williams, Jr. 1906. Game Laws for 1906.
        Farmers Bull. 265. U. S. Dept. Agric., Washington.

Peck, G. S. 1921. From a True Sportsman. Wis. Conservationist.
        3(1):15.

Peters, Virgil. 1944. Tells of Clubs' Fight to Save the Deer Herd.
        Save Wis. Deer 1(1):3.

.... 1946. Tells of His Experience on a State-Escorted Deer Yard
        Trip. Badger Sportsman. 2(10):2.

Philipp, Gov. E. L. 1920. Boyhood Life on the Farm in Wisconsin. Wis.
        Conservationist. 2(3):11-12.

Pollack, R. J. 1940. Mr. Buck--Your Acknowledged Superior. Wis. Cons.
        Bull. 5(3):51-53.

Polleys, Abner Dexter. 1948. Stories of Pioneer Days in the Black
        River Valley. Banner Journal, Black River Falls. 89 pp.

Pospichal, Carl E., Clark, Calvin E. and Little, Bejamin R. 1958.
        Necedah National Wildlife Refuge. Wis. Cons. Bull. 23(9):18-21.

Raeth, Valentine. 1920. Conserve Our Deer. Wis. Conservationist
        2(3):2-3.

Rausch, R. 1950. Observation on Histopathological Changes Associated
        With Starvation in Wisconsin Deer. Jour. of Wildl. Mgt.
        14(2):156-161.

Riegel, J. A. 1937. The Deer Question. Wis. Cons. Bull. 2(11):10-13.

.... 1937-38. More About Deer. Wis. Cons. Bull. 2,3(12,1):22-26.

.... 1938. Sportsman vs. Tourist. Wis. Cons. Bull. 3(4):39-45.

.... 1939. To Doe Or Not To Doe - Is That The Question? Wis.
Sportsman 3(5):3.

Robinson, A. J. 1941. Torture and Destruction. Wis. Cons. Bull.
6(5):19-24.

Rogers, Frederick Jay. 1940. The Babe of the Woods. Wis. Cons. Bull.
5(4):42-43.

Rollmann, W. L. 1958. Hit Where You're Looking. Wis. Cons. Bull.
23(10):8-10.

Rollmann, William L. and Hartman, George F. 1964. Good Deer Season - Why?
Wis. Cons. Bull. 30(2):18-19.

Rosenberry, M. B. 1941. A History of Deerfoot Lodge, 1910-1935.
Privately printed.

Sanders, Roy D. 1939. Results of a Study of the Harvesting of White-
tailed Deer in the Chequamegon National Forest. Trans. North
American Wildl. Conference. 4:549-553.

.... 1939. Deer Study Reveals Startling Facts. Wis. Sportsman.
3(8):3.

Schorger, A. W. 1942. Extinct and Endangered Mammals and Birds of the
Upper Great Lakes Region. Trans. Wis. Acad. Let. & Sci. 34:23-44.

.... 1948. Changing Wildlife Conditions in Wisconsin. Wis. Cons.
Bull. 13(6):53-60.

.... 1953. The White-tailed Deer in Early Wisconsin. Trans. Wis.
Acad. Sci. 42:197-247.

Schafer, Joseph. 1922. A History of Agriculture in Wisconsin. Wis.
Domesday Book, General Studies Vol. 1. 212 pp.

.... 1925. Outline History of Wisconsin, Annual Record. Wisconsin
Blue Book, pp. 61-93.

Schofield, H. C. Deer Hunting Diary, 1904-1926. Hist. Lib. U. of Wis.
Unpub. ms.

Schunke, William H. and Irven O. Buss. 1941. Trends in the Kill of
Wisconsin White-tailed Bucks, (1936-1940). Jour. Wildl. Mgt.
5(3):333-336.

Scott, Walter E. 1937-38. Conservation History. Wis. Cons. Bull.
2(3):10-15; 2(4):14-20; 2(5):23-30; 2(6):27-37; 2(9):26-31;
2(4):26-37.

.... 1938a. The Wisconsin Deer Situation as of September, 1938.
Wis. Sportsman. 3(2):3-5.

.... 1938b. Wisconsin's Large Deer. Wis. Cons. Bull. 3(11):3-4.

.... 1938c. New Small Refuges. Wis. Cons. Bull. 3(10):57-59.

.... 1939a. Fifth Archery Deer Season. Wis. Cons. Bull. 4(12):32-35.

.... 1939b. Rare and Extinct Mammals of Wisconsin. Wis. Cons. Bull. 4(10):21-28.

.... 1939c. Status of the Wisconsin Deer Herd. Wis. Cons. Dept. 7 pp. Unpub. ms.

.... 1940a. Department Begins Game Research. Wis. Cons. Bull. 5(10):11-12.

.... 1940b. Five Wildlife Research Projects Approved. Wis. Cons. Bull. 5(7):18-19.

.... 1943. Conservation Department Answers Questions on Deer Problems. Wis. Cons. Dept. Mimeo.

.... 1947. The 'Old North' Returns. Wis. Cons. Bull. 12(4):13-27.

.... 1948. Administrator's Dilemma--Sportsman's Burden. Mich. Conservation 17(11):6-7, 12-13.

Shiras, George III. 1921. The Wildlife of Lake Superior, Past and Present. Nat. Geog. Mag. 40(2):113-204.

Sholts, John A. 1913-14. Report of the State Fish and Game Warden 1913-1914. Madison, 95 pp.

Skinner, Alanson. 1925. Observations on the Ethnology of the Sauk Indians. Milwaukee Pub. Mus. Bull. 5(3):119-180.

.... 1926. The Mascoutens or Prairie Potowatomi Indians. Milwaukee Pub. Mus. Bull. 6(2):263-326.

Smith, Albert E. 1955. The Flag River Deer Yard. Wis. Cons. Bull. 20(10):25-27.

Smith, Huron H. 1930. Indian Place Names in Wisconsin. Yearbook of the Pub. Mus. of the City of Milwaukee. 10:256-257.

Smith, J. R. 1957a. Deer Management Units. Wis. Cons. Dept. 2 pp. Mimeo.

.... 1957b. Identification of Advanced Malnutrition in Dead Deer. Wis. Cons. Dept. 2 pp. Mimeo.

.... 1958. Instructions for Making Spring Deer Pellet Group Counts. General Letter Game Management No. 136. Wis. Cons. Dept. 3 pp.

.... 1961. Deer Range Acreage Figures. Wis. Cons. Dept. 3 pp. Mimeo.

Stephenson, Isaac. 1915. Recollections of a Long Life, 1829-1915. Privately printed. Chicago. 264 pp.

Stoeckler, J. H., Keener, John M. and Strothmann, R. O. 1958. Deer Browse Production from Felled Trees in the Northern Hardwood-Hemlock Forest Type. Jour. of Forestry. Vol. 56, No. 6. Reprint.

Stollberg, B. D. 1949. Deer Starve at Feeding Station. Wis. Cons. Bull. 14(2):18-19.

Stouffer, Russell. 1957. Let's Go Forward. Wis. Cons. Bull. 22(4):7-8.

Strong, Moses. 1883. List of the Mammals of Wisconsin. Geology Survey of 1873-1879. 1:437. Ch. 10.

Swift, Ernest F. 1936. Review of Deer Season. Wis. Cons. Bull. 1(12):4-7.

.... 1937. First Reports of 1937 Deer Season. Wis. Cons. Bull. 2(11):7-9.

.... 1938. Trail Blazing for the Deer Hunter. Wis. Cons. Bull. 3(3):3-13.

.... 1939. The Problem of Managing Wisconsin Deer. Wis. Cons. Bull. 4(2):8-27.

.... 1940-41. Biography of a Self-Made Naturalist (George Ruegger). Wis. Cons. Bull. 5(12):3-12; 6(1):41-52; 6(3):3-17; 6(4):3-8.

.... 1944. Let Us Examine the Record. Wis. Cons. Bull. 9(8,9):9-12.

.... 1946a. Deer As An Outdoor Problem. Wis. Cons. Bull. 11(7):6-10.

.... 1946b. A History of Wisconsin Deer. Pub. 323, Wis. Cons. Dept. 96 pp.

.... 1947. Wildlife as a Forest Crop in the Lake States. Proc. Soc. of Am. Forester's Meeting. pp. 483-492.

.... 1952. Deer Herd Control Methods and Their Results. Wis. Cons. Bull. 17(1):3-9.

.... 1961. They Laughed at Us. Am. Forests 67(5):20-22.

Taylor, Jim. 1961. Let's Even Up the Deer Kill. Wis. Cons. Bull. 26(1):14-15.

Thompson, D. R. 1955. Pre-season Deer Population Ratio Tallies, 1955. Wis. Cons. Dept. 2 pp. Mimeo.

.... 1956. Pre-season Deer Population Tallies, 1956. Wis. Cons. Dept. 2 pp. Mimeo.

.... 1957. Results of Spring Pellet Group Counts, 1957. Wis. Cons. Dept. 3 pp. Mimeo.

.... 1958. Results of Spring Surveys on Deer Management Units. Wis. Cons. Dept. 4 pp. Mimeo.

.... 1959. Results of Spring Surveys on Game Management Units. Wis. Cons. Dept. 3 pp. Mimeo.

.... 1960. Deer Management Unit Surveys, 1960. Wis. Cons. Dept. 9 pp. Mimeo.

.... 1961. 1961 Deer Management Unit Surveys. Wis. Cons. Dept. 8 pp. Mimeo.

.... 1962. 1962 Deer Management Unit Surveys. Wis. Cons. Dept. 12 pp. Mimeo.

Tiews, Lester C. 1962. Operation Browse Drop. Wis. Cons. Bull. 27(5):21-22.

Torkelson, M. W. 1931. Wisconsin Highways. Wisconsin Blue Book. pp. 9-30.

Trainer, Daniel O., Jr. 1958. Deer Whole Blood Collection. Wis. Cons. Dept. 2 pp. Mimeo.

.... 1962a. Protozoan Diseases of White-tailed Deer. Univ. of Wis.

.... 1962b. The Rearing of White-tailed Deer Fawns in Captivity. Jour. Wildl. Mgt. 26(3):340-341.

.... Bring 'Em Back Alive. Wis. Cons. Bull. 23(11):18-20.

Trainer, Daniel O., Jr., and Hanson, Robert P. 1960. Leptospirosis and Brucellosis Serological Reactors in Wisconsin Deer - 1957-58. Jour. of Wildl. Mgt. 24(1):44-52.

.... 1962. The Association of White-tailed Deer and Cattle in Wisconsin. Cornell Veterinarian 52(3):431-438.

Vail, E. C. 1920. Doesn't Favor One Buck Law. Wis. Conservationist. 2(1):23.

Vanderwall, E. J. 1946. The Department Reports on 1945. Wis. Cons. Bull. 11(3):3.

Voigt, L. P. 1957. What About the 1957 Deer Season? Wis. Cons. Dept. Circular.

.... 1961. Deer Management Policy Statement. Wis. Cons. Dept. 3 pp. Mimeo.

Wallin, Victor C. 1944. The Public Information Problem. Wis. Cons. Bull. 9(8,9):19-22.

Waskow, Ben and George Curran. 1954. Deer Hunting on the Apostle Islands. Wis. Cons. Bull. 19(10):3-7.

Wegg, Robert T. 1939. Managing Wisconsin Deer. Wis. Cons. Bull. 4(4):20-23.

Weitz, Chauncey A. 1963. Save The Deer. Wis. Cons. Bull. 28(5):6-7.

Welch, Stanley. 1939. Deer Damage in the Brule River Valley. Wis. Cons. Bull. 4(6):41-46.

Wildner, Clare L. 1936-37. Who Will Write the Final Chapter? Wis. Sportsman 1(5):4.

Wilson, E. 1938. More Deer Refuges Urged. Wis. Cons. Bull. 3(2):38-39.

Wisconsin Historical Collections 1856-1911. Year, volume and pages: 1856, 2, 520 pp; 1857, 3, 529 pp; 1868, 5, 432 pp; 1872, 6, 501 pp; 1882, 9, 486 pp; 1888, 11, 548 pp; 1895, 13, 515 pp; 1898, 14, 553 pp; 1900, 15, 491 pp; 1902, 16, 514 pp; 1910, 19, 528 pp; 1911, 20, 497 pp.

APPENDIX

CONSERVATION COMMISSION POLICY ON DEER-FOREST MANAGEMENT
(Adopted by the Conservation Commission on September 21, 1962)

In keeping with the Legislature's intent in the passage of the
Conservation Act (23.09 Wis. Stats.) for providing "an adequate and
flexible system for the protection, development and use of forests,
...and game", the Wisconsin Conservation Commission recognizes the need
to accelerate and implement the coordination of deer and forest
management programs.

It has been shown that the forests and deer of Wisconsin provide
invaluable economic and recreational benefits to this state. Therefore,
the entire public has a great equity in the sustained production of
timber and deer resources. The value of both present and future wood
and wildlife resources depends on ample and continuous forest regeneration.
An inadequately managed deer herd can damage forest regeneration to the
detriment of not only wood production but also its own range as well.
Also, it has become apparent that because of the inter-dependence of these
two resources they can't be managed as entities.

In 1961 a Department committee consisting of representatives of all
Divisions concerned with resource management was assigned to make a complete
evaluation of problems related to deer and forest management. This
evaluation together with plans and procedures for managing these resources
was set forth in a report "Deer-Forest Interrelationships in Forest Land
Management, 1962". The section on "Concepts and Conclusions" in this
report embodies recommendations of the Big Game Committee of the 1961
Conservation Congress.

To achieve the goal of a coordinated management program the Wisconsin
Conservation Commission adopts the following concepts and conclusions as
policy and instructs the Department to execute the attached action program.

CONCEPTS AND CONCLUSIONS

Needs and Background

Deer are a Wisconsin resource which must be managed equitably for the entire public, including all the people dependent on wood products, the hunter and sightseer. Deer are only one of several forest land resources and therefore cannot be managed as entities.

Extensive logging and other conditions during the late 1800's and early 1900's set the stage for a large deer herd during the 1940's.

Overbrowsing by deer, some destructive cutting practices, growth of the forest beyond the reach of deer and failure to adequately harvest the available crop of deer have reduced the quantity and quality of deer food and cover. Although some improvements can be achieved, the conditions which created the high deer populations of the 1940's will not be duplicated in the north.

Resources and Forest Land Management

The total value of Wisconsin's forest resource is tremendous. Although definite values can be determined for wood products, recreational values from these same lands are less tangible, but nevertheless highly significant.

Approximately 25 percent of the commercial forest area of the state is susceptible to deer damage.

To manage forested land for maximum production of either deer or timber products can result in a reduced yield of the other product. Since both are produced on the same land in most instances, coordination of management to achieve optimum production of each is imperative.

Public lands should be managed under a true multiple-use plan, i.e. all land should be managed to provide the maximum public benefits from both timber and recreation (wildlife). However, it must be recognized that not all lands can be managed in the same way. On certain public lands, forest management will predominate, while on certain others, wildlife management will take priority.

Private forest lands are normally managed to accrue the greatest economic benefits to the owner, regardless of the public interest. They normally are not managed for deer in the same way as public lands. However, deer are recognized as a valuable by-product of private forest lands.

Deer range is largely commercial forest land. In the long run browse production depends upon forest reproduction. Therefore, intensive forest management involving continous cutting and subsequent regeneration is good deer range management. Timber markets and available funds for intensive management will have important effects on the future overall deer range quality and resulting deer numbers. In fact the only practical means of cutting enough trees to allow significant amounts of browse to develop is through forest management practices. Such practices will also provide deer browse that is immediately available in the form of downed tree tops. Hence phases of the forestry program which deal with cutting operations will be emphasized in order to heighten benefits simultaneously to both forests and deer.

Intensive management for deer range alone, e.g. cutting or clearing out large areas of trees, is impractical and unnecessary to meet current deer population goals. However, it may be desirable at particular times and under particular conditions to increase productivity of the herd. This can be achieved as necessary by the modification of certain forestry practices within prescribed management units.

The responsibility for carrying out the mechanics of coordinating a timber and deer-range improvement program and any necessary modification of timber management practices rests with the district foresters, game managers and their assistants.

Forestry practices can benefit deer and wood production simultaneously but only if the herd is kept in balance with its range.

Current statewide population goals are a winter herd of 430,000 deer, which is larger than the state herd of 1961. Keeping the herd at this size will allow an annual legal harvest of 85,000 (75,000 to 100,000) and at the same time will alleviate forest damage and permit tree regeneration and deer-range improvement. Any increase in the harvestable crop should be brought about by creating range conditions which will result in an increased productivity rather than by carrying more deer in winter.

The maintenance of this level of population and harvest requires flexibility in hunting season regulations. Although deer of both sexes must be harvested at various times and places, it is necessary to develop seasons which will achieve such harvests only where needed. The variable-quota law provides the best current approach for harvesting deer at the highest sustained level and it in combination with buck and any-deer seasons will be used as the basis for future hunting regulations.

Deer hunting is a method of herd management but it is only a part of total resource management, and should not be regulated for deer management purposes only.

Education and Research

The production of optimum timber and wildlife resources requires a continuous research program to evaluate dynamic forest land changes and provide answers to unresolved technical problems.

To obtain the necessary information for managing deer resources, 77 management units have been established. Units with comparable conditions will be grouped together for setting hunting seasons.

A well-planned and persistent educational program for Department employees, technicians in other land use agencies and the general public is paramount to a sustained program of sound deer and forest management.

THE ACTION PROGRAM

Forest Management

Since intensive forest management involving increased cutting is good deer management, the following phases of the present forestry program will be emphasized in order to heighten benefits simultaneously to both forests and deer.

1. Attain a maximum program of timber sales on public lands and assist private landowners to do the same as markets allow.

2. Assist in expanding present wood-using industries and in obtaining new markets for wood products.

3. Develop the means and procure the funds to intensify forest improvement cuttings.

4. Where reforestation is desirable, ascertain that recommended accessways surrounding plantations are left and that clumps of hardwoods are left in the plantation area where feasible. Accessways are also important aids in the fire suppression program.

5. Efforts will be intensified to reduce grazing of woodlots, an important deterrent to larger deer herds in southwestern Wisconsin.

Deer-Range Management

Intensive mangement for deer range alone (e.g. cutting or clearing out large areas of trees) is impractical. The only practical deer-range management is dependent on forestry practices. But to achieve maximum benefits in some areas and under certain conditions, efforts must be made to redirect forestry operations for better coordination and implementation of forest and deer-range management.

1. Timing and distribution of normal timber-cutting practices will be coordinated wherever practical to achieve optimum returns of timber and wildlife production. These will be carried out immediately at the field level.

2. More intermediate cuts should be made. Such a program will result in a higher quantity and quality of forest products and, at the same time, improve deer-range conditions. Wherever possible, such cuttings should be made on a commercial basis. Where such cuttings are not commercially feasible, and important benefits would result to both forest and deer management, costs should be shared by both interests. Close coordination must be maintained so that such cutting will be done in critical areas where maximum benefits will result.

3. Guidelines will be prepared for forest managers by the game management administration, pointing out possible modification of forestry practices to benefit deer.

4. The Game Management Division in consultation with other Department divisions will determine when and where increased deer productivity is necessary to meet changes in statewide objectives. These recommendations will be submitted for administrative approval and implementation.

    (a) The area game supervisors and district game managers will review these recommendations with other area and district personnel.

    (b) Foresters and game managers at the field level will determine which of the various practices are to be implemented within the specified units. The decision will be based upon judgment with consideration of the major ownership of the land, the cost of instituting the practices, the cost of maintenance, and the loss of timber production values, all in relation to the expected increase in deer productivity (shootable population).

Herd Management

Proper forestry practices can benefit the deer herd only if the herd is kept in balance with the range. Therefore, management must be directed toward maintaining the herd at a level which will not only provide a high sustained yield but also at the same time permit the maintenance and improvement of present deer-range conditions, and provide for adequate forest regeneration by keeping the herd in line with range conditions and alleviating damage to forest and other crop resources.

1. Carry a winter herd of 430,000 deer - an increase of approximately 14% over the general 1961-62 winter level. A herd this size will allow an annual legal harvest of an average of 85,000 animals (75,000 - 100,000).

2. Complete the setting of specific population goals for deer-management units.

3. Utilize the variable-quota law in 1963 and in subsequent years in combination with a general season to concentrate or spread out hunting pressure as necessary. This will at the same time permit a man to hunt where he wants with possible restrictions only on his legal target.

4. In setting seasons, management units with similar needs and problems will be grouped together to keep down the number of unit seasons. This will be necessary to simplify hunting regulations and to facilitate law enforcement which will be important to the successful application of the variable-quota law. Management unit boundaries will be reevaluated and changes will be kept to a minimum.

5. Intensify present survey efforts -- aging, browse surveys, pellet group counts, etc.

6. Retain the present system for handling deer damage to agricultural crops. (No damage payments are available for forest crop damage but the goal of a winter herd of 430,000 deer will alleviate this problem when proper distribution is achieved.)

Education

As discussed in the Problems section, the success of deer-forest management demands an effective education program. This can be achieved only when a basic understanding of the value, equity, problems and approaches is obtained, first, by the agencies basically responsible for the custodianship and management of the resources, and then by other agencies responsible for cooperative phases of the management programs and the general public.

The process of education that will be followed includes five steps (the first two have been completed):

1. The best information available on forest-deer management was pulled together to form the background section of this report by representatives of the Forest Management, Forests and Parks and Game Management Divisions. From this information plans and procedures were developed.

2. A Department committee representing all divisions evaluated and approved the plans and procedures. Following this appraisal, these plans and procedures were adopted by the Conservation Commission as policy.

3. Now, the process of familiarizing all Department personnel concerned with this forest and deer management policy must be executed. The correct interpretation and use of this policy is essential to the success of the entire program. This will include a Department-wide training program specifically on deer-forest management.

4. Other key agencies having a responsibility or equity in the management of forest and deer resources will receive a copy of this report and explanations as necessary. These include the Natural Resources Committee of State Agencies, State Soil and Water Conservation Committee, Conservation Congress, Extension Service, Highway Commission, U. S. Forest Service and the U. S. Soil Conservation Service, college conservation teachers, state Conservation Curriculum Committee, key conservation club officers, vocational agriculture instructors, Conservation Committee of the State Legislature, and other groups where the need may arise.

5. Once Conservation Department personnel and representatives of other resource management agencies are familiarized with the background, the plans and procedures and the policy for managing Wisconsin's forest and deer resources, this information will be disseminated to the public using all media available. This will include radio and television coverage, with a special television program designated for spot news reporting prepared on this subject. A selection of deer-forest management slides will be prepared and made available to all Department employees who need them in disseminating this program.

There will be a continued need to keep Conservation Department personnel and other resource management agencies and the public appraised of progress in advancing an integrated deer-forest management program, new problems and proposed solutions. Special emphasis will be placed on the Department deer-forest program rather than divisional or unit interests that may arise. The entire policy and program is intended to be an ongoing and continuing program, rather than a one-shot or basic introductory crash program.

The emphasis of the education program will be based on recognizing the entire public's equity in forest and deer resources. In the past too much emphasis was placed on "too many deer". Our redefined goal will be to furnish hunters with the maximum number of high quality animals consistent with good land-use principles.

Research and Administrative Evaluation

The development of the background plans and procedures have emphasized the need for administrative evaluations and research studies to provide additional data to better implement the program. These are outlined below:

A. Deer-forest relationships

1. Development of methods of range analysis to permit determinations of limiting factors.

2. Openings -- the need where, when, how much and maintenance methods.

3. Development of methods for improvement and expansion of winter range, and feasibility of creating high browse production areas adjacent to deer yards through intensive management.

4. Projection of overall deer-range picture 20 and 40 years hence, i.e., what effect will gradual conversion of aspen to hardwoods, spruce or pine have on deer; is increased use of hardwood pulp likely -- this would benefit deer, etc.

5. Determination of deer population levels which will permit adequate regeneration in various forest types.

6. Determination of cutting practices which reduce the likelihood of damage by deer.

B. Deer biology and harvest

Determination of:

1. Productivity of unit herds

2. All mortality factors

3. Relative success on party permits

    a. In different forest types in the state

    b. With different deer herd levels

    c. Under various hunting pressures

C. Sociology and psychology of deer hunting and other factors regarding the deer herd, including the accumulation of information on:

1. The overall value of deer

2. How we can best sell good deer management

3. What makes a successful deer season

4. Importance of seeing deer to the tourist industry

5. Where hunters will go if a large portion of the state is open to unrestricted party permit seasons, and why.

PENALTIES RELATIVE TO HUNTING ACCIDENTS
AS PROVIDED BY WISCONSIN LAWS

29.221 LEAVING SCENE OF ACCIDENTAL SHOOTING. (1) Any person who, while
hunting any wild animal or bird, discharges a firearm or arrow, and thereby
injures or kills another person, shall forthwith give his name and address to
such person if injured and render such assistance to him as may be necessary
and obtain immediate medical or hospital care, and shall immediately thereafter report such injury or death to the sheriff or police of the locality
in which such shooting took place.
(2) Any person failing to comply with sub. (1) shall be fined not less than
$5 nor more than $5,000, or imprisoned in the county jail not less than 10
days nor to exceed one year, or both.

29.222 HUNTING ACCIDENT; FAILURE TO REPORT. (1) Every person who shall have
caused or been involved in an accident in which a human being has been injured
by gunfire or by bow and arrow while hunting or trapping, or shall have in-
flicted an injury upon himself with firearm or with a bow and arrow while
hunting or trapping, shall render a report to the state conservation commission of Wisconsin at any of its field offices within 10 days after such
injury unless such person be physically incapable of making the required report in which event it shall be the duty of the person or persons involved in
the accident to designate an agent to file the report within the specified
time.
(2) Any person who shall have been involved in an accident with firearm or
bow and arrow while hunting or trapping, and who shall fail to submit the report required by this section shall be fined not more than $50 or imprisoned
not to exceed 3 months, or both, and in addition the court may revoke any
license issued to him under ch. 29 and may further provide that no license
shall be issued to him under ch. 29 for such fixed period of time that the
court may deem just.

940.08 HOMICIDE BY NEGLIGENT USE OF VEHICLE OR WEAPON. (1) Whoever causes
the death of another human being by a high degree of negligence in the operation or handling of a vehicle, firearm, airgun, or bow and arrow may be fined
not more than $1,000 or imprisoned not more than one year in county jail or
both.
(2) A high degree of negligence is conduct which demonstrates ordinary negligence to a high degree, consisting of an act which the person should realize
creates a situation of unreasonable risk and high probability of death or
great bodily harm to another.

940.09 HOMICIDE BY INTOXICATED USER OF VEHICLE OR FIREARM. Whoever by the
negligent operation or handling of a vehicle, firearm or airgun and while
under the influence of an intoxicant causes the death of another may be fined
not more than $2,500 or imprisoned not more than 5 years or both. No person
shall be convicted under this section except upon proof of causal negligence
in addition to such operation or handling while under the influence of an
intoxicant.

940.24 INJURY BY NEGLIGENT USE OF WEAPON. (1) Whoever causes bodily harm
to another by a high degree of negligence in the operation or handling of a
firearm, airgun, or bow and arrow, may be fined not more than $1,000 or
imprisoned not more than one year or both.
(2) A high degree of negligence is conduct which demonstrates ordinary negligence to a high degree, consisting of an act which the person should realize
creates a situation of unreasonable risk and high probability of death or
great bodily harm to another.

941.20 RECKLESS USE OF WEAPONS. (1) Whoever does any of the following may be fined not more than $200 or imprisoned not more than 6 months or both:

(a) Endangers another's safety by reckless conduct in the operation or handling of a firearm, airgun, or bow and arrow; or

(b) Operates or goes armed with a firearm while he is under the influence of an intoxicant; or

(c) Intentionally points a firearm at or toward another.

(2) Whoever does any of the following may be fined not more than $1,000 or imprisoned not more than 3 years or both:

(a) Intentionally discharges a firearm into vehicle or building under circumstances in which he should realize there might be a human being present therein; or

(b) Sets a spring gun.

(3) Reckless conduct consists of an act which creates a situation of unreasonable risk and high probability of death or great bodily harm to another and which demonstrates a conscious disregard for the safety of another and a willingness to take known chances of perpetrating an injury. It is intended that this definition embraces all of the elements of what was heretofore known as gross negligence in the criminal law of Wisconsin.

29.63 (3) REVOCATION OF LICENSE. In addition to all other penalties for a violation of this chapter, or any conservation commission order made pursuant to this chapter, the court in its discretion may upon conviction revoke any license theretofore issued pursuant to this chapter to the person convicted and order that no such license shall be issued to such person for a period of not to exceed one year thereafter.

(d) If a person is convicted of reckless or highly negligent conduct in the operation or handling of a firearm or bow and arrow in violation of s. 940.08 or 941.20 and either death or bodily harm to another results from such violation, the court shall revoke every license issued to that person under this chapter and shall provide a fixed period during which no license may be issued to such person. If no death or injury to another results from the violation, the court in its discretion may revoke any license issued to that person under this chapter and may provide a fixed period during which no new license may be issued to such person.

GUN DEER SEASON INJURIES AND FATALITIES
1938-1964

Year	Season Type	Length	Deer Tag Sales**	Deer Hunting Accidents Total	Killed	Injured
1938	Forked-antlered buck or larger	7 days	103,721	17	11	6
1939	Forked-antlered buck or larger	7 days	109,630	34	11	23
1940	Forked-antlered buck or larger	8 days	105,198	20	7	13
1941	Forked-antlered buck or larger	9 days	124,305	31	8	23
1942	Forked-antlered buck or larger	9 days	120,605	29	12	17
1943	"Split season"*	8 days	157,824	20	9	11
1944	forked-antlered buck (fork one inch or over)	6 days	127,643	Not available		
1945	Forked-antlered buck (fork one inch or over)	5 days	133,548	Not available		
1946	Forked-antlered buck (fork one inch or over)	9 days	201,061	48	12	36
1947	Forked-antlered buck (fork one inch or over)	9 days	222,935	23	5	18
1948	Forked-antlered buck (fork one inch or over)	9 days	248,609	35	12	23
1949	Antlerless deer and forked-antlered, with fork less than 2"	5 days	286,299	46	7	39
1950	Any deer	7 days	312,570	40	8	32
1951	Any deer	7 days	296,795	46	8	38
1952	Forked-antlered buck (fork one inch or over)	7 days	238,287	32	9	23
1953	Forked-antlered buck (fork one inch or over)	7 days	234,032	22	6	16

Gun Deer Season Injuries and Fatalities - continued

Year	Season Type	Length	Deer Tag Sales**	Deer Hunting Accidents Total	Killed	Injured
1954	Forked-antlered buck (fork one inch or over)	7 days	247,310	23	7	16
1955	Forked-antlered buck	9 days	267,612	38	8	30
1956	Forked-antlered buck (3 inch spike or larger)	9 days	284,645	37	5	32
1957	Spike buck and party permit	9 days	288,903 (party permit- 32,027)	41	11	30
1958	Spike buck and party permit	9-16 days	335,866 (party permit- 58,438)	58	11	47
1959	Spike buck and party permit	9-16 days	349,443 (party permit- 61,018)	61	13	48
1960	Spike buck and party permit	9 days	338,208 (party permit- 47,522)	68	11	57
1961	Spike buck	9 days	307,863	28	9	19
1962	Spike buck and any deer	2-9 days	331,035	38	3	35
1963	Spike buck and any deer and party permit	2-9 days	360,552 (party permit- 5,578)	28	8	20
1964	Spike buck and any deer and party permit	3-9 days	24,624 (party permit-)	39	4	35

* Split season: Nov. 18-Nov. 21, forked-antlered bucks or larger.
Nov. 25-Nov. 28, antlerless deer (does and fawns).

** Includes resident big game, voluntary sportsmen's and nonresident big game licenses.

NOTE: This report lists only those casualties in which a person is injured by a weapon outside of the home and resulting from the activity of hunting.

ILLEGAL KILL DURING ANNUAL DEER SEASONS
Based on Warden Seizures Only
1932-1964

Year	No. of Seized Illegal Deer During Deer Season	Total No. of Seized Deer During Year	Type of Season
1932	608*	--	Antlered buck
1934	615*	--	Antlered buck
1936	713	--	Forked-horn buck
1937	542	--	Forked-horn buck
1938	846	--	Forked-horn buck
1939	995	--	Forked-horn buck
1940	816	--	Forked-horn buck
1941	1,548	--	Forked-horn buck
1942	934	--	Forked-horn buck
1943	1,018	--	Forked-horn buck and antlerless
1944	599	--	Forked-horn and antlered buck
1945	970	--	Forked-horn buck
1946	1,700	2,318	Forked-horn buck
1947**	2,092	3,126	Forked-horn buck
1948	1,637	2,932	Forked-horn buck
1949	848	1,884	Any deer except forked-horn buck
1950	157	--	Any deer
1951	104	--	Any deer
1952	434	--	Forked-horn buck
1953	744	--	Forked-horn buck
1954	976	--	Forked-horn buck
1955	1,702	--	Forked-horn buck
1956	1,592	--	Spike buck
1957	918	--	Spike buck and party permit
1958	706	--	Spike buck and party permit
1959	1,227	--	Spike buck and party permit

Illegal Kill During Annual Deer Seasons - continued

Year	No. of Seized Illegal Deer During Deer Season	Total No. of Seized Deer During Year	Type of Season
1960	518	--	Spike buck and party permit
1961	1,206	--	Spike buck
1962	995	--	Spike buck and any deer
1963	1,096	--	Spike buck and any deer
1964	1,057	--	Spike buck and any deer
TOTAL	29,913		

* Record is incomplete - a low estimate.

** Jackson County Sportsmen's Club members and Department men on a cross-country drive to locate and examine dead deer after the season, found in the heavy deer concentration area of Knapp Township 22 illegally killed deer per square mile, or an average of 1 deer per 28 acres. Systematic annual dead deer checks in Eastern Jackson County (1956-1964) have produced an estimated illegal and/or crippling losses of from 2.4 to 6.5 deer per square mile - equaling 35% to 150% of the registered legal harvest.
Illegally killed elk in Vilas County: 1941, 1; 1944, 1; 1945, 1; 1946, 2; 1947, 3; 1949, 5; and 1951, 1.

NOTE: This table includes salvaged deer for the most part. No record is available of the many spoiled deer left in the woods. Obviously, the total number of deer killed illegally during any season is much higher than is shown in this table.

AREAS CLOSED PRIMARILY FOR
THE PROTECTION OF DEER
1952-1953

County	Acres in County	1953 Season			1952 Season		
		Acres Closed	% of County Closed	No. of Units	Acres Closed	% of County Closed	No. of Units
Adams	433,280	42,920	9.90	3	137,900	31.83	5
Ashland	663,680	90	.01	1	28,250	4.26	3
Barron	554,240	none			35,362	6.38	3
Bayfield	943,360	none			none		
Burnett	537,600	none			79,367	14.76	5
Chippewa	656,000	none			13,460	2.05	1
Chippewa & Rusk	1,238,400	none			none		
Clark	782,080	none			78,490	10.04	6
Douglas	838,400	none			56,550	6.74	1
Dunn	549,120	none			860	.16	1
Eau Claire	415,360	21,980	5.29	2	57,600	13.87	5
Florence	312,960	5,200	1.66	2	22,400	7.16	5
Forest	646,400	none			32,680	5.06	3
Green Lake & Marquette	519,680	5,200	1.00	1	23,320	4.49	2
Iron	477,440	none			25,880	5.42	2
Jackson	640,000	none			57,248	8.95	10
Jackson & Monroe	1,225,600	none			none		
Juneau	508,800	1,920	.37	1	80,332	15.79	8
Langlade	549,120	none			131,450	24.34	2
Marathon	1,013,760	none			55,680	5.49	3
Marinette	888,320	none			20,500	2.31	2
Monroe	585,600	4,480	.77	1	33,160	5.66	3
Oconto	707,840	none			25,000	3.53	2
Oneida	712,960	28,930	4.06	5	97,940	13.74	3
Polk	597,760	none			76,418	12.78	5
Price	811,520	none			48,660	6.0	4
Rusk	582,400	none			10,160	1.74	1
Shawano	752,640	none			35,140	4.67	1
Sawyer	814,720	none			none		
Taylor	626,560	none			45,920	7.33	2
Vilas	554,880	42,570	7.67	7	262,920	47.38	2
Washburn	522,240	none			55,055	10.54	3
Wood	519,680	24,300	4.68	1	114,700	22.07	6
Price, Oneida & Vilas		none			24,880		1
TOTALS		177,590		24	1,767,282		100
Counties having closed areas			11			30	

AREAS CLOSED PRIMARILY FOR
THE PROTECTION OF DEER
1954

| County | Acres in County | 1954 Season | | |
		Acres Closed	% of County Closed	No. of Units
Adams	433,280	none		
Ashland	663,680	320	.05	1
Barron	554,240	none		
Bayfield	943,360	8,960	· .95	1
Burnett	537,600	none		
Chippewa	656,000	none		
Chippewa & Rusk	1,238,400	1,680	.14	1
Clark	782,080	none		
Douglas	838,400	none		
Dunn	549,120	none		
Eau Claire	415,360	13,400	3.23	1
Florence	312,960	5,200	1.66	2
Forest	646,400	none		
Green Lake & Marquette	519,680	2,775	.53	1
Iron	477,440	none		
Jackson	640,000	none		
Jackson & Monroe	1,225,600	3,220	.26	1
Juneau	508,800	1,920	.38	1
Langlade	549,120	none		
Marathon	1,013,760	none		
Marinette	888,320	none		
Monroe	585,600	none		
Oconto	707,840	none		
Oneida	712,960	41,775	5.86	6
Polk	597,760	none		
Price	811,520	none		
Rusk	582,400	none		
Shawano	752,640	none		
Sawyer	814,720	21,560	2.65	2
Taylor	626,560	5,150	.82	1
Vilas	554,880	53,005	9.55	15
Washburn	422,240	3,520	.67	1
Wood	519,680	none		
Price, Oneida, & Vilas		none		
TOTALS		162,485		34
Counties having closed areas			16	

AREAS CLOSED PRIMARILY FOR
THE PROTECTION OF DEER
1955

County	Acres in County	1955 Season		
		Acres Closed	% of County Closed	No. of Units
Ashland	663,680	320	.05	1
Bayfield	943,360	8,960	.95	1
Chippewa	656,000	1,300	.20	1
Chippewa & Rusk	1,238,400	none		
Eau Claire	415,360	14,020	3.38	2
Florence	312,960	3,680	1.18	2
Green Lake & Marquette	519,680	none		
Jackson & Monroe	1,225,600	none		
Juneau	508,800	1,920	.38	1
Kewaunee	211,840	5,760	2.72	1
Manitowoc	276,960	1,680	.45	1
Marquette	292,480	1,960	.67	1
Monroe	585,600	3,220	.55	1
Oneida	712,960	37,245	5.23	5
Sawyer	814,720	none		
Taylor	626,560	none		
Vilas	554,880	53,285	9.60	15
Washburn	522,240	3,520	.67	1
TOTALS		136,870 (15% less than 1954)		33
Counties having closed areas		13		

AREAS CLOSED PRIMARILY FOR
THE PROTECTION OF DEER
1956

| County | Acres in County | 1956 Season | | |
		Acres Closed	% of County Closed	No. of Units
Ashland	663,680	320	.05	1
Bayfield	943,360	8,960	.95	1
Florence	312,960	3,680	1.18	2
Green Lake & Marquette	519,680	2,775	.53	1
Juneau	508,800	1,920	.38	1
Kewaunee	211,840	5,760	2.72	1
Manitowoc	376,960	770	.20	1
Oneida	712,960	35,125	4.93	4
Vilas	554,880	53,289	9.60	15
Washburn	522,240	3,520	.67	1
TOTALS		116,119 (15.2% less than 1955)		28
Counties having closed areas		11		

AREAS CLOSED PRIMARILY FOR
THE PROTECTION OF DEER
1957

| County | Acres in County | 1957 Season | | |
		Acres Closed	% of County Closed	No. of Units
Ashland	663,680	320	.05	1
Bayfield	943,360	8,960	.95	1
Florence	312,960	4,400	1.4	2
Green Lake	227,200	1,125	.5	1
Juneau	508,800	1,920	.38	1
Kewaunee	211,840	5,760	2.72	1
Manitowoc	376,960	700	.20	1
Oneida	712,960	35,705	5.0	4
Vilas	554,880	50,760	9.14	13
TOTALS		109,720 (6% less than 1956)		25
Counties having closed areas		9		

DEER FEEDING COSTS AND DEER YARD EXPENDITURES

1935-1956*

Year	Hay	Concentrate	Tonnage Grain or Concentrate	Total
1935-36	23.0	.5		23.5
1936-37	28.0	3.5		31.5
1937-38	39.0	2.0		41.0
1938-39	41.0	1.5		42.5
1939-40	13.0	12.0	2.0	27.0
1940-41	20.0	21.0		41.0
1941-42	2.5	7.0		9.5
1942-43	25.0	22.5		47.5
1943-44	107.0	106.0	58.0	271.0
1944-45	202.0	173.0	110.0	485.0
1945-46	377.0	355.0	35.0	767.0
1946-47	282.0	175.0		457.0
1947-48	492.0	491.0	2.5	985.5
1948-49	521.0	393.0		914.0
1949-50	625.0	362.0		987.0
1950-51	775.0	356.0		1,131.0
1951-52	584.0	170.0		754.0
1952-53	113.0	58.0	6.0	177.0
1953-54	224.4	50.0		274.4
1954-55	204.5			204.5
1955-56	273.8		94.2	368.0

Year	Feed Costs	Other Costs**	Total	Browse Improvement*** Acres	Cost
1935-36	$ 377.20	$ 204.54	$ 581.74		
1936-37	457.50	249.01	706.51		
1937-38	1,327.50	739.26	2,066.76		
1938-39	577.15	329.18	906.33		
1939-40	965.43	549.08	1,514.51		
1940-41	1,438.67	797.19	2,235.86		
1941-42	391.50	220.44	611.94		
1942-43	1,407.43	823.69	2,231.12		
1943-44	8,237.71	9,338.43	17,576.14		
1944-45	18,149.13	9,605.37	27,754.50		
1945-46	45,910.38	33,419.96	79,330.34		
1946-47	15,861.45	18,460.71	34,322.16		
1947-48	55,094.71	17,843.31	72,938.02		
1948-49	45,866.43	15,044.33	60,910.76		
1949-50	43,687.77	21,209.55	64,897.32		
1950-51	50,049.34	44,354.32	94,403.66		
1951-52	31,431.70	34,795.85	66.227.55	858.5	$ 8,357.47
1952-53	9,000.01[1]	28,821.10	37,821.11	1,254.0	13,989.93
1953-54	12,329.85	10,159.59	22,489.44	818.0	9,026.25

Deer Feed Costs and Deer Yard Expenditures (continued)

Year	Feed Costs	Other Costs**	Total	Browse Improvement***	
				Acres	Cost
1954-55	$ 6,160.15	$13,059.37	$19,219.52	206.0	2,368.00
1955-56	10,834.96	21,080.71	31,915.67	213.0	1,555.35

   * Winter deer feeding costs prior to 1943-44 are estimated.
  ** Includes the feed distribution costs of salaries, travel expense,
     materials, services, supplies and miscellaneous charges.
 *** Includes deer browse improvement work such as the cutting of palatable
     species of trees and shrubs.
[1] Credit of $495.50 received through sale of unused hay is not included.

DEER YARD ACQUISITION AND EXPENDITURES SINCE 1943-44

Fiscal Year	Acres Acquired	Cost of Land Purchased	Total Deer Yard Cost*
1944-45	4,239.59	$13,149.45	$27,113.69
1945-46	9,486,28	30,708.93	40,357.05
1946-47	5,373.67	36,460.00	29,387.10
1947-48	1,428.28	5,948.19	13,413.13
1948-49	3,184,69	28,506.80	30,375.70
1949-50	578.96	2,625.00	22,958.85
1950-51	640.00	6,510.00	20,082.21
1951-52	1,443.45	11,064.00	39,653.32
1952-53	565.55	2,840.00	16,859.76
1953-54	906.95	9,048.50	16,816.42
1954-55	105.12	930.00	6,152.02
1955-56	40.00	170.00	6,346,68
1956-57	80.00	570.00	
1957-58	--	--	--
1958-59	--	--	--
1959-60	--	--	--
1960-61	--	--	--
1961-62	40.00	50.00	
1962-63	20.00	400.00	
1962-63	162.93	(gift)	--
TOTALS	28,295.47	$148,980.87	

*Includes deer yard acquisition and management costs.

NOTE: From 1943-1953 revenue derived from $.50 of each deer tag or resident
deer hunting license fee was used exclusively for the purchase of
winter feed and the acquisition of winter deer yards in the northern
major deer counties. Included in the program of deer feeding during
recent years is browse improvement -- the cutting or bulldozing of
trees and saplings of little value so that deer can browse the tops,
and the stumps can set out new shoots within reach of the deer.

DEER DAMAGE EXPENDITURES

Year**	Total Appropriations*	Expenditures Deer	Fence	Total	Number of Paid Claims
1932	$ 12,000.00	$ $4,259.70	$ -	$ 4,259.70	71
1933	-	1,773.85	-	1,773.85	72
1934	12,000.00	5,746.14	-	5,746.14	143
1935	-	5,040.09	-	5,040.09	172
1936	12,000.00	5,413.24	-	5,413.24	207
1937	12,000.00	6,578.54	381.06	6,959.60	223
1938	12,000.00	6,428.09	1,161.01	7,589.10	223
1939	12,000.00	9,427.67	2,276.79	11,704.46	271
1940	12,000.00	12,405.73	1,840.17	14,245.90	308
1941	12,000.00	11,623.95	545.21	12,169.16	479
1942	13,033.65	19,006.45	-	19,006.45	353
1943	23,216.35	14,690.04	21.04	14,711.08	372
1944	33,926.20	23,725.50	7.40	23,732.90	182
1945	53,073.80	26,329.77	2,217.06	28,546.83	405
1946	25,000.00	25,402.59	2,119.08	27,521.67	459
1947	60,000.00	52,726.16	2,256.59	54,982.75	307
1948	58,000.00	45,839.29	1,605.81	47,445.10	554
1949-50	40,000.00	39,998.93	500.00	40,498.93	460
1950-51	40,000.00	37,442.61	-	37,442.61	414
1951-52	40,000.00	21,378.55	-	21,378.55	198
1952-53	40,000.00	8,084.57	13.09	8,097.66	73
1953-54	40,000.00	13,049.14	-	13,049.14	104
1954-55	40,000.00	35,138.00	-	35,138.00	215
1955-56	40,000.00	17,219.60	-	17,219.60	114
1956-57	40,000.00	31,396.97	-	31,396.97	202
1957-58	40,000.00	25,474.94	-	25,474.94	212
1958-59	40,000.00	28,611.99	-	28,611.99	299
1959-60	40,000.00	27,384.80	-	27,384.80	170
1960-61	40,000.00	18,103.07	-	18,103.07	122
1961-62	40,000.00	22,014.29	-	22,014.29	135
1962-63	40,000.00	20,344.71	-	20,344.71	145
1963-64	40,000.00	29,855.51	-	29,855.51	197
TOTALS	**$962,250.00**	**$651,914.48**	**$14,944.31**	**$666,858.79**	**7,861**

* Annual Appropriations also provide for bear damage payments.

** Years up to 1949-50 represent calendar years. Subsequent payments were made on a fiscal year basis.

NOTE: Deer damage to agricultural crops has occurred since the time of settlement in Wisconsin. The first appropriation ($12,000.00) for payment of damage claims was made in 1931. Since 1949-50 deer and bear damage claims have been paid on a prorata basis at the end of the fiscal year from a $40,000.00 annual appropriation. More than 7,800 valid claims have received payment since the inception of the program.

TOTAL DEER DAMAGE EXPENDITURES BY COUNTY
1950-51 through 1963-64
(13 years)

( ) Number of claims

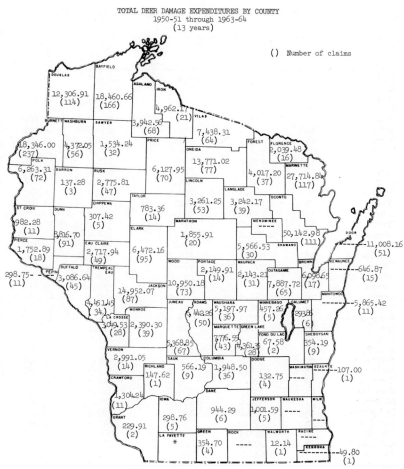

* Claims were paid in Lafayette County in 1948.

LAND AREA OF WISCONSIN DEER COUNTIES

County	Rank in Size	Square Miles Including Lakes*	Estimated Square Miles of Deer Range*	Area in Farms (Square Mi.)**	1960 Population***
Adams	45	642.4	409.3	268.4	7,566
Ashland	17	975.3	852.8	188.1	17,375
Barron	24	889.5	349.6	729.3	34,270
Bayfield	2	1,508.9	1,400.7	252.2	11,910
Brown	56	525.0	73.1	457.8	125,082
Buffalo	42	712.0	435.7	602.6	14,202
Burnett	25	883.5	702.5	255.3	9,214
Calumet	68	314.9	44.7	297.4	22,268
Chippewa	11	1,052.0	522.3	771.8	45,096
Clark	8	1,226.6	597.7	873.4	31,527
Columbia	35	786.9	381.2	642.4	36,708
Crawford	55	544.1	253.5	498.0	16,351
Dane	7	1,230.4	242.0	1,082.8	222,095
Dodge	23	908.0	122.0	784.3	63,170
Door	59	495.5	177.9	353.1	20,685
Douglas	5	1,328.8	1,230.9	164.4	45,008
Dunn	27	863.1	338.3	747.7	26,156
Eau Claire	43	655.1	415.2	422.7	58,300
Florence	58	496.5	476.3	53.6	3,437
Fond du Lac	40	726.8	97.8	640.3	75,085
Forest	12	1,044.3	980.0	96.3	7,542
Grant	10	1,142.4	233.9	1,020.0	44,419
Green	49	586.0	122.9	565.2	25,851
Green Lake	64	377.3	114.0	294.8	15,418
Iowa	36	761.0	398.4	710.1	19,631
Iron	34	798.2	706.4	47.6	7,830
Jackson	15	1,000.0	592.6	475.6	15,151
Jefferson	50	584.9	170.9	485.2	50,094
Juneau	33	804.5	515.7	342.3	17,490
Kenosha	69	278.1	27.0	192.9	100,615
Kewaunee	67	331.5	60.0	316.4	18,282
La Crosse	61	469.0	252.7	385.0	72,465
Lafayette	44	643.0	182.2	600.3	18,142
Langlade	26	873.0	766.3	324.1	19,916
Lincoln	21	917.1	611.8	342.5	22,338
Manitowoc	48	590.7	115.0	525.2	75,215
Marathon	1	1,618.0	618.7	1,241.4	88,874
Marinette	3	1,407.7	1,086.0	433.2	34,660
Marquette	62	463.4	214.9	334.1	8,516
Menominee	65	360.0	350.0	--	--
Milwaukee	70	239.0	11.0	51.3	1,036,041
Monroe	22	916.7	497.4	644.9	31,241
Oconto	13	1,022.9	576.8	508.2	25,110
Oneida	9	1,221.8	1,050.8	110.4	22,112
Outagamie	47	634.0	198.8	540.6	101,794
Ozaukee	72	235.0	28.4	182.5	38,441
Pepin	71	237.7	92.1	213.9	7,332

Land Area of Wisconsin Deer Counties (continued)

County	Rank in Size	Square Miles Including Lakes*	Estimated Square Miles of Deer Range*	Area in Farms (Square Mi.)**	1960 Popu- lation***
Pierce	51	584.7	154.5	524.2	22,503
Polk	18	966.7	439.4	684.6	24,968
Portage	30	815.9	375.6	623.9	36,964
Price	6	1,286.9	1,091.4	342.7	14,370
Racine	66	342.7	43.2	233.4	141,781
Richland	52	584.0	284.6	549.5	17,684
Rock	41	722.4	123.6	652.5	113,913
Rusk	20	919.3	693.9	415.2	14,794
St. Croix	38	745.3	126.4	627.0	29,164
Sauk	29	841.7	310.4	719.1	36,179
Sawyer	4	1,365.6	1,270.3	164.6	9,475
Shawano	19	939.9	677.7	705.1	34,351
Sheboygan	57	508.7	92.1	430.7	86,484
Taylor	16	984.8	747.0	555.7	17,843
Trempealeau	39	739.0	238.3	680.4	23,377
Vernon	32	805.0	423.9	741.6	25,663
Vilas	14	1,008.0	843.5	218.6	9,332
Walworth	54	560.0	89.7	478.6	52,358
Washburn	28	859.9	714.3	270.9	10,301
Washington	63	430.4	84.3	340.8	46,119
Waukesha	53	576.2	80.3	360.5	158,249
Waupaca	37	760.4	363.3	574.5	35,340
Waushara	46	635.9	251.5	426.4	13,497
Winnebago	60	490.3	77.7	369.7	107,928
Wood	31	813.0	352.0	509.4	59,105
TOTALS			29,547.1		3,951,777

* Deer range acreage figures, 1961.
** U. S. Census of Agriculture, Volume 1, Part 14.
*** U. S. Population Census, 1960.

RANK OF COUNTIES IN RESIDENT DEER LICENSE SALES
1947-1954

County	Year				
	1947	1948	1949	1950	1951
Adams	1,144	1,370	1,546	1,435	1,192
Ashland	2,930	3,069	3,796	3,848	3,355
Barron	4,501	4,847	6,087	6,642	5,858
Bayfield	2,590	2,772	3,059	3,167	2,643
Brown	5,807	6,327	7,368	8,517	7,972
Buffalo	1,303	1,641	1,697	1,770	1,625
Burnett	2,055	2,080	2,643	2,740	2,435
Calumet	693	724	927	1,094	976
Chippewa	4,445	4,638	5,941	6,152	5,299
Clark	4,630	5,038	5,979	6,183	4,933
Columbia	3,409	3,558	3,920	4,285	4,001
Crawford	759	1,155	1,227	1,080	1,084
Dane	6,531	7,028	8,333	9,379	8,374
Dodge	2,268	2,526	2,874	3,400	3,156
Door	858	977	1,204	1,481	2,378
Douglas	5,042	5,400	6,936	7,165	6,716
Dunn	1,884	2,955	3,601	3,836	3,309
Eau Claire	4,901	5,213	6,158	6,730	5,530
Florence	979	973	1,164	1,187	1,010
Fond du Lac	2,264	2,660	3,310	3,946	3,782
Forest	2,162	2,269	2,677	2,661	2,347
Grant	1,430	2,597	2,905	2,915	2,618
Green	661	746	814	1,168	953
Green Lake	1,028	1,397	1,598	1,902	1,892
Iowa	864	1,032	1,031	1,156	947
Iron	1,434	1,509	1,809	1,897	1,691
Jackson	2,494	2,674	3,091	3,201	2,447
Jefferson	1,010	1,172	1,591	1,918	1,680
Juneau	2,716	2,709	3,003	3,170	2,540
Kenosha	1,326	1,461	2,187	2,671	2,535
Kewaunee	680	831	1,058	1,227	1,134
La Crosse	4,838	5,370	5,526	6,158	5,429
Lafayette	380	488	582	659	576
Langlade	3,504	3,716	4,230	4,226	3,728
Lincoln	3,727	3,891	4,535	4,905	4,182
Manitowoc	2,386	2,554	3,085	3,712	3,304
Marathon	6,717	7,538	8,747	9,472	8,680
Marinette	5,258	5,638	6,187	6,252	5,772
Marquette	945	1,364	1,477	1,605	1,473
Milwaukee	13,166	15,548	20,562	25,765	25,360
Monroe	3,789	3,884	4,220	4,462	3,460
Oconto	3,879	4,066	4,731	4,905	4,198
Oneida	4,517	4,747	5,747	5,711	4,903
Outagamie	4,105	4,582	5,945	6,855	7,064
Ozaukee	481	574	786	896	804
Pepin	820	904	892	1,019	906
Pierce	1,367	1,690	2,408	2,77	2,480
Polk	3,407	3,763	4,402	4,	4,422
Portage	3,429	3,618	4,322	4, 3	4,051

- 264 -

Rank of Counties in Resident Deer License Sales (continued)
1947-1954

County	Year				
	1947	1948	1949	1950	1951
Price	3,178	3,352	4,260	4,282	3,701
Racine	2,242	2,544	3,019	3,691	3,682
Richland	1,326	1,475	1,745	2,043	1,565
Rock	3,163	3,473	4,290	5,009	4,498
Rusk	2,520	2,761	3,279	3,454	2,919
St. Croix	1,588	2,150	2,658	2,976	2,629
Sauk	3,682	3,910	4,142	4,429	3,688
Sawyer	1,828	1,797	2,398	2,355	1,894
Shawano	3,595	3,999	4,702	5,304	4,820
Sheboygan	2,100	2,410	2,773	3,207	3,014
Taylor	2,657	2,806	3,328	3,567	3,100
Trempealeau	2,158	2,416	2,632	2,818	2,558
Vernon	1,846	2,065	2,219	2,449	2,094
Vilas	2,383	2,509	3,225	3,102	2,437
Walworth	1,124	1,277	1,607	1,875	1,611
Washburn	2,783	2,911	3,481	3,420	3,106
Washington	1,226	1,375	1,597	1,830	1,736
Waukesha	2,490	2,568	3,485	4,305	4,009
Waupaca	3,307	3,628	4,658	5,101	4,572
Waushara	1,930	2,280	2,440	2,612	2,380
Winnebago	3,586	3,923	5,262	6,235	6,079
Wood	7,063	7,092	8,371	8,500	6,840
TOTALS	199,234	220,004	263,489	289,420	260,136

County	Year			Average Annual Sales	Rank
	1952	1953	1954		
Adams	897	932	867	1,173	62
Ashland	2,530	2,411	2,505	3,056	29
Barron	3,958	3,964	4,239	5,012	11
Bayfield	1,757	1,516	1,637	2,393	43
Brown	6,412	6,350	6,778	6,941	4
Buffalo	1,816	1,502	1,551	1,613	53
Burnett	1,495	1,515	1,684	2,081	48
Calumet	654	636	677	791	68
Chippewa	4,272	4,189	4,401	4,917	12
Clark	3,800	3,735	3,885	4,773	14
Columbia	3,011	2,830	3,099	3,514	26
Crawford	1,151	926	1,040	1,053	63
Dane	6,892	6,085	6,362	7,373	3
Dodge	2,235	2,119	2,268	2,606	38
Door	1,813	1,520	1,026	1,407	58
Douglas	4,886	4,330	4,642	5,640	7
Dunn	2,512	2,491	2,750	2,917	31
Eau Claire	4,283	4,262	4,522	5,200	10
Florence	814	818	787	967	64
Fond du Lac	2,647	2,538	2,861	3,001	30
Forest	1,829	1,798	1,783	2,191	46
Grant	2,491	2,209	2,281	2,431	42
Green	700	615	621	785	69
Green Lake	1,220	1,165	1,294	1,437	57
Iowa	959	749	782	940	65
Iron	1,355	1,260	1,356	1,539	54
Jackson	2,401	2,273	2,353	2,617	37
Jefferson	1,173	1,119	1,255	1,365	60
Juneau	1,880	1,819	2,070	2,488	40
Kenosha	1,870	1,805	1,798	1,957	51
Kewaunee	861	835	800	928	66
La Crosse	5,208	4,514	4,971	5,252	9
Lafayette	476	438	392	499	71
Langlade	2,877	3,018	3,095	3,549	24
Lincoln	3,456	3,365	3,448	3,939	19
Manitowoc	2,663	2,604	2,761	2,884	33
Marathon	6,519	6,499	6,835	7,626	2
Marinette	4,604	4,607	4,673	5,374	8
Marquette	1,055	1,083	1,143	1,268	61
Milwaukee	18,091	17,127	18,954	19,322	1
Monroe	3,188	3,099	3,282	3,673	22
Oconto	3,402	3,270	3,259	3,964	18
Oneida	3,633	3,841	3,937	4,630	15
Outagamie	5,819	5,425	6,009	5,726	6
Ozaukee	663	596	710	689	70
Pepin	806	752	856	869	67
Pierce	1,946	1,882	2,063	2,077	49

Rank of Counties in Resident Deer License Sales (continued)
1947-1954

County	Year			Average Annual Sales	Rank
	1952	1953	1954		
Polk	2,784	2,909	3,092	3,709	21
Portage	2,951	2,848	3,092	3,622	23
Price	2,731	2,721	2,914	3,392	27
Racine	2,652	2,663	2,785	2,910	32
Richland	1,321	1,188	1,222	1,486	56
Rock	3,424	3,357	3,522	3,842	20
Rusk	2,103	2,119	2,296	2,681	36
St. Croix	1,980	1,995	2,099	2,259	45
Sauk	3,008	2,748	2,773	3,548	25
Sawyer	1,392	1,323	1,475	1,808	52
Shawano	4,070	4,054	4,316	4,358	16
Sheboygan	2,389	2,331	2,471	2,587	39
Taylor	2,494	2,547	2,530	2,879	34
Trempealeau	2,499	2,115	2,312	2,439	41
Vernon	1,900	1,733	1,835	2,018	50
Vilas	1,459	1,565	1,785	2,308	44
Walworth	1,218	1,247	1,264	1,403	59
Washburn	1,997	2,027	2,133	2,732	35
Washington	1,306	1,343	1,559	1,497	55
Waukesha	3,060	3,043	3,315	3,284	28
Waupaca	3,579	3,542	3,742	4,016	17
Waushara	1,630	1,638	1,834	2,093	47
Winnebago	4,513	4,362	4,702	4,833	13
Wood	4,504	4,833	5,592	6,599	5
TOTALS	199,944	192,687	205,022		

County	1955	1956	1957	1958	1959	Average Annual Sales	Rank
Adams	993	1,080	1,044	1,264	1,224	1,121	62
Ashland	2,487	2,538	2,610	2,979	2,916	2,706	39
Barron	4,359	4,354	4,349	5,312	5,566	4,788	15
Bayfield	1,541	1,618	1,737	2,001	1,974	1,774	55
Brown	7,711	8,034	7,977	9,229	9,291	8,448	3
Buffalo	1,905	1,605	2,000	2,166	2,205	1,976	49
Burnett	1,588	1,637	1,766	2,082	2,177	1,850	53
Calumet	837	1,015	991	1,248	1,354	1,089	63
Chippewa	4,507	4,486	4,661	5,262	5,355	4,854	14
Clark	3,892	3,989	4,043	4,654	4,198	4,155	18
Columbia	3,389	3,540	3,215	4,008	4,265	3,683	23
Crawford ,,,......	1,118	1,132	1,277	1,406	1,517	1,290	59
Dane	7,222	7,847	7,944	9,556	10,207	8,555	2
Dodge	2,504	2,519	2,735	3,254	2,971	2,796	36
Door	1,399	1,534	1,496	1,875	1,745	1,609	57
Douglas	4,404	4,425	4,695	5,490	5,280	4,858	13
Dunn	3,050	2,557	2,613	3,365	3,353	2,987	33
Eau Claire	4,819	4,842	5,224	5,916	5,715	5,303	10
Florence	805	781	796	837	870	817	69
Fond du Lac	3,124	3,352	3,276	4,088	4,347	3,637	24
Forest	1,700	1,795	1,808	1,948	1,888	1,827	54
Grant	2,418	2,709	2,821	3,290	3,689	2,985	34
Green	672	808	854	1,162	1,201	939	68
Green Lake	1,434	1,464	1,415	1,851	1,884	1,609	57
Iowa	810	894	908	1,080	1,193	977	67
Iron	1,192	1,175	1,185	1,360	1,276	1,057	66
Jackson	2,349	2,357	2,450	2,708	2,398	2,452	42
Jefferson	1,477	1,621	1,521	2,079	2,740	1,887	52
Juneau	2,103	2,114	2,111	2,488	2,136	2,190	46
Kenosha	2,052	2,345	2,550	3,008	3,734	2,737	38
Kewaunee ,........	1,091	1,132	1,200	1,430	1,418	1,254	61
La Crosse	5,634	5,553	5,924	6,372	6,098	5,916	8
Lafayette	425	506	549	759	567	561	70
Langlade	2,983	3,061	2,993	3,417	3,336	3,154	30
Lincoln	3,422	3,511	3,608	4,070	4,121	3,746	22
Manitowoc	3,450	3,742	3,602	4,242	4,484	3,904	20
Marathon	7,090	7,410	7,502	8,820	8,987	7,961	4
Marinette	4,481	4,951	5,033	5,355	5,357	5,087	12
Marquette	1,177	1,222	1,105	1,431	1,413	1,269	60
Milwaukee	21,332	24,091	25,311	29,376	32,193	26,460	1
Monroe	3,152	3,337	3,285	3,787	3,125	3,337	28
Oconto	3,383	3,390	3,260	3,815	3,765	3,522	27
Oneida	3,978	4,038	4,113	4,555	4,339	4,204	17
Outagamie	6,669	7,019	6,885	8,496	9,113	7,636	5
Ozaukee	857	960	1,009	1,191	1,362	1,075	65
Pepin	1,035	918	1,041	1,193	1,218	1,081	64

Rank of Counties in Resident Deer License Sales (continued)
5 Year Period - 1955-1959

County	1955	1956	1957	1958	1959	Average Annual Sales	Rank
Pierce	2,395	2,185	2,292	2,560	2,700	2,426	43
Polk	3,259	3,228	3,353	4,078	4,163	3,616	26
Portage	3,274	3,508	3,366	4,088	4,148	3,677	25
Price	2,806	2,921	2,934	2,342	3,206	3,041	32
Racine	3,132	3,406	3,579	4,346	4,660	3,824	21
Richland	1,332	1,472	1,519	1,845	1,770	1,587	58
Rock	4,093	4,737	3,923	5,630	6,157	5,108	11
Rusk	2,342	2,408	2,324	2,651	2,643	2,473	41
St. Croix	2,311	2,080	2,170	2,463	2,700	2,344	44
Sauk	2,915	2,994	2,741	3,514	3,567	3,146	31
Sawyer	1,414	1,473	1,642	1,992	1,912	1,686	56
Shawano	4,162	4,361	4,379	5,092	4,831	4,565	16
Sheboygan	2,836	3,055	3,032	3,526	3,786	3,247	29
Taylor	2,564	2,597	2,701	2,963	3,003	2,765	37
Trempealeau	2,732	2,430	2,774	3,093	3,295	2,864	35
Vernon	1,827	2,071	2,368	3,562	2,523	2,270	45
Vilas	1,810	1,813	1,926	2,209	2,025	1,955	50
Walworth	1,498	1,615	1,760	2,175	2,561	1,921	51
Washburn	2,111	2,125	2,410	2,969	2,884	2,499	40
Washington	1,675	1,899	1,975	2,414	2,706	2,152	47
Waukesha	4,008	4,593	5,180	6,505	7,492	5,555	9
Waupaca	3,687	3,675	3,398	4,460	4,992	4,042	19
Waushara	1,914	1,994	1,923	2,425	2,417	2,134	48
Winnebago	5,260	5,459	5,389	6,832	7,571	6,102	7
Wood	5,874	6,190	6,624	7,799	7,516	6,800	6
TOTALS	219,611	229,297	235,125	276,808	284,693	241,649	

Rank of Counties in Resident Deer License Sales (continued)
5 Year Period - 1960-1964

County	1960	1961	1962	1963	1964	Average Annual Sales	Rank
Adams	1,022	800	692	648	576	3,738	68
Ashland	3,018	2,078	1,950	1,863	1,795	10,704	36
Barron	5,665	3,637	3,348	3,297	3,206	19,153	13
Bayfield	1,928	1,425	1,346	1,283	1,306	7,288	51
Brown	8,881	5,287	5,285	5,278	5,334	30,065	3
Buffalo	2,252	1,355	1,657	1,503	1,438	8,205	47
Burnett	2,135	1,555	1,552	1,392	1,326	7,960	49
Calumet	1,128	699	718	845	703	4,093	64
Chippewa	5,449	3,485	3,228	3,003	3,049	18,214	14
Clark	4,251	2,650	2,655	2,311	2,292	14,159	21
Columbia	3,522	2,238	2,229	2,059	2,066	12,114	28
Crawford	1,565	904	830	842	792	4,933	60
Dane	9,294	5,898	5,914	5,725	6,270	33,101	2
Dodge	2,668	1,915	2,026	1,962	1,748	10,319	39
Door	1,534	1,178	1,109	1,025	1,058	5,904	56
Douglas	5,450	3,767	3,522	3,347	3,386	19,472	12
Dunn	3,447	2,140	2,005	2,140	2,030	11,762	30
Eau Claire	5,671	3,634	3,608	3,529	3,565	20,007	11
Florence	725	511	506	508	480	2,730	71
Fond du Lac	3,870	2,451	2,408	2,597	2,402	13,728	23
Forest	1,628	1,095	972	1,002	1,005	5,702	58
Grant	3,702	2,321	2,140	2,019	1,991	12,173	27
Green	1,200	873	878	781	728	4,460	62
Green Lake	1,436	932	915	889	886	5,058	59
Iowa	1,131	746	639	683	712	3,911	67
Iron	1,250	793	721	606	582	3,952	66
Jackson	2,477	1,766	1,675	1,685	1,511	9,114	44
Jefferson	2,333	1,088	968	1,126	1,143	6,658	55
Juneau	1,965	1,446	1,451	1,340	1,275	7,477	50
Kenosha	3,926	2,501	2,465	2,481	2,466	13,839	22
Kewaunee	1,231	677	656	755	723	4,042	65
La Crosse	5,896	3,643	3,906	3,508	3,420	20,373	10
Lafayette	802	608	513	498	481	2,902	70
Langlade	3,291	2,061	2,001	1,854	1,803	11,010	33
Lincoln	4,035	2,607	2,373	2,292	2,208	13,515	24
Manitowoc	3,876	2,170	2,206	2,369	2,077	12,698	25
Marathon	8,800	5,496	5,026	4,864	4,836	29,022	4
Marinette	4,925	3,351	3,302	3,067	3,058	17,703	15
Marquette	1,072	652	644	616	679	3,663	1
Menomonie	--	--	12	54	68	134	72
Milwaukee	30,803	20,811	19,786	19,181	18,966	109,547	1
Monroe	3,202	2,198	2,185	2,074	2,097	11,756	31
Oconto	3,616	2,085	2,133	2,047	1,999	11,880	29
Oneida	4,222	2,901	2,757	2,602	2,546	15,028	19
Outagamie.........	8,050	5,012	4,815	4,781	4,812	27,470	5
Ozaukee..........	1,252	763	710	809	764	4,298	63
Pepin	1,258	732	847	871	777	4,485	61

Rank of Counties in Resident Deer License Sales (continued)
5 Year Period - 1960-1964

County	1960	1961	1962	1963	1964	Average Annual Sales	Rank
Pierce............	2,711	1,778	1,892	1,943	2,014	10,338	38
Polk	4,135	2,956	2,752	2,693	2,725	15,261	18
Portage	3,580	2,007	2,343	2,200	2,280	12,410	26
Price	3,076	2,094	1,992	1,810	1,812	10,784	35
Racine	4,837	3,102	2,968	3,008	3,196	17,111	16
Richland	1,613	1,034	1,054	1,074	1,074	5,849	57
Rock	5,813	3,600	3,660	3,758	3,682	20,513	9
Rusk	2,578	1,796	1,668	1,548	1,640	9,230	43
St. Croix	2,745	1,958	1,887	1,846	1,975	10,411	37
Sauk	2,914	1,847	1,816	1,750	1,751	10,078	41
Sawyer	1,939	1,342	1,176	1,176	1,185	6,818	53
Shawano	4,617	2,693	2,579	2,547	2,541	14,977	20
Sheboygan	3,528	1,936	2,032	2,237	1,963	11,696	32
Taylor	3,005	1,934	1,869	1,676	1,601	10,085	40
Trempealeau	3,193	1,889	2,081	1,853	1,956	10,972	34
Vernon	2,398	1,500	1,535	1,616	1,490	8,539	45
Vilas	2,017	1,355	1,301	1,199	1,157	7,029	52
Walworth	2,206	1,440	1,441	1,473	1,598	8,158	48
Washburn	2,821	1,842	1,817	1,685	1,811	9,976	42
Washington	2,398	1,430	1,419	1,503	1,504	8,254	46
Waukesha	7,248	4,963	4,682	4,880	4,787	26,560	6
Waupaca	4,301	2,837	2,840	2,653	2,693	15,324	17
Waushara	1,798	1,268	1,248	1,225	1,226	6,765	54
Winnebago	6,669	4,340	4,459	3,933	4,177	23,578	8
Wood	6,873	4,628	4,483	3,999	3,894	23,877	7
TOTALS	269,867	174,504	170,278	165,296	164,167	944,112	

COMPARATIVE DEER SEASON RECORDS
1955-1964

Year	1955	1956	1957	1958	1959	1960	1961	1962	1963	1964	Total
License Sales											
License Sales*	267,612	284,645	288,903	335,866	349,443	338,208	307,863	331,035	360,552	386,519	3,250,646
Party Permit**	--	--	32,027	58,438	61,018	47,522	--	--	5,578	24,624	229,207
Nonres. Bow & Arrow Lic.***	2,022	3,017	3,343	4,225	4,510	3,939	3,796	4,289	4,892	6,356	40,389
Harvest											
Regular Gun	35,060	35,562	42,779	50,247	57,900	35,490	38,772	45,835	60,507	73,888	476,040
Party Permit	--	--	25,359	44,987	47,696	25,515	--	--	4,513	19,557	167,627
Total Gun	35,060	35,562	68,138	95,234	105,596	61,005	38,772	45,835	65,020	93,445	643,667
Bow and Arrow	1,131	1,267	1,753	1,885	1,320	1,091	1,167	1,625	2,194	3,164	16,597
Total Lic. Sales	269,634	287,662	324,273	398,529	414,971	389,669	311,659	335,324	371,022	417,499	3,520,242
Total Harvest	36,191	36,829	69,891	97,119	106,916	62,096	39,939	47,460	67,214	96,609	660,264
Percent of Licensees Successful	13.4	12.8	21.6	24.4	25.8	15.9	10.2	14.2	18.1	23.1	18.8
Car Kill	1,472	2,137	2,470	3,172	2,980	3,046	3,756	4,483	5,995	8,107	37,618
Illegal Seizures	1,702	1,592	918	706	1,227	518	1,206	995	1,096	1,057	11,017
Total Deer Kill	39,365	40,558	73,279	100,997	111,123	65,660	44,901	52,938	74,305	105,773	708,899

*Includes resident big game, voluntary sportsmen and nonresident big game licenses.

**The party permit system, innovated in 1957, allowed groups of four or more hunters to apply for a hunting party permit which entitled the party to take one deer of any age or sex in addition to spike or antlered deer each could take under regular licences.

***The number of resident bow hunters is unknown, since holders of resident big game and voluntary sportsmen licenses could hunt with either gun or bow.